EXTRACTS FROM HUMAN NUTRITION

A health perspective

PARTS ONE AND THREE

Mary E. Barasi

BA, BSc, MSc, R. Nutr.
Principal Lecturer in Nutrition,
University of Wales Institute, Cardiff, UK

Hodder Arnold

A MEMBER OF THE HODDER HEADLINE GROUP

The Open University

This edition first published in Great Britain in 2005 by Hodder Arnold on behalf of the Open University, presenting extracts from *Human Nutrition: A health perspective*, second edition, published in 2003 by Hodder Arnold, an imprint of Hodder Education and a member of the Hodder Headline Group, 338 Euston Road, London NW1 3BH

British Library Cataloguing in Publication Data
A catalogue record for this book is available from the British Library

Library of Congress Cataloging-in-Publication Data
A catalog record for this book is available from the Library of Congress

ISBN-10: 0 340 91297 9
ISBN-13: 978 0 340 91297 3

1 2 3 4 5 6 7 8 9 10

Typeset in RotisSerif 9.5/12 by Charon Tec Pvt. Ltd, Chennai, India
www.charontec.com
Printed and bound in Spain

CONTENTS

PREFACE

Every day we make choices about our nutrition and health. At a conscious or subconscious level we decide for example what, if anything, we are going to eat for breakfast, whether we are going to buy a snack on our way past the local shop, or even if we are going to walk up the stairs or take the lift. Each of these single choices does not by itself make a large difference to our nutritional state and our health, but taken over a period of weeks and months contributes to our long-term health status. To optimize the health benefits from our diet, we need to learn more about nutrition and how it can influence the way our bodies function.

At first glance, this may seem to be very easy to do. It is clear that there is an enormous amount of nutritional information in the public domain, ranging from advice on healthy eating, weight loss, dietary supplements to a multitude of diets for almost every possible health problem. By its very existence, it has increased the level of interest in nutrition and health. These messages about diet and food are to be found in diverse places, including health centres and hospitals, in the supermarket and leisure centre, in the bank and even on public transport. In addition, electronic communication has opened up an almost overwhelming amount of information, available via the internet. Some of this is sound and reliable, based on scientific evidence, supported by reputable sources, and can be used with reasonable confidence. However, there is also unscientific and uncontrolled information, with no traceable scientific basis, often merely reflecting an individual opinion or that of an uninformed group, which can be misleading, inaccurate, confusing and potentially dangerous. Unfortunately, this can also apply to information presented by the broadcasting and print media. The ability to distinguish between reliable and unreliable sources is therefore important for anyone who wishes to improve their nutrition and health reliably, sensibly and safely.

This desire for a clearer understanding of nutritional principles is likely to be driven by various motivating factors. It may be related to a responsibility at work, the need to feed a growing family, a new vegetarian or looking after an older relative, eating on a limited budget, controlling weight, managing an illness or improving physical performance. It may simply stem from a curiosity about the plethora of products available in the typical supermarket and a desire to understand their relative merits and functions. Whatever the reason, the student of nutrition needs to have the tools to inform their decision-making skills in choosing how to eat. It is only by understanding the components of the human diet and how the food we eat is processed in the body that we can start to work out for ourselves what would be beneficial to have in our diet and what is less useful to us. The decisions we make about this may vary depending on our individual condition, but practising these skills in different contexts will build confidence.

For some students, there may be an anxiety about technical language, and a preconceived notion that scientific concepts are difficult. However, by focusing on desired outcomes such as understanding the links between foods and normal growth, development, health and performance, it becomes easier to absorb the underlying scientific principles.

It is such an approach that is offered in this course book, abridged from the original 'Human Nutrition' textbook, and focusing on the more social aspects of nutrition, areas to which the majority of students can relate. The accompanying OU study guide provides the introduction to the nutrients found in food and the concept of energy balance. Thus the course book provides the framework for the study of nutrition, how to look at food intakes and nutritional needs, and how to assess what constitutes a healthy diet. These are the basic tools, against which all information about nutrition needs to be judged.

Once these principles have been established, the student is encouraged to think of applying them within different age groups in the population, taking into account specific nutritional needs. In addition, situations that can pose a practical challenge to achieving adequate nutrition are considered, such as having a low income, being a vegetarian, or belonging to a minority ethnic group. Also considered are situations where dietary intakes need to be modified, for example in the case of allergies or to optimize physical performance. Using nutrition to improve our health, in particular in relation to the biggest disease threats in the UK, forms an important part of the book. One of the major threats to health facing populations, not just in the UK but across many other countries, is the growing prevalence of overweight and obesity which is accompanied by increased risk of other diseases. Improving our understanding of the many nutritional and lifestyle factors that contribute to the problem, and finding ways of helping people lose weight and avoid weight gain, are ongoing issues.

The book provides information about foods that have been developed by the food industry to fulfil specific needs, that perhaps may be less readily achieved through the normal diet. This area leads into thoughts of the future and whether 'designer' foods will be produced that will be suitable for individuals with specific needs to ward off the threats of ill health. The world of molecular biology, which brings an understanding of the most fundamental ways in which our cellular structures are programmed and operate, offers prospects for a much deeper understanding of the interaction of nutrients with our genetic blueprints. How quickly this will lead to better tailoring of nutritional advice to the individual is difficult to predict; foods contain so many diverse chemical compounds that we are far from understanding how all of them influence physiological or biochemical processes, and what impact they have on our health.

In the meantime, we can make some very positive changes to our diets and our health by following the principles of healthy eating that have been established, and which are founded on a sound evidence base developed from work over the last 50 to 60 years.

Once the reader has an understanding of these basic principles, they can consider the challenges of assessing not only their own diet, but that of others, as well as being in a better position to judge whether the information they encounter is credible and worth taking seriously.

Mary E. Barasi
Cardiff
June 2005

ONE

THE STUDY OF NUTRITION AND FOOD HABITS

1 WHAT IS NUTRITION?

The aims of this chapter are to:

- define nutrition as a discipline for study and reflect on its importance;
- look at ways in which dietary information is collected;
- encourage the reader to think about their own food intake, their own and others' perceptions of nutrition;
- consider why nutrition is important and how it is included in nutrition policies.

On completing the study of this chapter, you should be able to:

- think about nutrition and food in relation to yourself;
- understand what is meant by nutrition, and why it is an important science, involving many different disciplines;
- explain and discuss the various ways in which nutrition is studied, together with their advantages and disadvantages;
- understand and evaluate the information about nutrition that is disseminated in the scientific as well as the non-specialist literature;
- explain how nutritional status can be assessed;
- understand the basis on which nutrition policy may be made at government level.

DEFINITIONS OF NUTRITION

Everybody has their own experience of food and eating, so it is likely that people will have different ideas about what is meant by nutrition. Some may see eating as a means of meeting our basic physiological needs and warding off hunger, and others as a pleasurable experience in its own right and something to anticipate and plan. These represent the two extremes implied by the sayings 'eat to live' and 'live to eat'.

In reality, eating is far more complicated than this, involving aspects of our psychological make-up and current state of mind, our genetic blueprint, the social environment of which we are a part, our economic situation and external factors relating to the availability of the food. These will be explored in more detail in Chapter 2. Eating also does more than just keep us alive. When insufficient food or specific nutrients are supplied, some physiological adaptation may occur to minimize the consequences. Eventually, however, a deficiency state will arise.

At the beginning of the twentieth century, most of the science of nutrition was directed at discovering the essential nutrients, studying the effects of insufficient intakes and determining the quantities needed to prevent deficiency states. Since then it has gradually been recognized that good nutrition is not simply a matter of providing enough of all the nutrients. We now realize that diets in the affluent Western countries, although apparently containing all the necessary nutrients, are probably contributing to many of the diseases afflicting these populations. Much research has been focused on finding which nutrients are linked to which diseases, in an effort to promote a change in the dietary intake and hence an improvement in health. Since the 1970s a great deal of advice has been aimed at encouraging people to eat a healthier balance of foods, thereby reducing disease. The emphasis in the twenty-first century has started to move towards promoting positive health through diet, know as optimum nutrition. However, nutritionists recognize that altering people's food intake is complicated because diets are influenced by many factors other than the need to eat and the desire for well-being.

It can be seen that arriving at a definition of nutrition is far from straightforward. Two rather different definitions have been suggested, describing nutrition as:

> 'the study of foods and nutrients vital to health and how the body uses these to promote and support growth, maintenance and reproduction of cells' or
>
> 'the study of the relationship between people and their food'.

The first definition deals only with the nutrients, what happens to them within the human body and what the results are if insufficient amounts are provided. However, people do not eat nutrients, they eat food. This definition ignores all the external factors that play a role in our approach to food and that are crucial in any study of what people are eating. These factors are different for each individual, depending on cultural background and the circumstances of a person's life.

The second definition takes a much broader perspective, from the supply of food and all the influences thereon, to the individual's food selection and, finally, to the physiological and biochemical effects of the nutrients in the human body, and the consequences for health and survival. It also recognizes that nutritionists do not only study the effects of nutrients on biochemical and physiological functioning, they have an additional responsibility to translate their knowledge for those who produce, process and market the foods. Furthermore, nutritionists must be involved in the formulation of policy that determines the access by consumers to food. Finally, consumers need the help of nutritionists to enable them to make the best of the food available. Only by broadening our definition of the subject across the full range of human relationships with food can nutrition have its justified place in human well-being.

WHY IS NUTRITION IMPORTANT?

To answer this question, it is perhaps useful to consider the various levels at which nutrition can be studied. Table 1.1 illustrates some examples of the application of nutritional science in other fields of study. In each case, nutrition plays a specific role, and the emphasis required may differ from its application in all other roles. Thus, nutrition is a science with many different applications and meanings to different specialists. Nevertheless, each of these specialists, working in their own particular field of expertise, needs to have knowledge of nutrition in order to apply the findings of their work to the nutritional context.

There has been an upsurge of general interest in nutrition in the last 20–30 years; this has not just been among the scientific community, but also among the general population. Why has this happened?

First, it is notable that dietary intakes have been and are changing rapidly. In the Western world, we have an ever-increasing selection of foods available to us. People can now eat every day the foods our ancestors had only on special occasions. New foods are appearing that have been conceived and developed by food

Activity 1.1

Why are you studying nutrition?

At what level will you be applying your nutritional knowledge?

At what level might the following be using nutrition:

nurse	pharmacist
dietitian	journalist
obstetrician	parent?
home economist	

Try to think of some other examples of people working with nutrition, at each of the different levels in Table 1.1.

TABLE 1.1 Different levels of studying nutrition

Level of study	Examples of application
Macro/population studies	Government statistics (for formulation of policy, e.g. about agriculture, or health)
	Epidemiology (to study relationship between diet and disease)
	Food producers (to respond to changes in consumer demand and to lead demand)
Individual/whole person studies	Sociology (to study patterns of behaviour related to food)
	Food science/technology (to identify changes in individual preferences for food; sensory qualities)
	Sports science (to identify links between diet and performance)
	Medicine (to study influences of diet on the health of the individual and recovery from illness)
Micro/laboratory studies	Physiology (to understand the role of nutrients in functioning of body systems)
	Biochemistry (to investigate the biochemical role of nutrients in normal and abnormal functioning)
	Molecular biology (to study gene–nutrient interactions)

technologists; sometimes these contain unusual ingredients, which provide nutrients in unexpected amounts (this can be a problem for the nutritionist in giving advice). New processing techniques, such as irradiation, may affect the nutrients in food. New products, specially designed to promote health are now available; these are discussed in Chapter 17.

In modern society, meal patterns have become less rigid and many people no longer eat meals at regular mealtimes. The members of a family may each have an independent meal at different times of the day and the traditional family meal is a rare event.

Concerns about food safety and environmental issues have resulted in changes in dietary habits, the most notable amongst these being the rise in vegetarianism in the UK and the growth of demand for organically grown food. Nevertheless, the great majority of food bought comes from large retail supermarkets that exert a great deal of influence over customer choice.

Health issues have been given a great deal of prominence in the media. Statistics show that populations in Western countries have excess mortality (i.e. death rates) and morbidity (i.e. rates of illness) from many diseases related to diet, such as cardiovascular disorders, bowel diseases and cancers, as well as a high prevalence of obesity and diabetes. At the same time, we are often shocked by images of starvation in other parts of the world where conflict, drought and other disasters have resulted in millions of people suffering acute malnutrition and starvation.

As greater numbers of nutritionists are trained and the discipline becomes more widely studied, knowledge accumulates based on sound evidence. Public health nutrition is now a discipline in its own right, with a specific remit of promoting health through good nutrition. However, as with all scientific research, more questions follow every finding. Consensus is being reached on some of the ways in which diet is involved in Western diseases, and advice can now be based on much firmer evidence. However, new research may cause current advice to be modified. New angles on nutrition research, particularly from the field of molecular biology, are explaining observations made earlier at the whole-body level. Improved methodologies allow more sensitive and appropriate measurements to be made. For example, in the study of energy balance, the use of radioactively labelled water has provided a means of measuring energy expenditure in subjects during their normal lives. This has provided a wealth of information about this important area of nutrition.

The media are very sensitive to public concern, so that news about nutritional findings receives a great deal of publicity. Unfortunately, the style of reporting may distort the scientific detail, so that what is eventually presented by the media may not accurately represent the findings. Moreover, excessive prominence may be given to very minor and insignificant findings, especially if they appear to contradict earlier results. Consequently, rather than being better informed, the public may become confused. It is essential, therefore, that those trained in nutrition have a clear understanding of nutritional issues, and are able to disentangle some of the inaccuracies presented by the media.

WHAT DO PEOPLE EAT?

Different peoples around the world have different dietary patterns, determined by a number of factors. The major factors influencing what is eaten in different cultures are the foods available in that particular culture, traditional practices and beliefs, and any religious prescriptions. The relative importance of these foods is the starting point for many of the published pyramid-shape food guides (Figure 1.1).

The basis of the diet for most people is a core food, referred to as the 'staple', around which the majority of meals are constructed. Without the staple, a meal would not be perceived as a meal. There are usually only a very few core

Activity 1.2

You read the following article in your local paper:

> **Amazing Weight Loss Breakthrough!!**
>
> Doctors at the University of Nirvana have made a revolutionary new discovery, which will change the life of literally millions of people. Volunteers in their laboratories have been eating only three different foods a day and have lost an astonishing 30 lbs in a month!
>
> The secret of their success is eating just one food at each meal. It doesn't matter what food you eat, but it must never be eaten with anything else. So, if you feel like ice cream for breakfast, chocolate for lunch and a steak for dinner – go ahead, the weight will still fall off and you will emerge a slimmer, fitter person.
>
> Doctors claim that anyone can get the same results, as long as they stick to the diet regime of only one food at each meal. They explain that the body needs other foods to help the digestion process. When we eat only one food at a time, food breakdown stops, and so the calories can't pile on!
>
> Results like this have never been obtained before, and it is likely that the whole country will become 'One Food a Meal' crazy.
>
> The scientists do offer a word of caution, however. The weight loss is so astonishing that you should not need to stay on the diet for more than 4 weeks at a time. It may be dangerous if you continue on it for longer than this.

- What effect would you expect this article to have if it were published in the national newspapers?
- What alternative explanations for the findings might there be?
- Why might an article like this be nutritionally dangerous?

Try to find some articles in newspapers or magazines that you feel are misleading and potentially harmful.

- Attempt to identify what it is about the articles that concerns you.
- Try to think of an explanation for the way the article has been written.

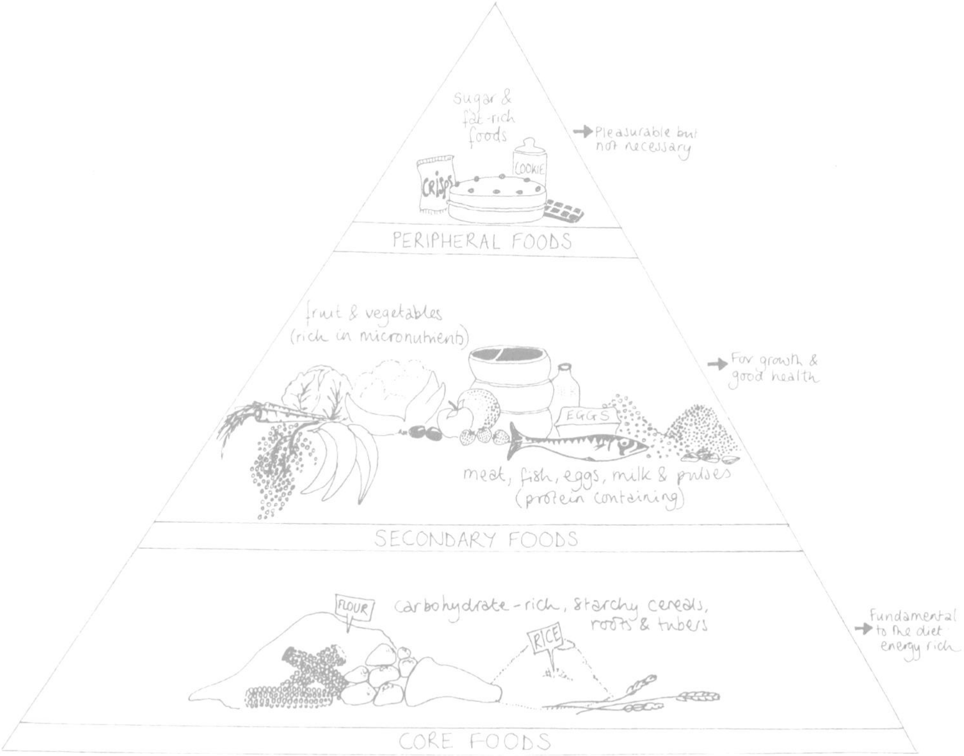

Figure 1.1 A pyramid represents the contents of the diet and can be used as the basis of a food guide.

foods in any one culture, sometimes only one. They are generally cereals, or roots and tubers.

Secondary foods are also eaten; these enhance the meal, but are not an essential part of it. They may be endowed with specific properties of their own; for example they may promote strength (protein-rich foods, such as meat) or good health (fruit and vegetables), or they may maintain bodily forces in balance ('hot' and 'cold' foods as in some Eastern cultures). In addition, some secondary foods may be important at particular life stages.

The third category of foods are peripheral foods. These are non-essential, but pleasant to eat. Examples include biscuits, cakes, confectionery, preserves, sauces, puddings and alcoholic beverages. They may also include flavourings and seasonings.

Thus, despite the huge diversity of foods eaten around the world, it is possible to identify common patterns in the foods that people eat. In general, a greater part of the diet comes from the staple in the poorer parts of the world, and the peripheral foods make an excessively large contribution in richer countries. Clearly, the core and secondary foods in any national or cultural diet must supply the essential nutrients in appropriate amounts to sustain life and promote health. Some diets appear to achieve this better than others, as is shown by the fact that mortality rates from diseases that can be attributed to diet are lower in some countries of the world than in others.

HOW IS INFORMATION ABOUT PEOPLE'S DIETS COLLECTED?

To permit any exploration of the role of food in the health and welfare of the whole individual, rather than its biochemical effect at the system or cellular level, it is necessary to investigate what people eat. It is relatively straightforward for individuals to think about their own food intake, and to keep some sort of diary of what they have eaten. Most people can identify foods that they like or dislike, that they eat often or rarely. However, not everyone possesses enough interest in or knowledge about their own food intake to keep a detailed record over a period of time and, for most people, keeping a food record will be quite difficult.

Many of us would also be able to make some statements about the food intake of members of our family, or close friends. However, this information would inevitably be less detailed than our own, as we can rarely know about absolutely everything someone else has eaten. For a nutritionist, trying to find out what people eat poses a number of problems and requires varied approaches.

Population and household information

Information about the diet of a population can be obtained either in a very general way or with progressively more detailed techniques. In many countries, data are collected together in 'food balance sheets', which estimate the amount of food moving into and leaving a country, in much the same way as monetary transactions on a financial balance sheet. This can provide an overview of the theoretical availability of food in a country. Such statistics are collated and published by the United Nations' Food and Agriculture Organization (FAO) for most countries of the world, and are used to provide an overview of food availability.

In Europe, several Household Budget Surveys exist, each providing valuable data about dietary intakes in the specific country. The DAFNE (Data Food Networking) initiative is a collaborative effort across Europe to develop a bank of regularly updated and comparable data in order to assess and monitor trends in dietary patterns.

In the UK, data have been collected by the Household Food Consumption and Expenditure Survey, in particular, the National Food Survey (produced annually by the Ministry of Agriculture, Fisheries and Food) since 1940. This has provided a continuous surveillance of the food coming into households for consumption, together with money spent on food according to household composition, economic status and geographical location. In 1994, the Survey started to collect data about food eaten outside the home, a reflection of the growing importance of eating out. The National Food Survey in this form ended in March 2001, and has been replaced by a new Expenditure and Food Survey (EFS), which will be published by DEFRA (Department for Environment, Food and Rural Affairs). Information about food consumption, nutrient intakes and food expenditure will, therefore, continue to be collected and published.

A study of this nature, however, cannot tell us the intake of an individual, as all of the data are collected with the household as the unit, without any indication of food distribution within. More information is required on food distribution patterns within households. The EFS will continue to publish information at the level of the household, although individual members will keep their own diaries. It is hoped that this will reduce the incidence of underreporting and increase accuracy.

The use of supermarket till receipts collected over 4 weeks, together with 4-day individual diaries has been used to assess patterns of fat and energy intake and has been shown useful. The involvement of supermarket checkout data to obtain information about population dietary patterns has potential in dietary surveys. Novel ways to collect data continue to be developed.

Individual information

Information on dietary intake of individuals is usually obtained by asking subjects to keep a record of everything they have eaten over a period of time. The level of precision with which this is carried out and the duration of the study have been subject to debate. In general, the more exact the method of measurement tries to be, the less it is likely to reflect the normal, freely chosen diet of the subject.

The exact method used will be determined by the aims of the study. Decisions have to be taken by the researcher to determine the reliability and validity of the methods used. In other words, if the method chosen provides results that can be reproduced on a subsequent occasion, it has a reasonable degree of reliability. A second more difficult question to answer relates to the validity of the information, i.e. how well it measures the subject's intake. Since food and, therefore, nutrient intakes are not constant from day to day for the majority of people, an average intake over a period of time would reflect 'habitual' intakes. The duration over which food intake has to be recorded to obtain a valid measure of habitual intake has been studied and shown to vary for different nutrients. Ultimately, the decision on how long a recording period should be depends on the nutrients to be analysed. For example, for energy and macronutrient intake, Black (2001) reports that a 7-day intake record will provide a result within 15–20 per cent of the true level of intake. For micronutrients, the variability is up to 30–40 per cent for those that are widely distributed in foods, and very large for vitamins, such as A and C, which occur in large amounts in fewer foods. Some of the methods used are discussed below.

The weighed inventory

This is considered to be the 'gold standard' of dietary intake studies. In this method, all the food eaten by the subject during a period, usually 1 week, is weighed and recorded, together with any plate waste. Actual nutrient intakes are then calculated, using data from food composition tables applicable to the particular country (in the UK McCance and Widdowson's tables, published by the Royal Society of Chemistry, are the most widely used – see Food Standards Agency, 2002b). The major drawback of the method is that it requires a considerable degree of motivation and cooperation on the part of the subject. It is quite an intrusive method, which takes time at meals and may thus deter a busy person.

Most subjects tend to underrecord their habitual food intake, possibly because they actually eat less during the study period, or forget/omit to record some of the foods eaten. This seems to be a particular problem in those who are trying to restrain their food intake in some way. Snack foods are often omitted, perhaps because of inconvenience or forgetfulness. Recent work has shown that the fat and carbohydrate intakes are underreported to a greater extent than protein intakes. Food choice may also be altered to facilitate weighing.

Food diaries

In this technique, the food eaten is simply recorded in a notebook, without being weighed. Comprehensive instructions are provided to the subject to explain the procedure. Cooking methods, brand names and recipes are requested. The respondent is asked to provide an estimate of the portion size using household measures, e.g. spoons, cups, units, slices or recording packet weights. The researcher then has the task of quantifying portions eaten. Food models or pictures may help in the quantification of portion sizes. A number of photographic atlases of food portions have been developed and validated in recent years. Other visual images, including those generated by computer may be used in the future, but would also need to be validated. Tables of average portion sizes are available in the UK, based on measurements of typical portions (Food Standards Agency (FSA), 2002a). Database information is available for a large number of typical servings of foods, although they remain only an estimate for each particular subject. A large database, known as DINER (Data Into Nutrients for Epidemiological Research) has been developed as part of the EPIC study, which contains information on over 7000 foods and portion sizes. The food diary method requires that the subject is literate and physically able to write. Alternative ways of recording the size of portion eaten include photographing the meal, and the use of computerized scales with an associated tape-recorder, for example, the PETRA (Portable Electronic Tape Recording Automated) Scales system, which can both weigh and store a description of the meal. In both cases, however, the data still require interpretation and collation by the researcher.

The diary method remains subject to possible changes in the diet by the respondent and failure to record all foods eaten. However, if respondents are adequately instructed, reasonably comprehensive records can be obtained. Generally, women produce more reliable records by this method than men.

A record of foods eaten with no attempt to assess the quantity (a menu record) is a further modification of this approach. Average servings can be used by the researcher and, although the accuracy of individual intake calculation is reduced, this method can provide an overview of dietary patterns.

A simpler and more straightforward approach used increasingly is to compile a food intake record based on food groups, such as those in the Balance of Good Health (FSA, 2001a). This allows an overall profile of the diet to be obtained and the balance to be assessed against a standard desirable pattern.

Food frequency questionnaires

These provide a means of studying intake retrospectively. The use of questionnaires is an inexpensive technique: it can be self-administered by large numbers of people and requires only a short period of time. This tool is often used in epidemiological research. It has the advantage that current diets are not altered. Analysis of the data can be done rapidly using a computerized scoring system. Disadvantages are that the results are culture-specific and a different group may require a new questionnaire. Additionally, individuals with unusual diets within the study group may not fit the predetermined criteria for coding. Even for people with a relatively consistent dietary pattern, it can be quite a complicated task to convert information about a habitual food intake into a frequency over a week, for specific foods. This is complicated further by trying to assess portion sizes of these foods. This type of questionnaire often looks at a subset of foods providing specific nutrients, rather than at the whole diet, and is generally tailored to the aims of a particular study.

In general, questionnaires can give useful information, which may be used to rank individuals within groups into subsets according to intake, rather than to provide precise data on actual intakes.

The diet interview

This technique is widely used by dietitians to obtain a general picture of a person's food intake. It requires a skilled interviewer to elicit an accurate picture of a person's diet history. The time frame is usually 7 days. This can be sufficient to pinpoint potential excesses or deficiencies. The interview may be more or less detailed, depending on the type of information required and its purpose. It usually consists of questions about the daily eating pattern, along the lines of 'What do you usually have for breakfast, mid-morning, lunch, etc.?' It then aims to draw a more precise picture by focusing on the current (or previous) day's intake, by asking 'What did you have for breakfast, mid-morning, lunch, etc. today, or yesterday?' Many people have little awareness of what they eat, so that it may be quite difficult for them to remember even the previous day's food intake. An estimation of portion sizes may also be made, often with the help of food models. A checklist of foods may be used to remind subjects about foods that they do eat, but forgot to mention.

Some of the limitations of a diet history are that it requires both a skilled interviewer and a subject with a reasonable memory. For the latter reason, it is unlikely to be suitable for children and for anyone with a failing memory. It also depends on the subject having a recognized dietary pattern, and a 'usual intake'. In addition, it is time consuming both to complete the interview and to carry out any subsequent analysis of the data collected. Hand-held computers with dietary analysis packages can simplify the process, allowing information from the subject to be entered directly.

A dietary recall interview can be simplified to focus just on the previous 24 hours and obtain a 'snapshot' of a typical intake. This can be done by telephone and need not take more than 15–20 minutes. However, bias is introduced as the day chosen may be atypical. It is also likely that food portion sizes are inaccurate, and the completeness of the record is memory dependent.

Practical issues in dietary survey methods

The way in which food is perceived by the subject may affect what is recorded. This might include perceptions of what their culture group believes they 'should' be eating as well as what the interviewer might expect.

Interaction at a subtle level between an interviewer and subject in the diet history interview may produce varying results when different people carry out the interview with the same subject.

Obtaining dietary intake information from children and adolescents poses particular challenges. With young children, below the age of 8 years, the limiting factors are likely to be knowledge of the names of foods as well as limited attention span and memory. The use of a surrogate reporter may introduce bias. As children become older, the ability to record the food intake increases, but at the same time there may be a greater desire to 'please' the interviewer and accuracy of records may be low. There are no easy solutions to collecting dietary intake data in these age groups, and new or refined survey methods are needed. Some of the problems found in this group include underreporting and non-response, which are also discussed below.

In the last few years, there has been recognition among nutritionists that much of the dietary intake data that are collected contain an element of underreporting. This is confirmed by comparison of energy intake with calculated or measured energy expenditure in many different groups. Measurements of energy expenditure using the doubly labelled water technique are available in some research settings. Biomarkers such as urinary nitrogen levels can also be used to confirm the accuracy of food intake records, although these increase the intrusion of the method, and could reduce compliance.

General findings, for example, based on studies of 77 groups (reported by Black, 2001) show a ratio of energy intake to energy expenditure of 0.83 (when a ratio of 1.0 would be expected). In addition, there is variability between subjects in the extent of misreporting. For 29 per cent of the groups studied, results for energy were within 10 per cent of those for expenditure. In 69 per cent of the groups, energy intake figures were more than 10 per cent below energy expenditure. Only in 2 per cent of the groups were the intake results more than 10 per cent greater than the expenditure results.

In summary, food intakes are usually underreported. This has implications for the calculation of energy intakes, but also nutrient intakes. If nutrient intakes are expressed in relation to the total energy intake, a measure of the nutrient density of the diet can be obtained, expressed as the weight of nutrient/MJ or 1000 Calories. This can then be used for comparison between individuals, even if underreporting has occurred. These findings raise concerns about the accuracy of dietary intake studies, and underline the need for new methods to be developed that can more accurately capture information about individual intakes. Alternatively, more precise techniques for validating the intake records are needed.

Activity 1.3

1. With a partner, try out a diet history interview on one another.
   - **a** Go through all of the times in the previous day when your partner might have eaten something, and ask him/her questions about it.
   - **b** Try to find out how much of everything they ate, how it was prepared, what brand name they had.
   - **c** Did they eat all of it, or were there any left-overs?
2. Reflect on how easily you managed to complete this activity.
   - **a** Did you and your partner have a pattern of eating?
   - **b** How easy was it to assess amounts of food eaten?
   - **c** Did you have the same ideas about what was a small/medium/large serving of a food?
   - **d** Could you remember everything you had to eat 2 days ago, 3 days ago, etc.? How far back would your memory of your diet be reliable?

STUDIES OF NUTRITIONAL STATUS

These include measurements of:

- anthropometric indicators
- biochemical indicators
- clinical indicators.

Anthropometric indicators

Anthropometric (literally 'measuring man') indicators are basic measurements of the human body. By relating these to standards typical of the test population, any deviations indicate abnormal nutritional status. Measurements commonly used are height and weight; these can be used to calculate the body mass index (BMI):

$$\text{BMI (or Quetelet's index)} = \frac{\text{Weight (in kilograms)}}{[\text{height (in metres)}]^2}$$

The desirable range for BMI is given as 20–25, with values above 30 being associated with obesity. Similarly, values below 18 are indicative of undernutrition.

In children, height and weight results can be compared with standard growth curves (see Chapter 12), which indicate the rate of physical development of a child, particularly when a sequence of measurements is made. In addition, head and chest circumference measures can also be useful in children to indicate rates of growth of the brain and body.

Skinfold thickness measurements at mid-triceps, mid-biceps, subscapular and supra-iliac sites using Harpenden or similar callipers give a surprisingly accurate value for body fat, when used by a skilled person. Figure 1.2 shows the sites for skinfold measurements.

Arm muscle circumference can be calculated by subtracting the thickness of the fatfold from a mid-arm circumference measurement. This can indicate muscle development or wasting, and can be a useful indicator in clinical situations of change in muscle mass, for example, during illness and rehabilitation.

Waist: hip ratio is increasingly used as an indicator of body fat distribution: the circumference of the waist at the umbilicus and of the hips around the fattest part of the buttocks are used to calculate this ratio. A nomogram may be used, or a simple calculation performed to obtain the ratio. Values above 0.8 in women and 0.9 in men are indicative of a tendency for central fat deposition, and a possible increased health risk. Waist measurements alone have been shown to correlate well with body fatness, and may be used in future as a quick indicator of risk from overweight. Other ratios, such as waist to height, have also been suggested to be equally useful, as they tend to be 'unisex' and, therefore, a single figure can be used as a cut-off point.

Demispan is a measurement of skeletal size, which can be used as an alternative to height measurement, where it is difficult to obtain an upright posture in a subject. Demispan is the distance between the sternal notch and the roots of the middle and third fingers with the arm stretched out at shoulder height to the side of the body. It is particularly useful in elderly people, in whom height might have been lost due to vertebral collapse. The demispan value can then be used to produce two alternative indices

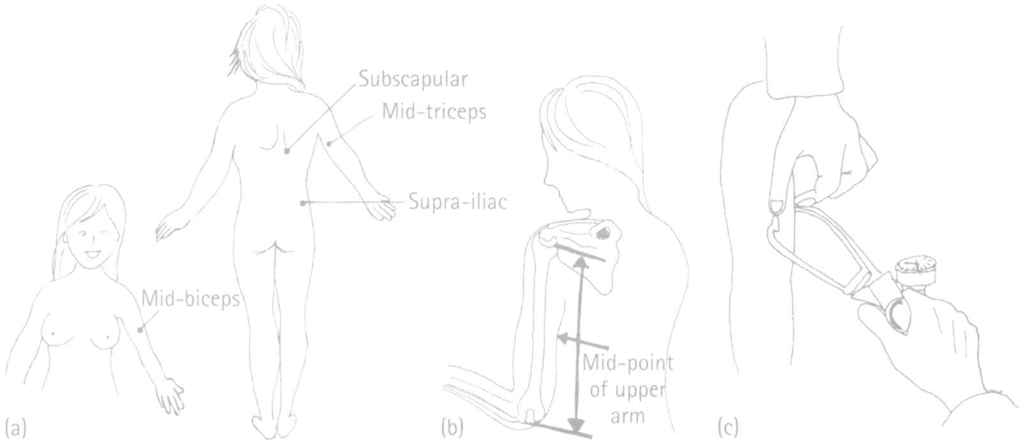

Figure 1.2 Measurement of skinfold for assessment of body fat content. (a) The four commonest sites used are subscapular, supra-iliac, mid-biceps and mid-triceps. Measurements from all four sites are added together for use in formulae to obtain fat mass. (b) For mid-triceps measurement the mid-point of the upper arm is found. (c) The callipers in use. The skinfold is taken lengthways along the arm, grasped firmly between thumb and forefinger, avoiding underlying muscle. The callipers are applied about 1 cm below the operator's fingers and the fold is held throughout the measurement. Three measurements are made and the results averaged.

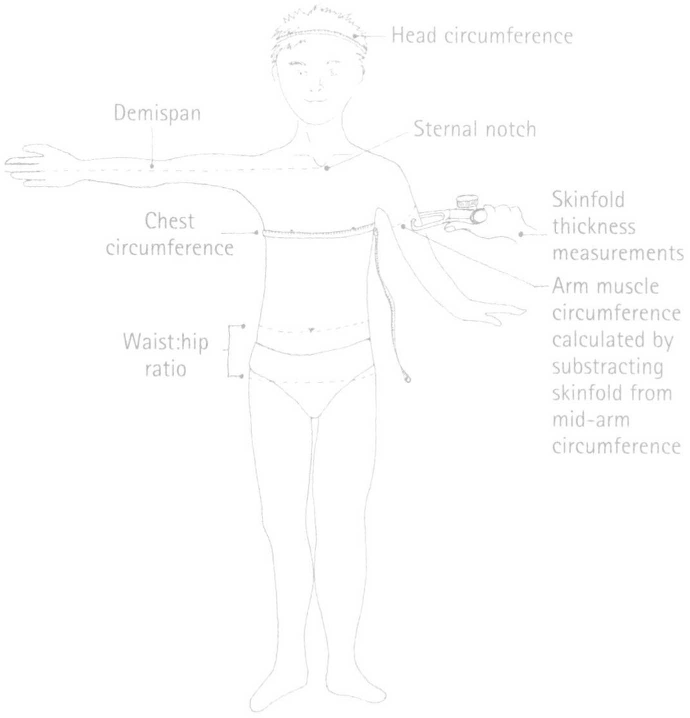

Figure 1.3 Summary of the main methods of anthropometry.

which show good agreement with BMI. These are demiquet, which uses weight/demispan^2 and mindex which is weight/demispan. The methods of anthropometry are summarized in Figure 1.3.

Biochemical indicators

Biochemical indicators can include assessment of blood and urine samples for levels of a variety of nutrients and/or their byproducts or for levels of nutrient-linked enzyme activities. In addition, analysis may be performed on samples of hair or bone marrow.

Blood (plasma, cells or serum) can provide a great deal of information. Analysis can be used to determine:

- actual levels of a nutrient in relation to expected levels (e.g. vitamin B_{12}, folate, carotenes, vitamin C in white blood cells);
- the activity of a nutrient-dependent enzyme (e.g. transketolase for thiamine);
- the activity of a nutrient-related enzyme (e.g. alkaline phosphatase for vitamin D);
- the rate of a nutrient-dependent reaction (e.g. clotting time for vitamin K);
- the presence of a nutrient carrier or its saturation level (e.g. retinol-binding protein, transferrin (iron)); or
- levels of nutrient-related products (e.g. lipoprotein levels).

Urine samples may be used to monitor the baseline excretion of a water-soluble nutrient or to follow its excretion after a loading dose. Metabolites of nutrients also appear in the urine and their levels can be monitored. Twenty-four-hour urine collections can be assayed for creatinine to indicate muscle turnover rates or for nitrogen content to check protein intakes.

Analyses of bone include bone marrow biopsies, which will show the blood-forming cells, and radiographic examination, which can detect stages of bone development or rarefaction in ageing. Bone densitometry can provide an essential measure of the density of the skeleton.

It is also possible to measure the levels of some trace elements in the hair, although the scientific accuracy of these assays is not proven and, therefore, they should not be relied upon.

A large amount of research is currently directed at finding new and sensitive biomarkers for the activity of nutrients in the body. Developments in molecular biology have opened up possibilities of assessments at gene level to provide much more precise indicators of what role the nutrient is fulfilling and at what levels it needs to be present. A major challenge is to translate *in vitro* findings from laboratory studies to meaningful measures of nutritional status in humans.

Clinical indicators

Clinical indicators are used to detect changes in the external appearance of the body. A number of nutritional deficiencies may cause alterations in superficial structures, although many are non-specific. In addition, changes in appearance may also be unrelated to nutritional state. Signs occur most rapidly in those parts of the body where cell turnover is frequent, such as hair, skin and digestive tract (including mouth and tongue). Therefore, a clinical examination may include the hair, face, eyes, mouth, tongue, teeth, gums, glands (such as the thyroid), skin and nails, subcutaneous tissues (to detect fat thickness, oedema), and the musculoskeletal system (to note bone deformities, ability to walk, muscle wasting). Some internal organs, like the liver, may be felt to note any enlargement. Reflex tests may be performed to test nerve pathways and muscle function. A trained observer will be able to detect many changes in appearance; generally, these are followed up with more specific tests of nutritional status.

WHAT CAN WE LEARN FROM NUTRITIONAL ASSESSMENT?

The techniques described above can be combined to obtain a more detailed picture of the dietary intake and nutritional status of a population. Food intake at the household level has been monitored in the UK for over 50 years in the National Food Survey produced by the Ministry of Agriculture, Fisheries and Food (MAFF). However, this does not collect information about health. In the mid-1980s a new approach was adopted in the UK, with the introduction of a series of studies organized by the Department of Health and MAFF. The first of these was the Dietary and Nutritional Survey of British Adults (commissioned in 1986-87, published as Gregory et al., 1990). This collected information about food intake using 7-day records, together with blood and urine analyses, anthropometry and lifestyle features. The Health Survey for England was set up in 1991 to monitor trends in the nation's health, using a health and socio-economic questionnaire, physical measurements and blood analysis. This is now running continuously and provides an ongoing picture that includes key nutrition-related health indicators.

The National Diet and Nutrition Survey (NDNS) is a cyclical programme, which collects dietary information from surveys of the different age groups in the UK. In this way each subsection of the population should be re-studied every 8 years. Surveys have been published of pre-school children, older people over 65 years, the 4–18 age group; a new survey of adults is due for publication. Other groups, such as vegetarians, people living on a low income and pregnant women are likely to be studied. Monitoring of people's diet is an essential part of the work of the Food Standards Agency, set up in 2000 in the UK. This now has responsibility for commissioning surveys of nutritional intake, as part of its Nutrition Strategy Framework (FSA, 2001b).

Diet is dynamic and, for this reason, ongoing programmes of study and surveillance are necessary, to monitor both what people are eating and the effects of any dietary changes on the patterns of disease.

The NDNS programme aims to:

- provide detailed quantitative information about intakes and sources of nutrients, and the nutritional status of the population;
- measure blood and other indices that give evidence of nutritional status, and relate these to dietary, physiological and social data;
- monitor the diet for its nutritional adequacy;
- monitor the extent to which dietary targets are being met.

In Scotland, both the Scottish Heart Study, which included over 10 000 subjects aged 40–59, and one part of the European MONICA project have provided more specific information about the Scottish diet.

Other countries approach the monitoring of nutrition in similar ways. In the USA, the National Health and Nutritional Examination Survey (NHANES) collects data about food intakes, anthropometric indices, blood pressure and blood levels of minerals and vitamins. Surveillance of the diets of populations occurs in Australia, Canada and several European countries. Cross-population studies are also performed; the SENECA (Survey in Europe on Nutrition and the Elderly, a Concerted Action) study is one such example.

HOW IS THE INFORMATION GOING TO BE USED?

The declared purpose of any nutritional surveillance programme is to identify links between diet and disease, and thereby to formulate policy and advice aimed at minimizing the risk of disease, by altering the diet.

All countries have food policies that relate to the provision of a safe food supply, and that incorporate a wide range of measures relating to production, taxation, trade, politics and social and consumer issues. In some cases these may run counter to health policies, for example, by the promotion of fats, dairy produce and meat. These policies may also concentrate on legislation about pesticide residues, additives or food processing. Incorporating a nutrition policy into a food policy is, however, more problematic as there may be conflicting interests between food producers and the health professionals. Where nutrition is supported at government level, it is necessary for the government to facilitate the nutrition policy by changes to legislation, taxation, food labelling or other measures. Without such changes, a nutrition policy might not be workable. It is, therefore, important that government policy-making is informed by good-quality nutrition surveillance information, and that appropriate policy decisions are made.

The UK Food Standards Agency works with the Department of Health to improve the health of the UK population through encouraging and facilitating the adoption of a healthy balanced diet. The FSA has put forward its plans in the Nutrition Strategic Framework to enable it to achieve the following objectives.

- Secure a sound evidence base for action to promote a healthy diet.
- Develop appropriate means of informing the general public.
- Identify and address barriers to changing dietary behaviour.
- Evaluate and monitor the effectiveness of the action taken.

In order to achieve these objectives, the FSA is working with many other key players, including the Scientific Advisory Committee on Nutrition (SACN), which has replaced Committee on Medical Aspects of Food Policy (COMA), government departments including Health and Education, the food industry and the scientific community. Their work will build on many of the goals already achieved since the publication of 'The health of the nation' white paper, which set out specific health goals for England to be achieved within a decade (DoH, 1992). These related to heart disease and stroke, accidents, mental health, sexual health and cancer. A Nutrition Task Force (NTF) was set up to discuss ways in which the targets relating to nutrition could be achieved, using all the parties involved in the food chain to form 'healthy alliances'.

One of the major aims of the NTF was to produce a simple and easy to understand National Food Guide to provide a basic tool for teaching the elements of a balanced healthy diet. This was to be available to all educators, at whatever level, so that a consistent message was given from all sides. The National Food Guide (the Balance of Good Health) was developed, tested and eventually launched in 1994 (HEA, 1994). This is still used in the UK and has recently been reissued by the FSA as the Balance of Good Health; it is discussed more fully in Chapter 3. The NTF set in train a great number of initiatives and, as a consequence, nutritional issues are now much more to the fore in the national health agenda. The FSA now has the responsibility for taking these forward into the first decade of the twenty-first century. There is more information about food policy in Chapter 18.

SUMMARY

1 Nutrition is a very broad discipline. It may be of interest to people from a variety of backgrounds, who can also make useful contributions to its knowledge base.
2 There has been a huge increase in interest in nutrition in the last decade and people want to be better informed.
3 To be informed about nutrition, it is necessary to know what people eat and how his can be measured. The advantages and disadvantages of these methods are important to consider.
4 The dietary information must be supplemented by information about health. Both of these need continual updating, as neither remains static.
5 This information is used in making policy decisions about dietary advice to improve health.

STUDY QUESTIONS

1 Which methods of obtaining information about food intakes would you use in each of the following examples, and for what reason:
   a A study to identify groups in a population who have a high, or low, intake of dietary fibre (non-starch polysaccharide; NSP).
   b An investigation into iron intakes in a group of children who do not eat meat.
   c A comparison of food intakes between two populations who have different disease patterns.
   d A pregnant woman who needs advice about her diet.
2 Discuss with a colleague the benefits and disadvantages of adding specific nutrients to manufactured foods. Do you think this practice would help or hinder the work of a nutritionist?
3 What factors, apart from nutrition, might play a role in the health of a population? How could these be taken into account in results of nutritional assessment?
4 Perform a small survey among your acquaintances and friends to discover:
   a what they understand by the term nutrition;
   b how relevant to their health and well-being they consider their food intake to be;
   c if they would consider changing their diet to improve their health.

Draw some conclusions from your findings.

REFERENCES AND FURTHER READING

Bassey, E.J. 1986: Short report: demispan as a measure of skeletal size. *Annals of Human Biology* 13(5), 499–502.

Beaglehole, R., Bonita, R., Kjellstrom, T. 1993: *Basic epidemiology*. Geneva: WHO.

Beghin, I., Cap, M., Dujardin, B. 1988: *A guide to nutritional assessment*. Geneva: WHO.

Bingham, S.A., Gill, C., Welch, A. et al. 1994: Comparison of dietary assessment methods in nutritional epidemiology: weighed records v. 24 hr. recalls, food-frequency questionnaires and estimated-diet records. *British Journal of Nutrition* 72, 619–43.

Bingham, S.A., Welch, A.A. McTaggart, A. et al. 2001: Nutritional methods in the European Prospective Investigation of Cancer in Norfolk. *Public Health Nutrition* 4(3), 847–58.

Black, A.E. 2001: Dietary assessment for sports dietetics. *British Nutrition Foundation Nutrition Bulletin* 26, 29–42.

Cade, J., Thompson, R., Burley, V. et al. 2002: Development, validation and utilisation of food-frequency questionnaires – a review. *Public Health Nutrition* 5(4), 567–87.

Colhoun, H., Prescott-Clarke, P. (eds) 1996: *Health survey for England 1994*. London: HMSO.

DoH (UK Department of Health) 1992: *The health of the nation. A strategy for health in England*. London: HMSO.

Food Standards Agency 2001a: *The balance of good health*. London: FSA.
Food Standards Agency 2001b: *Your food – farm to fork*. London: FSA.
Food Standards Agency 2002a: *Food portion sizes*, 3rd edn. London: The Stationery Office.
Food Standards Agency 2002b: *McCance and Widdowson's the composition of foods*, 6th summary edn. Cambridge: The Royal Society of Chemistry.
Gregory, J., Foster, K., Tyler, H. et al. 1990: *The dietary and nutritional survey of British adults*. London: HMSO.
HEA (Health Education Authority) 1994: *Introducing the National Food Guide: The balance of good health. Information for educators and communicators*. London: Health Education Authority.
Livingstone, M.B.E., Prentice, A.M., Strain, J.J. et al. 1990: Accuracy of weighed dietary records in studies of diet and health. *British Medical Journal* 300, 708–12.
Livingstone, M.B.E., Robson, P.J. 2000: Measurement of dietary intake in children. *Proceedings of the Nutrition Society* 59, 279–93.
Margetts, B.M. Nelson, M. 1997: *Design concepts in nutritional epidemiology*, 2nd edn. Oxford: Oxford University Press.
Nelson, M., Haraldsdottir, J. 1998: Food photographs: practical guidelines II. Development and use of photographic atlases for assessing food portion size. *Public Health Nutrition* 1(4), 231–8.
Ransley, J.K., Donnelly, J.K., Khara, T.N. et al. 2001: The use of supermarket till receipts to determine the fat and energy intake in a UK population. *Public Health Nutrition* 4(6), 1279–86.
Trichopoulou, A., Naska, A. (eds) 2001: The DAFNE initiative. Assessment of dietary patterns across Europe using household budget survey data. *Public Health Nutrition* 4 (5B).
Welch, A.A., McTaggart, A., Mulligan, A.A. et al. 2001: DINER (Data Into Nutrients for Epidemiological Research) – a new data-entry program for nutritional analysis in the EPIC-Norfolk cohort and the 7-day diary method. *Public Health Nutrition* 4(6), 1253–65.

2 WHAT ARE THE INFLUENCES ON EATING HABITS?

The aims of this chapter are to:

- ❑ discuss the reasons for eating and possible mechanisms controlling eating;
- ❑ describe food habits;
- ❑ explore the factors influencing food choice, the interactions between them and how they change;
- ❑ help the reader understand how their own food habits are determined.

On completing the study of this chapter, you should be able to:

- ❑ describe the physiological and metabolic signals that determine food intake;
- ❑ discuss how social and cultural influences play a part in modifying basic physiological mechanisms;
- ❑ analyse your own food habits, and show how these have developed and are influenced currently;
- ❑ recognize the importance of individuals' particular food habits and appreciate how these may be resistant to change.

Activity 2.1

Before studying this chapter, spend a little time thinking about:

- why you eat;
- what you eat;
- what are some of the reasons for choosing the particular foods.

You may find that this is a surprisingly difficult task. We are generally quite unconscious of our reasons for eating and choosing particular foods. Only when we have a basic framework with which to study these influences can we begin to gain insight into our own behaviour related to food.

Most people, if asked why they eat, would respond with 'to stay alive' or 'because of hunger'. Both of these are appropriate answers: the body has a physiological need for food and, when deprived for even a short period of time, a sensation of hunger is experienced. This is a normal physiological response, which is designed to balance the output and storage of nutrients with their input from food.

In addition, however, people eat for a number of other reasons. In the West, eating is a matter of habit because food is usually widely available, often at all hours of day or night. There are also socially accepted 'mealtimes', when there is an expectation of eating, regardless of hunger, and there are social norms associated with eating, which define what behaviour is and is not acceptable.

Food provides us with sensory satisfaction, it is (usually) pleasant to eat, and this aspect of certain foods can induce people to eat when they have no physiological need to do so.

We have a very personal relationship with food. It is something we deliberately take into our body and which becomes part of us. This can have very profound meanings for some people, but for everyone it implies that there are psychological influences on eating.

Each of these influences on eating will be discussed in turn, to demonstrate that even something as basic as supplying the body with the energy for its survival can involve more than an understanding of physiology.

REASONS FOR EATING

Physiological need

Signals relating to all of the processes involved in the initiation and cessation of eating are integrated and organized by the brain. These controlling mechanisms have been studied mainly in experimental animals. This is because humans are more complicated, with many cultural and social conventions, which influence food intake, and which can override the physiological mechanisms. A schematic diagram of the various components of the control mechanism integrated by the brain is given in Figure 2.1.

In an individual whose weight remains constant, there is evidently a balance between the input of food and its metabolism and energy output. Consideration of the various stages of the process helps to identify where control mechanisms could be operating.

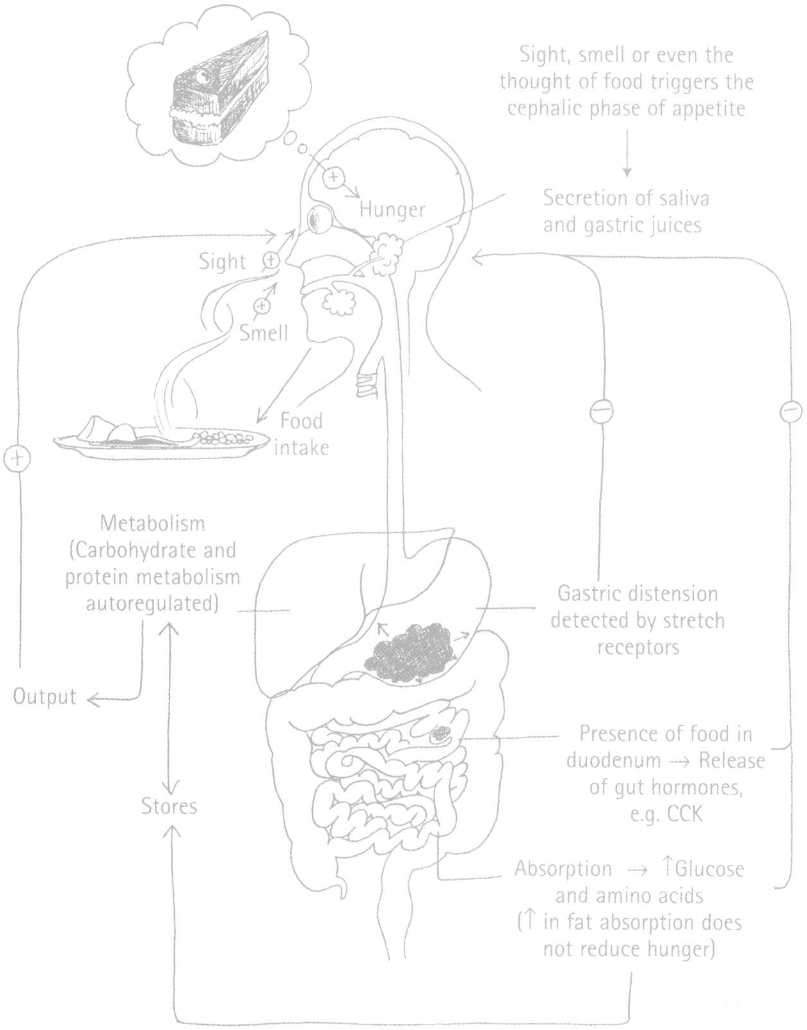

Figure 2.1 Physiological factors controlling hunger and food intake.

Sensory signals

The sight, smell or even thought of food triggers the cephalic phase of appetite, which stimulates hunger and prepares the digestive tract for the ingestion of food by secretion of saliva and gastric juices. When eating starts, the food stimulates the senses of taste and touch (via the texture and consistency of the food). Variety in the sensory properties of foods offered in a meal can further stimulate eating, whereas a meal that contains only one item rapidly leads to satiation. This is the sensation that stops food intake at a meal and is associated with a feeling of fullness.

Pre-absorptive information

Ingested food causes gastric distension. This is detected by stretch receptors, which send signals to the brain. The presence of food and early digestion products in the duodenum causes the release of a large number of gut hormones, some of which have been shown to inhibit food intake. The most extensively studied of these is cholecystokinin (CCK), which has been shown to produce satiety in many animal species, including humans. CCK is stimulated particularly by the presence of protein and fat digestion products in the duodenum. The presence of residual protein in the stomach at the start of a meal has a restraining effect on food intake, and particularly on the intake of protein. Newly discovered peptides, such as PYY and ghrelin signal to the brain that the stomach is full (Wilding, 2002). Satiety is described as the sensation that delays the next food intake, thus affecting the interval between meals.

Ingestion of liquids, even those containing macronutrients, is less well regulated by these mechanisms than ingestion of solids.

Post-absorptive signals

All of the digestion products have been proposed as regulators of food intake. Fluctuations in blood glucose level and, therefore, its availability to the cells of the nervous system and brain, were originally believed to be the cornerstone of feeding behaviour regulation. Carbohydrate-rich meals suppress further intake for between 1 and 3 hours after eating. This may be associated with the period during which insulin levels are raised after a meal. This is the glucostatic theory of food intake. However, it cannot satisfactorily explain control of eating in all situations.

A further theory, the lipostatic theory, proposes a relationship between body fat reserves and eating behaviour, such that an increase in stored fat would reduce intake. It is only recently, however, that a mechanism to support this has been identified.

Leptin is a relatively recently discovered (in 1994) protein, released principally from adipose tissue as well as other tissues. Because it is released at one site and acts at a distant site, it fulfils the criteria of a hormone. Amounts produced reflect the size of the fat store in both humans and animals. Leptin release from adipose tissue is also influenced by levels of feeding, such that fasting results in a rapid fall in leptin secretion and levels rise again on refeeding. In addition, exposure to cold inhibits leptin release. Leptin secretion from adipose tissue is also influenced by several other hormones. Release is stimulated by insulin, glucocorticoids, oestrogens and cytokines (released as part of immune reactions). The major inhibitors of leptin release are adrenaline and noradrenaline, mediated by the sympathetic nervous system. One of the functions of leptin is to act in the hypothalamus, where it causes the release of a number of neuropeptides, including neuropeptide Y. This has a potent action to inhibit food intake. In obese humans and animals, leptin receptors have a low sensitivity, resulting in poor recognition of the size of fat stores and, therefore, dysregulation of food intake.

Further regulation of food intake may occur via the activity of lipoprotein lipase, an enzyme found in adipose tissue.

Amino acid levels also have an effect on feeding behaviour, with shifts in plasma and brain concentrations of particular amino acids causing changes in intake. There is competition between different amino acids for uptake across the blood–brain barrier; consequently, an elevation of one amino acid may inhibit the uptake of others. The importance of some amino acids lies in their role as precursors for brain neurotransmitter substances; these may be the effectors of changes in feeding behaviour.

Metabolism

The blood levels of metabolites are regulated by the liver and peripheral tissues, which remove them from the circulation and may also have an effect on feeding behaviour.

It is becoming clear that metabolism of the energy-providing nutrients is regulated with different levels of precision. Alcohol, as a potential toxin, must be oxidized completely and removed as quickly as possible. Its metabolic regulation is perfect and all alcohol is completely metabolized.

The capacity of the body to store carbohydrate and protein is limited, and blood levels of glucose and amino acids are carefully controlled. It is now believed that under normal circumstances very little carbohydrate is actually converted to fat. The conversion of carbohydrate to fat is very inefficient, with approximately 25 per cent of the potential energy wasted as heat. Metabolism of both glucose and amino acids is thought to 'autoregulate' to match the intake level.

Fat metabolism, however, exhibits no such 'autoregulation', probably because of the large capacity for fat storage in the body. Therefore, fat metabolism does not correlate well with fat intake and there is no evidence that fat oxidation adjusts when intake increases. Consequently, one can conclude that fat intake plays a smaller role in the control of food intake than do either carbohydrates or proteins. This may provide an explanation for the 'fattening' effects of high-fat diets, which can be consumed without any consequent change to fat oxidation. Also evidence from feeding studies of diets where fat content has been covertly increased shows that a change in fat levels has no effect on satiety and subsequent food intakes. This means that such diets are easy to consume leading to 'passive overconsumption', and may be a significant contributory factor in obesity.

Integration by the brain

Early research identified hunger and satiety centres in the hypothalamus; these could be artificially stimulated or destroyed, resulting in starvation or overeating. The function of these centres was thought to be the maintenance of adequate levels of energy-providing nutrients in the blood. The dietary macronutrients, carbohydrates, fats and proteins, were the primary candidates for these regulatory factors. It is now clear that this is an oversimplified picture. The brain receives information from receptors and metabolites about the whole feeding process, from the initial thought about food to the final metabolism of its breakdown products. Changes in plasma concentrations of nutrients resulting from metabolism in the liver and peripheral tissues are also monitored. A number of these have been mentioned in the earlier sections. In particular, leptin levels are believed to be important, through their action on neuropeptide Y, causing inhibition of food intake. Low levels of leptin are thought to cause a number of adaptive changes to minimize weight loss, including increased food intake. In addition, levels of serotonin, which promotes feelings of satiety, are influenced by the amounts of tryptophan crossing the blood–brain barrier. By these means, food intake and metabolic processes can be regulated to match the body's needs. This complex integration occurs in the brain, probably by appropriate changes in the levels of neurotransmitters.

In addition, it has been proposed that unconscious reflex pathways are established, particularly during childhood, whereby the body 'learns' the metabolic consequences of particular eating patterns and responds accordingly. If such reflexes are not established, perhaps due to erratic eating behaviour in childhood, then control mechanisms remain less efficient. Much remains to be learned about the complex control of eating.

Habit as an influence on eating behaviour

In parts of the world where food is readily available, intake could occur at any time of day or night. Most people do not eat continuously, but usually at fairly clearly defined 'mealtimes', with 'snack times' interspersed between them. This behaviour has become a habit, and many Westerners believe that they should have three meals a day together with two or three snacks, with the main meal either in the middle of the day or in the evening (see Figure 2.2). In other societies, especially among the poor, fewer meals are eaten, maybe only one or at most two

Figure 2.2 Habit influences eating behaviour.

within a day. Therefore, it appears that there is no physiological need to eat so frequently, although it will be necessary to eat to satiation when mealtimes are infrequent. If eating is more continuous, the sensations of satiety or hunger may never be experienced. The brain, therefore, lacks the necessary input to recognize these, which may result in poor regulation of eating behaviour at some point in life.

What is the difference between meals and snacks?

A snack is an eating occasion where just one type of food is eaten, perhaps accompanied by a drink, and might include biscuits, chocolate or sandwiches, for example. Often this is eaten in an informal setting, or perhaps in the street, or while travelling. In the last 20 years, more informal eating has been taking place, as lifestyles become more flexible. In some instances, all of the food taken during the course of a day may be classified as 'snacks', with perhaps as many as ten or more being consumed. This is particularly prevalent among young people, and causes concern to nutritionists as some of the snack foods eaten are low in micronutrients, but may contain substantial amounts of fat and/or sugar. However, not all snack foods are nutritionally poor: sandwiches, fruit, nuts and drinks, such as milk or fruit juice, can provide useful nutrients.

A meal generally contains a selection of different separate items, usually eaten with utensils (although in some cultures this is not usual), and takes some time to prepare and to eat. Traditionally, this would be eaten in a designated eating place, for example, at a table. More flexible lifestyles, however, mean that meals now may be eaten in more informal settings, perhaps from a tray while watching the television, or in the street out of the packaging in the case of fish and chips or a burger. Because it includes more items, a meal is more likely to contain a greater number of nutrients, although there are still meals which can be nutritionally very poor.

There needs to be a degree of organization of mealtimes in a society that operates by the clock. Chaos would ensue if in every office, classroom and business organization people wandered off to eat whenever they felt like it. Some accepted schedule is essential, both from the consumers' and from the cooks' point of view. It could be argued that rigorous timing of meals is introduced too early in life. Some infants in the first months of life are still fed 'by the clock', usually 4-hourly. Feeding 'on demand' gives the infant the opportunity to be fed when actually hungry, although it does introduce a level of unpredictability into the mother's life.

Some people eat just because food is available. They are unable to resist the desire to eat, and are apparently less sensitive to their own internal cues about needing food than to external signals. Others may deliberately avoid food or eat in very small amounts, disregarding their internal signals and gauging what they eat by external cues related to the size of the plate, what other people are having or what they think is an appropriate amount for them.

Both of the above types have developed particular habits that control their eating, which are usually more powerful than the physiological need. In the extreme, these can result in disordered eating – both overeating, or bingeing, and compulsive dieting, or perhaps a cycling between these two extremes.

Figure 2.3 Psychological need as a trigger to eating.

Psychological need

Eating is a pleasurable activity, and can satisfy some of our internal needs. Boredom provides a major incentive to eating and may fill many empty hours for people. Depression or anxiety can also make people turn to food for comfort. This is believed to stem from the reassurance given by food provided by parents to children, linking positive feelings about parental care and love with the food. It is important that the 'food as comfort' response is not made too frequently, as it is likely to result in overweight, often with associated emotional problems (see Figure 2.3).

We may also offer food to people to comfort them; for example, a child who has fallen and been hurt may be cuddled and then offered something to eat (often a sweet or biscuit). After a funeral, people may come together to share food. This acts as a comforting gesture for both those providing the food, as well as those eating it. If we remember that provision of food is linked with loving and caring, it is easy to see how rejection of the food by the intended recipient can be hurtful and painful. This happens with young children who are learning about food, but can become manipulative and cause their carers considerable hurt. They may use food rejection to express feelings of anger, jealousy or insecurity, or to gain attention. Children who have to follow a special diet for health reasons may be particularly at risk of this type of behaviour. Using food as a weapon can become a habit maintained into adult life. Sometimes this weapon is turned against the self, in situations where food intake is chaotic.

Sensory appeal

The way in which a food stimulates our senses by its appearance and smell, taste and texture may also increase our desire to eat it. Most people claim that the taste of the food is the prime consideration, although for adolescents the appearance also rates highly.

The visual appeal of the food, although important to attract the eye, can be quite deceptive, however, and gives no indication of nutritional value. Most sighted people would be very wary of accepting and eating a food they could not see. Our expectations of the taste of a food are prepared by its appearance – we expect an orange-coloured drink to have a sweet, citric taste; anything else might lead to rejection. The food industry is well aware of the importance of the 'correct' visual stimulus and uses a range of colorants to produce an acceptable finished appearance. However, the numbers of these are less than they were 10–20 years ago as consumers become more concerned about safety aspects, and are increasingly prepared to buy foods with a more 'natural' colour (see Figure 2.4).

The smell of the food must also meet our expectations. We use this to detect if food has 'gone off' and we are enticed to eat by pleasant aromas. We can recognize many foods purely from their smell. Smell and taste interact to produce the flavour of the food; if the sense of smell is lost; for example, when suffering from a cold, food may seem tasteless. The number of taste buds is highest in children, who have them on the insides of the cheeks and throat, as well as over the surface of the tongue. These begin to decrease from adolescence and are considerably reduced by the age of 70.

Figure 2.4 Sensory appeal as a trigger for eating.

Children's food preferences and choices are driven primarily by taste. Relative to adults, children have a preference for very sweet taste, and avoid bitter tastes. The liking for intense sweetness declines into adolescence, more so in girls than boys. There is also a link between energy density and sweetness, and this is believed to be a means by which intake of high-energy foods is assured to support growth and development in children. Once adulthood is reached, the need for such energy-dense foods is reduced, and the liking for intense sweetness tends to disappear. The taste acuity for the bitter taste also declines, and adults accept bitter tastes more readily. There is also a move to less energy-dense foods, which are often those associated with a healthier diet, with increasing age. Taste perception can change in certain circumstances: pregnant women, surgical patients and people with cancer all report an altered ability to taste certain foods. It has been suggested that zinc status plays a role in this. Unusual appetites for particular foods may also develop. People can become accustomed to a particular taste if this is perceived to be an advantage. The bitter tastes found in beer, quinine (in tonic water) and coffee appear to be an acquired taste for many people, although some find them unpleasant all their lives.

The texture and taste of the food in the mouth provide us with the pleasurable aspects of eating. The feel of the food in the mouth can include its texture, temperature and even any pain it produces. We expect particular foods to be presented at a certain temperature (e.g. ice cream or hot tea). Extremes of temperature can cause pain to the mouth and teeth. Chilli contains a chemical substance (capsacin), which irritates the nerve endings, triggering pain. Some substances can cause a local anaesthetic effect in the mouth – chewing coca leaves (widespread practice in parts of South America) has this effect; its purpose is to dull the hunger sensation among peoples who have little food.

Food technologists can measure optimal levels of various sensory characteristics (such as sugar content, aroma, water content, temperature), which are associated with the highest level of pleasure. These are aptly named 'bliss points'. These are not fixed forever and can become modified if the diet changes, although the initial alteration to the diet will be associated with a reduction in pleasure. For example, an individual who normally takes two spoonfuls of sugar in their tea probably will have that concentration of sugar as their 'bliss point'. Cutting out sugar will result in a reduction in 'bliss'. In time, the subject is likely to adapt to the newer taste, the level of 'bliss' is restored at a lower sweetness, and drinking tea with the original level of sugar will no longer be acceptable. This sequence will apply to other changes made to the diet that have sensory implications, including cutting down fat or salt intakes.

Variety also encourages us to eat. Studies on both animals and humans have shown clearly that, when offered a variety of food, total intake is greater than when just a single food is offered. Thus, it is possible to make rats overweight by offering them a 'cafeteria diet', containing chips, burgers, crisps, chocolate, etc., rather than ordinary rat pellets; they eat more of the mixed diet. Humans will also overeat when offered something new; for example, having apparently eaten their fill of a main course, many people will still manage to have a dessert afterwards. It has also been noted that more food is eaten when meals are accompanied by wine and taken in a social setting. These factors occurring together can promote an unconscious overconsumption.

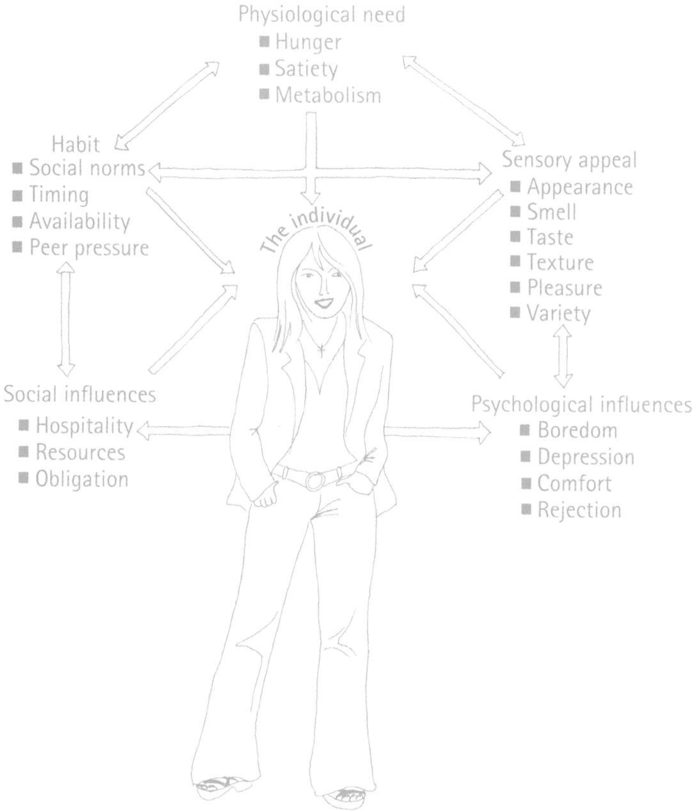

Figure 2.5 Why do we eat?

Overweight is much less common in communities around the world where only a few foods appear regularly in the diet – it seems that monotony imposes its own limits on eating. On the other hand, organizing food into different courses, with different flavours, seems to enhance the food intake.

Social influence

Food may also be used in a social context to please or displease others. Offering food or drink is recognized as a gesture of hospitality, and refusal may be interpreted as rejection. This may extend to the obligation to eat food that is not wanted or even disliked, to avoid offending the giver. This may be a particular problem for visitors to other countries, who may be presented with unknown or even unacceptable food, yet feel obliged to consume it.

In situations where food is scarce, or budgets are very restricted, wasting food may be socially unacceptable, and individuals may feel it necessary to eat everything provided. The opposite may also apply – waste may be quite acceptable where food supplies are plentiful, or where left-over food can be put to other uses, such as feeding pigs or poultry.

All of these influences and some of their interrelationships are summarized in Figure 2.5.

FOOD HABITS

So far, we have learned that the primary reason for eating is to satisfy our hunger, but that what and when we eat can also reflect who we are, the society we live in, our upbringing and how we perceive ourselves. We can define food habits as the typical behaviour of a particular group of people in relation to food. They provide an important signal of the identity of the group. They will determine food choice, as well as eating times and numbers of meals, size of portions, methods of food preparation and

Activity 2.2

Using your experience, try to identify which of the factors given in Figure 2.5 are likely to be most important for the following people:

a yourself
b a pre-school-age child
c a mother with young children
d a teenage girl/boy
e an elderly woman, living on her own.

Account for your answers.

who takes part in the meal. Food habits are a product of the environmental influences on a culture and, in general, are resistant to change.

Some of the components of an individual's food habits are shown in Figure 2.6.

Acquisition of food habits

The acquisition of food habits is largely unconscious, since they are acquired at a young age from parents, which incidentally ensures transmission between generations. The strongest influence on a child in its acquisition of food habits is generally its mother, who is likely to be the most closely involved with the provision of food. Children learn what is acceptable as food, and what is not. Foods that are associated with good times are often preferred to those that do not have these connotations. We may remember particularly foods that we ate on holiday and seek these out to help relive happy memories. Children are dependent on the food practices and beliefs of the adult caregivers; this may restrict a child's opportunities to try many foods, if they are not part of the adult's food choice. In addition, some foods may be seen as inappropriate for children and, therefore, not offered.

After the initial socialization within the home environment, children learn more food practices from other people, or institutions outside the home. A major force may be the school, where behaviour is learned from other children, as well as through the food provided in school meals and tuck shops, and more formal teaching about food in lessons. All of these will broaden the child's view of food and will affect the food practices.

Later still, other people may influence food habits as different views are encountered with a widening social circle. Foreign travel also provides experience of different food habits.

Changing food habits

Although food habits are resistant to change, they are not static. Change may come from within the culture. For example, the increase in female employment in the West has resulted in a dramatic increase in the availability of convenience food. Fewer households now eat meals prepared from basic ingredients on a regular basis. Weekday meals in particular are composed to a great extent of convenience items, with perhaps the addition of a home-prepared vegetable or starchy staple (such as rice or potato). The prevalence of microwave ovens, together with widespread ownership of freezers, has meant that meals can be ready in minutes, and that even quite young children can prepare themselves

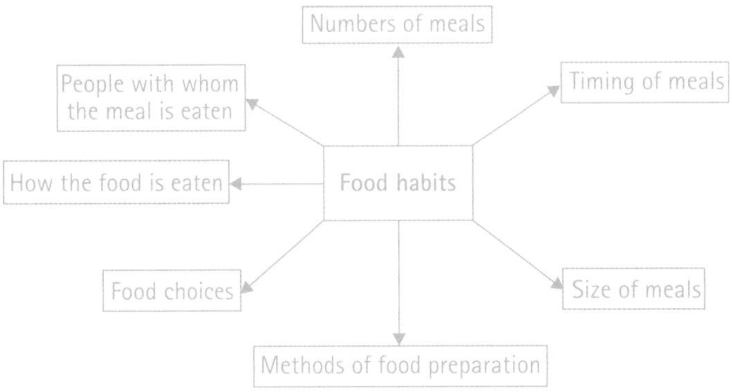

Figure 2.6 Some of the main components of a person's food habits.

something hot to eat with little risk of accident. The consequence of this has been that, in many families, mealtimes are no longer taken together. Instead, individual members of the family may eat at times convenient to themselves, often heating up different meals in the microwave. In addition, around 30 per cent of meals eaten are likely to be consumed away from home, in work or school canteens, cafes, fast-food outlets, restaurants or in the car. The National Food Survey (Department for Environment, Food and Rural Affairs (DEFRA), 2001) showed that on average three meals per week were eaten outside the home (not from the home food supply), and this represents 30 per cent of the expenditure on food.

Another source of change is the increase in the availability of information about world cookery. Examples of the cuisine of different cultures are found in restaurants, supermarkets and as cookery programmes on the television, and the wide availability of many exotic ingredients makes it possible for these 'foreign' dishes to be included into traditional food habits. Many books describe how to prepare these dishes.

The media are also responsible for changing food habits. This may occur through the following.

- Advertising and the promotion of new food products (although the information given here may be biased).
- Programmes or articles that aim to increase people's knowledge about food, perhaps in the context of nutrition and health.
- Providing role models in the form of characters in programmes and advertising. These contribute a subtle force towards change in food habits by the food they eat and the attitudes they express. Some of the messages put forward are not necessarily conducive to health; for example, there is believed to be a prevailing message that only thin women are healthy and attractive, which causes often disastrous changes to food habits among the female population.

Food habits may have to change when an individual suffers from an illness requiring dietary alteration for its management. The difficulty of changing food habits is best seen in such subjects, who often struggle to maintain dietary changes, even when there are very good health reasons for doing so.

Nutrition educators and health promoters aim to change food habits towards a healthier balance. This is a very complex process because of the multi-faceted influences on food habits. Different influences may be at work in determining what is eaten from day to day or even from meal to meal. A further factor is the strength of the attitude of the subject towards food and healthy eating. If they are ambivalent about either of these, change may be difficult to bring about. Finally, the subjective recognition that change is needed to the diet is a powerful influence in determining whether it is undertaken.

Therefore, an educator may need to consider the strength of the subject's belief:

- that food and healthy eating are important;
- that these can influence their individual health in a beneficial way;
- that making changes to food and eating has a high priority amongst factors that influence food choice.

Studies have identified many barriers to making changes towards healthy eating that are more prevalent amongst those subjects who make fewer changes. In the study by Margetts et al. (1998), these included:

- a perception that there is a lack of clear messages about healthy foods;
- a belief that the tastiest foods are the ones that are 'bad';
- confusion about what to eat;
- difficulty of eating healthy food away from home;
- costs of healthy eating;
- lack of concern about what is eaten.

In addition, changes towards healthier eating are less likely to be found among younger, lower income groups and those who smoke. This emphasizes that dietary change is closely linked to other lifestyle indicators in complex ways.

Food choices

Within the context of a culture's food habits, each individual makes their own, personal food choices, which are likely to be different from those of anyone else. There are many ways to study individual food choices, and much has been written about them. There are still areas of uncertainty, however, and research into determinants of food choice, especially within family groups, is ongoing. Viewpoints may be anthropological, economic, physiological or administrative, political, psychological or sociological, as well as nutritional. The following is a nutritional perspective on food choice.

In very broad terms, people can only choose from the range of food available to them; thus, factors that determine food availability are important. Given a range of foods, an individual will not necessarily choose to eat all of them. The choice will depend on what is acceptable to them, personally. Hence the two main determinants of food choice are availability and acceptability. The main factors influencing these are shown in Tables 2.1 and 2.2.

Availability

Physical/environmental factors

In the West, this factor is less important now than it was 20 or more years ago. Food preservation, storage and distribution around world markets are so efficient that it rarely matters whether the local area produces a food or not. It can generally be imported from elsewhere. This creates a uniformity of foods available, and there is concern that many interesting varieties of locally produced foods are being lost, or remain available only in a speciality market. Differences exist, however, in what food is available to buy in a locality. This will be dependent on factors such as population density and, therefore, the number of shops in the vicinity, and ease of access, which will determine the cost of transporting food into the area. The perishability of a food will also determine the range over which it can be transported. For these reasons, rural areas in most countries generally have a smaller range of food available than urban areas.

However, in places not reached by the world market, where locally grown produce is eaten, physical factors such as type of soil, rainfall or transportation are important determinants of what food is actually available. Perishability of food and the means of preservation available will also determine how long food can be kept. Thus, for a subsistence family in a developing country, physical factors are extremely important determinants. Their access to the local market and the range of foods available there will have a major impact on the food they eat.

TABLE 2.1 Factors influencing the availability of foods

Physical/environmental	**Legislative**	**Economic**	**Food handling**
Locality (soil/climate)	National/international laws	Money	Access to shops
Transport/marketing		Budget priorities	Cooking skills
Distribution costs	Health recommendations	Cost of foods	Knowledge
Perishability		Significance of foods	Cooking facilities
		Variety	Time available

TABLE 2.2 Factors influencing the acceptability of foods

Cultural	**Physiological**	**Social/psychological**
National identity	Physiological need	Status (of self/of foods)
Culture group	Hunger/satiety	Group identity
Core, secondary and peripheral foods	Appetite/aversion	Communication
Meal patterns	Sensory appeal	Ritual
Religious ideology	Personal preference/choice	Emotional support
Taboos/prohibitions	Therapeutic diets	Reward/punishment

Legislative factors

Government legislation aims to ensure that food available for purchase is of a suitable quality and has not been adulterated. There is also agricultural policy, which regulates the prices received by the producers of crops. Trade agreements and sanctions may operate at particular times between different countries. In addition, the UK, as a member state of the European Union, is subject to Europe-wide laws relating to food and agricultural production. All these factors will influence the type of food available for sale in shops and its exact composition, especially in terms of additives and minimum standards of composition.

In recent years, the labelling of foods has become more explicit, with more information about the nutritional composition appearing on the label. This is to be applauded as an important means of educating people about nutrition, as well as providing useful information for anyone who wishes to understand more about the food they eat. European laws on labelling affect products marketed in the UK.

Legislation has also been needed to control the introduction of some of the new foods resulting from developments in food technology. Recent introductions in Britain have included irradiated foods, items produced from research in genetic engineering and foods containing synthetic substitutes (e.g. for fat). In addition, there is a growing market in 'functional foods'. All have been the subject of safety testing, and have needed to obtain government approval before being marketed.

Economic factors

The cost of food is a major determinant of what people perceive as available to them; it ranks only after taste in general surveys of influences on choice. Within the range of foods available to them, people can only eat what they can afford, or choose to afford. The second point is important, since it brings into consideration the priorities that exist in spending money. The annual National Food Survey shows that in 2000 (DEFRA, 2001) on average people in Britain spent 9.5 per cent of their budget on food, although this is less among the better off, and can be much more (up to 30 per cent or more) among lower income groups. Even though the percentage of income spent is higher, the amount of money spent is actually less; in 2000, households in the lowest income group spent 15 per cent less than the UK average on food and drink. People see their food budget as one of the more flexible items in their expenditure; other expenses such as fuel, rent, cigarettes and alcohol may take priority. When income is small and food budget cuts are made, food distribution within the family may change, food treats may still be bought and the children's likes and dislikes attended to. The variety of foods eaten becomes smaller and the diet becomes more monotonous. These issues are discussed further in Chapter 13.

Food handling

If food is available and there is money with which to buy it, bringing it home and preparing it for eating remain as possible areas of difficulty. Getting to the shops and bringing food home may be a major problem, especially for families with no car, older people or those with disabilities. This will determine where the shopping is done, how often and the sorts of foods that can be bought and carried home. Many supermarkets in Britain have moved to peripheral locations outside towns, which makes shopping easier for the car-owning customers who spend a lot of money, but very difficult for those families living further away, without transport. These then rely on the local shops, which inevitably keep less stock, thereby restricting choice.

Once the food is in the kitchen, most of it has to be prepared in some way for eating. This will depend largely on the knowledge and skill of the cook, facilities and time available. Cooking skills are variable; it has been suggested that fewer people now know how to cook. This has been attributed to the escalating reliance on pre-prepared convenience foods, which eliminate the need for cooking skills. Often the only skill required is the ability to open a packet or can and heat the contents. Some foods can even be eaten cold out of the packaging in which they were bought. In families where cooking does take place, the complexity of the preparation of the food will reflect the cook's personal experience of food and cooking, education, interest and time available.

Acceptability

Cultural factors

Each cultural group possesses its own typical food selection patterns. These may be similar to those of related cultural groups, but are unlikely to be the same. Even within a relatively small country such as the UK, there are different regional foods, such as haggis in Scotland, laver bread in Wales and jellied eels in London. However, all these groups also share similar 'British' food choices, such as fish and chips or roast beef. It is not just the choice of food that may vary between the cultures, but also the way in which it is cooked, the seasonings and flavourings used and the way it is served.

Traditional foods confer a sense of identity and belonging. This is very deeply held, since for most people it derives from the socialization process in childhood, discussed earlier. The strength and persistence of this cultural identity may be illustrated by two examples. First, when people holiday in another country, many will seek out foods with which they are familiar. Although they may be prepared to try the local dishes, it is often with a sense of curiosity and a preconceived idea that they will be strange. More importantly, when people emigrate to another country for long-term settlement, they often suffer a sense of alienation or difference from the adopted environment. They may adopt the host country's style of dress and speak the language, but the food that is eaten in the privacy of their home may remain very traditional. This provides a link with the homeland and support in an alien environment.

If in addition to providing a cultural identity, the food is also associated with religious beliefs, traditional food habits may persist longer still. Studies on migrants to Britain show that first-generation members adhere strongly to traditional food practices. With the second generation, these practices are less widespread, unless they are associated with religious prescription. Conflict may arise between the generations as a result. Short-term migration does not, however, bring about changes to the diet, with evidence pointing to a reluctance to include host-country foods and an adherence to traditional foods, even if they are hard to find.

The types of foods that may be served to form a meal are culturally determined. People may classify foods in different ways: for example, into 'sweet' and 'savoury', or 'healthy' and 'less healthy', 'snack food' (or 'junk food') and 'proper meal'. Nutritionists categorize foods more systematically in terms of their main nutritional role in the diet. Currently, most Western countries use five food groups: cereal/grain (or starchy) foods, fruit and vegetables, meat and meat substitutes, milk and dairy produce, fatty and sugary foods. An appropriate amount of each group should be eaten to provide a nutritionally balanced diet.

Foods can also be described in terms of their place in the diet, as core, secondary or peripheral foods (Table 2.3).

As well as providing the accepted norms for what can be eaten, cultural identity will also determine what should not be eaten. Each culture has clearly defined ideas about what is 'food' and 'non-food'. In many instances, these distinctions have arisen for sound reasons, including scarcity of a particular plant or animal, or its potential harmfulness. In addition, there may be prohibitions on particular foods at certain times of life, particularly in infancy and during pregnancy. Many cultures have prohibitions associated with pregnancy, based on beliefs about possible effects on the fetus. Although generally harmless, some may restrict intakes of foods, such as meat or other useful sources of iron, for which needs are increased in pregnancy. It is also believed by some that eating a particular mixture of foods around the time of conception can influence the gender of the embryo.

A taboo that occurs in most world cultures is that against cannibalism, but even this deep-rooted taboo is not universal. There are records throughout history of people reverting to cannibalism in times of severe hardship, such as wartime siege, or following an air crash in an inaccessible region, as well as some cases of murder followed by cannibalism.

Many world religions also forbid the eating of particular foods completely or at special times. These include a prohibition on pork among Muslims and Jews, and on all animals

TABLE 2.3 Core, secondary and peripheral foods

Core foods	Secondary foods	Peripheral foods
The most important foods in the diet – the staple of the region (normally a cereal or a root)	Enhance the meal, but not essential	Non-essential, but pleasant to eat
Usually one or two foods only (in Britain: bread/cereals and potatoes)	May have specific perceived properties (e.g. protein-rich, healthy, promoting balance, suitable for particular ages/ conditions in life)	Special occasion foods, e.g. eaten at festivals, celebrations (e.g. turkey at Christmas or Thanksgiving, birthday cake)
Tend to appear in most meals	May include meat/fish, vegetables, pulses, fruit	Food with special properties, e.g. bedtime drinks
Nutritionally, a source of carbohydrate, some protein and a range of minerals and vitamins		May include biscuits, cakes confectionery, alcoholic drinks, exotic fruit, sauces, drinks, e.g. tea/coffee

Activity 2.3

Make a list of your food intake over the previous few days. For each food, identify to which of the categories in Table 2.3 it belongs.

- Which of the categories appears most frequently?
- Are your meals made up of all three categories?
- What about your snacks?

among the Hindus. These are considered further in Chapter 13.

Physiological factors

Appetite is associated with memories of particular foods, and is the desire for a specific food or foods. In animals, there is some evidence that such desires for particular foods are linked to a specific nutritional need. This is very difficult to demonstrate in humans and has, therefore, not been proven. The opposite is an aversion to a specific food; this is often linked to an unpleasant memory of that food or an experience associated with it.

Personal preferences for foods are usually linked to a liking for the sensory attributes of the food, which contribute to the pleasure of eating it. Liking a food is frequently given as the main reason for choosing it; however, people will eat foods they feel neutral about, or even dislike in certain circumstances, for example, to please others. Most people select their food from a relatively small number of items that appear frequently in their diet. New foods may be tried on occasions, often as a result of advertising or promotion of the product in the media. The wealthier members of society include more variety in their choices than those on a low income. Compared with traditional hunter–gatherer societies, who would eat a wide range of wild products from the land at different seasons, our Western diet is quite limited.

Children are considered to be the age group most reluctant to diversify their diet, with some individuals eating so few foods that they threaten their nutritional status.

Because of the importance of personal preference in making food choice, it is important that individuals are allowed to exercise some control over what is eaten. Loss of control can lead to loss of appetite. This can be a reason for poor intakes in hospitalized patients or residents in other institutions, where menus are centrally determined, perhaps repetitive and little choice is offered.

The need to follow a special diet for therapeutic reasons will affect personal food selection, and is a further area where loss of control and self-determination may cause problems with compliance. This is a particular problem in adolescents, who may refuse to comply with dietary restrictions, as part of the maturing process. Food selection may be deliberately restricted in those wishing to control their weight: eating behaviour becomes inhibited, and less food than is required to alleviate hunger may be eaten. Also, specific food groups (the 'fattening foods') may be avoided, while others are eaten in their place (the 'slimming foods'). If the inhibition of intake is broken, for a number of reasons, food intake may become excessive, resulting in binge eating, until the inhibitory influence is restored. This pattern of restrained eating appears to exist, to a greater or lesser extent, in up to 80–90 per cent of women in Western society. In some it results in clinically recognized conditions of anorexia or bulimia nervosa.

Special diets may be adopted for moral or ideological perspectives, and these will impose constraints on individual food choice. Of these, the vegetarian diet has become the most prevalent in Britain in recent years. The extent to which people stop eating all animal produce varies, and some of those claiming to be vegetarian may still actually consume some animal foods, even white meat as well as fish, eggs, cheese and milk. Reasons for choosing this diet may stem from abhorrence of the killing of animals (and the methods used), and concern about the exploitation of animals reared in cramped conditions for food. More recent publicity about aspects of food safety related to foods of animal origin, such as beef, chicken, eggs and milk, has convinced others that avoiding these foods may be healthier (see Chapter 13 for further discussion).

Whatever the rationale for the special diet, the individual's freedom of choice is restricted. It makes the person different from the rest of their culture group (this may be one of the objectives!). Consequently, it may create barriers to the sharing of food, causing alienation and possibly avoidance of social eating situations, or lack of compliance with therapeutic diets. Giving as much freedom of choice as possible within the constraints of a special diet will help the individual to regain their self-determination and enhance compliance.

Choosing to follow a 'healthy' diet is a positive choice made by an increasing number of people. This has arisen from the recognition that many of the diseases prevalent in Western society may have a dietary origin. The understanding of these links may not be very accurate and even confused, as may also the understanding of what constitutes a 'healthy' diet. A common belief is that eating too much fat causes heart disease in men, or that too much chocolate will make women fat. Thus, one or two aspects of current dietary guidelines may be adopted, while others are ignored. Only a tiny percentage of the population manage to achieve all of the dietary guidelines, and the idea of a 'whole-diet' approach to healthy eating has not been widely recognized. The concept of 'healthiness' also becomes blurred by food safety issues, including concerns about additives in foods, genetically modified products, food that is not fresh, ready-made foods containing unknown ingredients and possible contamination by microorganisms, such as *Listeria* or *Salmonella*.

Social/psychological influences

Although our own physiological needs and wants are important determinants of what we find acceptable to eat, we are nevertheless also influenced in our actions by the prevailing social conditions, as well as our own psychological make-up.

Food and the way it is presented can be used to express status in society. The most obvious distinction is that between having and not having food. The wealthy generally have access to more and varied food, while the poor have less choice and are more likely to go hungry. In some societies, it is a sign of wealth and status to be obese.

Individual foods may also have differing status: those that are more expensive or difficult to get, such as grouse, venison or caviar, will be perceived as being high status. On the other hand, foods such as tripe or pig's trotters may be equally unusual, but because of their association with low-income diets, have a low status. Everyday foods, such as potatoes, sausages and baked beans, will also have relatively low status. The status of foods may change with time, depending on how they are valued. For example, in the nineteenth century, brown bread was considered coarse and fit only for the lower classes; now it is seen as healthy and desirable in the diet, and its status has increased considerably.

What is eaten in particular circumstances is likely to reflect the assumed status of the food. When eating alone, it does not matter what we eat, and people may 'treat' themselves to combinations of foods that they would not eat in company. As soon as food is eaten in company, value judgements are made on the basis of the foods. The status of the foods served reflects the implied status in which the diners are held. Thus, the type of food shared in a meal implies more than satisfying a physiological need. Sharing food with others is very symbolic: it confirms previously established links, and a sense of mutual identity. There is also powerful peer pressure in food selection.

Relationships within groups of people are confirmed in the sharing of food: usually the most powerful or most important members of the group are served first. This not only confirms their superiority, but allows them to choose the prime parts of the meal.

The food preferences of men and women often differ; in most cultures men consume more meat and women consume more fruit and vegetables. Women tend to eat more of the foods that are regarded as 'healthy'. It is suggested that these differences are associated with the traditional gender roles, which still exist in society. Women remain in charge of the food-related activity; therefore, they tend to know more about food. Information about healthy diets tends to be seen more by women, as it features in women's magazines, or in leaflets available from supermarkets or in doctors' surgeries. However, despite this greater knowledge, or level of information, decisions about what is eaten are shown to be dictated in many families by the men and children, rather than the women. Studies of changes in food intake on marriage show that both partners make some adjustments, with husbands adopting more of the wives' habits initially, but reverting to their original habits in time. Nevertheless, married men tend to have healthier diets than single men.

Differences have also been reported in the way food is eaten, with men taking gulps and mouthfuls, whereas women nibble and pick. As a consequence of this, it is suggested that some foods are more appropriate for women (such as fish or fruit) and other foods for men (red meat, bread).

Food can be a powerful means of communication. A box of chocolates given as a present is perhaps the most widely used example of food acting as a token of affection. Some may find it easier to give the chocolates than to put into words what they are feeling. A cup of tea is a typically British answer to a difficult social situation, when words are hard to find. A family eating a meal together is sharing not only food, but the affection they feel for each other. Rejecting the meal in this situation can, therefore, be a very potent dismissal of the love being offered. Reciprocal invitations to meals or parties by both adults and children strengthen the social bonds. Children may exchange small items of food, such as sweets, to communicate their friendship.

A special form of communication by means of food exists in the ritual use of food. Many religions use foods as offerings to their deities. Christians use bread and wine. The end of the growing season and the harvest are marked in many communities by a festival, with a sample of the crops being offered in thanksgiving, often to the poorest members of the community.

Certain life events are marked by specific ritual meals – baptismal feasts, wedding breakfast, the funeral wake. Group membership may also be marked by rituals involving food or drink; for example, the pre-wedding ritual of stag night and hen party, where the men and the women separately undergo a 'rite of passage', usually involving large amounts of alcohol.

Food represents security from the earliest age, so that in times of stress it can form an important support. Anxiety can provoke eating as a means of coping with tension, although in some individuals stress can result in a loss of appetite and an inability to eat. Anxiety may also lead to feeding others, for example, anxious mothers may overfeed their children to relieve their own anxiety about them. Abnormal eating patterns have also been linked with uncertainty about a person's role or position in society. It has been suggested that both overweight and anorexia nervosa may originate from a dissociation between the socially desirable body image and that with which the individual feels psychologically at ease.

In the case of obesity, it is argued that overeating occurs as a deliberate attempt to add substance to the body (generally female) in an effort to cope with the demands of the world. In anorexia nervosa, the body size is deliberately reduced to escape from the pressures of society on the adult female, and return to the child shape.

SUMMARY

1. Eating is regulated by the brain, which integrates many afferent signals coming from external and internal sources. This allows food intake to be matched to metabolic needs. However, this regulation is more efficient for some components of the diet than for others.
2. Apart from the physiological need to eat, food intake is also regulated by psychological needs, social influences, the sensory satisfaction obtained from eating, and by habit.
3. What is eaten is also influenced by many factors that determine both the availability of food and its acceptability to the individual.
4. Despite many differences between cultures in actual foods eaten, influences on eating and food choice are similar.
5. The interaction of influencing factors may be a key determinant in achieving dietary change.

STUDY QUESTIONS

1. What information is available to the brain to allow food intake to be regulated? Consider the macronutrients in the diet and discuss how precise this regulation is for each one.
2. The sensory appeal of food in very important. Give examples of some situations where:
   a. sensory properties may not be detected by the eater;
   b. additional care needs to be taken to enhance sensory appeal.
3. Consider the food habits of members of your family or your immediate friends.
   a. Have they changed in the last 10 years?
   b. If so, can you account for any changes?
   c. If they have remained the same, what have been the major factors maintaining this consistency?
4. Suggest ways in which government action could influence food habits. What barriers to change might this encounter?
5. What might be the nutritional consequences of a diet composed entirely of:
   a. core foods
   b. secondary foods
   c. peripheral foods?
6. In what ways can the following influence food habits:
   a. travel
   b. education
   c. multi-ethnic societies?

REFERENCES AND FURTHER READING

Blundell, J.E., Halford, J.C.G. 1994: Regulation of nutrient supply: the brain and appetite control. *Proceedings of the Nutrition Society* 53, 407–18.

Burnett, C. 1994: The use of sweets as rewards in schools. *Journal of Human Nutrition and Dietetics* 7, 441–6.

Charles, N., Kerr, M. 1988: *Women, food and families.* Manchester: Manchester University Press.

Cotton, J.R., Burley, V.J., Weststrate, J.A. et al. 1994: Dietary fat and appetite: similarities and differences in the satiating effect of meals supplemented with either fat or carbohydrate. *Journal of Human Nutrition and Dietetics* 7, 11–24.

Craig, P.L., Truswell, A.S. 1994: Dynamics of food habits of newly married couples: who makes changes in the foods consumed? *Journal of Human Nutrition and Dietetics* 7(5), 347–62.

DEFRA, 2001: *National Food Survey 2000 Annual report on food expenditure, consumption and nutrient intakes.* London: The Stationery Office.

Margetts, B.M., Thompson, R.L., Speller, V. et al. 1998: Factors which influence 'healthy' eating patterns: results from the 1993 Health Education Authority health and lifestyle survey in England. *Public Health Nutrition* 1(3), 193–8.

Mennell, S., Murcott, A., van Otterloo, A.H. 1992: *The sociology of food: eating, diet and culture.* London: SAGE Publications.

Stubbs, R.J., Harbron, C.G., Murgatroyd, P.R. et al. 1995: Covert manipulation of dietary fat and energy density: effect on substrate flux and food intake in men eating ad libitum. *American Journal of Clinical Nutrition* 62(2), 316–29.

Weststrate, J.A. 1996: Fat and obesity. *British Nutrition Foundation Nutrition Bulletin* 21, 18–25.

Wilding, J.P. 2002: Neuropeptides and appetite control. *Diabetic medicine* 19, 519–27.

Wood, R.C. 1995: *The sociology of the meal.* Edinburgh: University Press.

3 BASICS OF A HEALTHY DIET

The aims of this chapter are to:

- review the development of ideas about healthy eating;
- describe the basis and application of dietary reference values;
- discuss the dietary goals that have been put forward, and some of the dietary planning tools and mechanisms that are available to assist with constructing a diet.

On completing the study of this chapter, you should be able to:

- explain the fundamental ideas about healthy eating and the goals that have been developed;
- understand the significance of dietary reference values and be able to use them appropriately;
- use a dietary planning guide to evaluate diets;
- understand and show how to make use of information available on food labels in constructing a diet;
- evaluate information given in pamphlets about healthy eating;
- explain the health implications of alcohol consumption.

In Chapter 2 the factors affecting food habits and food choice were discussed. The choice of foods offered to people in Western societies is enormously diverse, with novel foods being developed by food technologists. However, instead of making it easier for us to choose what to eat according to our particular desires at a specific time, the increased variety makes it more difficult. Consequently, many people cope with the huge selection, often over 6000–9000 different items in a major supermarket, by consistently selecting only a very narrow range of foods.

In addition, many people are increasingly concerned with improving their health, and consumers wish to make food choices that will help in this. Various views are put forward to support particular dietary choices; the most polarized are those between plant-based or meat-based diets. There is now a substantial body of evidence to support the view that, where food is abundant, increasing the intake of plant-based foods, in particular fruit and vegetables, can help to reduce the incidence (i.e. the number of new cases in a given time period in a population) of chronic disease. However, the exact proportions of meat-based and plant-based foods in the diet that might support optimal health are impossible to determine. Epidemiological evidence does, however, support the view that diets based largely on plant foods are most associated with health and longevity, where food supplies are adequate. It is thus particularly important to provide some guidance for people to be able to select foods that will help to maintain their health.

A HEALTHY DIET – WHICH FOODS TO CHOOSE?

If we are interested in and committed to taking care of ourselves and others, the 'healthiness' of our selection of food needs to be considered. However, 'healthiness' is not the only feature we look for in our food. Most of us would be very reluctant to eat an unfamiliar food just because we were told it was healthy; the property of healthiness would be included in the general consideration of the food in deciding whether or not to include it in the diet.

However, food that constitutes a 'healthy diet' is in the main not very different from that which makes up a less healthy diet – it is the balance of the parts making up the total meal or diet that is important. As has been said elsewhere in this book, there are no 'bad' foods; it is their place in the general picture of the diet that is important. Some foods provide only a very narrow range of nutrients, perhaps even just one. If such foods comprise a substantial part of the daily intake, the consumer will run the risk of not meeting nutritional requirements for a range of nutrients. The greater the range of foods, the less likely are there to be 'gaps' in the nutrient intake, and the more likely it is that the consumer will meet the nutritional needs.

We are attracted by variety in foods, and would find a diet containing just one or two foods very monotonous. This might result in a smaller intake of the foods. The converse is also true: when presented with a variety of foods, we move from one to another and are likely to eat more. The appearance of a tempting dessert after a filling meal can readily override feelings of satiety, simply because of the novelty aspect!

Selecting several foods is, therefore, beneficial for our nutrient intake. Traditional meal patterns can help us to decide on combinations of foods to make up meals, as well as what foods to have at specific points of our day. The pattern of core, secondary and peripheral foods discussed in Chapter 2 serves as a general guide. It must be recognized that there is increasing variation in this pattern. It is possible that, in future generations, meals may be quite different, although there are also signs of a 'traditionalist revival', which may take us back to the old-established food patterns.

Activity 3.1

Make a list of foods that you usually eat during the course of a week. Divide them up into four columns: foods eaten at breakfast, lunch, evening meal, and snack foods.

- Is this easy to do? If so, you have got strong ideas about what foods are appropriate at what times, and in what meals. If you found it quite hard to do, this may be because you have a much 'freer' food structure, and the items in your diet may serve several roles.
- Check with a partner how easy their list was to write into columns.
- Finally, check how much agreement there is between your list and your partner's – do you consider the same foods as appropriate at particular times?

A HEALTHY DIET – HOW MUCH TO EAT?

In addition to deciding what foods to eat, each person makes a decision about the quantity to consume. From experience we have learned what is an adequate serving size for us and this obviously varies between individuals.

Our ability to assess how much of a food we would like to eat relies on learned responses established during our childhood and added to whenever a new food has been introduced. The sensations arising from the stomach when a particular serving size has been eaten will be remembered and will help to determine our behaviour in the future. Other reflex pathways, linked to the metabolic consequences of the meal, may also be part of the regulatory process. It is believed that this type of learning is an important component of the control of food intake (as discussed in Chapter 2).

The variability of 'normal' serving sizes between individuals is a dilemma for those studying food intakes in populations. There is no such thing as an 'average' serving size, which would apply to everyone. However, for the sake of expediency, such a measure is quoted and used in many contexts. However, in relation to this 'average', it is recognized that different people will also have 'large' and 'small' servings. Interpretations of these are also subjective and, therefore, variable.

Activity 3.2

1 *Observation*: During the next few days, use any opportunities you may have to observe people at mealtimes. Notice whether the amounts of food items they consume are similar to or greater/smaller than you would choose.

2 *Quantitative assessment*: If you have access to dietary or household weighing scales, make measurements of the typical serving size that you select of everyday foods. Ask members of your family or your colleagues/friends to do the same. Collate the information from as many different people as possible.
- How much variation do you find?
- Are portion sizes for some foods more variable than others?
- Can you offer explanations for this?
- What are the health implications of people's different concepts of 'appropriate' serving size?

Dietitians try to resolve this issue by using replica foods, which generally represent the 'average' serving. Patients may then indicate whether the amount they would consume is similar to this or different. There is always, of course, the tendency to claim that one's intake follows the average.

WHAT ARE THE FEATURES OF A 'HEALTHY' DIET?

This question is likely to produce a number of different responses from people, depending on their level of interest in nutrition and their understanding of the principles of health.

Answers will fall into one or several of the following categories.
- Eating more or less of particular foods.
- Eating more or less of particular nutrients.
- Eating specific foods that are believed to have 'healthy' properties. (This may include taking nutritional supplements or eating organically produced food.)
- Adopting particular diet-related practices, as well as lifestyle changes.
- Having a 'balanced diet'.

Each of these will be discussed in turn to consider how well they answer the question of what are the features of a healthy diet.

Eating more or less of particular foods

This response derives from the belief that there are 'good' foods and 'bad' foods, and that we should eat less of the latter and more of the former. Unfortunately, it is not a straightforward matter to classify foods in this manner; individual foods are less important than the way in which they are combined in diets. However, foods that contain a lot of fat or sugar, or those which have been extensively refined or processed, are likely to be of less value in a complete diet, since they reduce the nutrient density. This means that the remaining foods in the diet must contain more of the micronutrients to compensate.

This can be a particular problem in people who have relatively small appetites, or who are sedentary and, therefore, have low energy needs, since their potential intake of the more nutritious foods in the diet will be limited.

Eating more or less of particular nutrients

This has been one way in which advice about healthy eating has been promoted. In many countries, initial dietary guidelines included advice to eat less fat (especially saturated fat), reduce salt and increase dietary fibre. It is not surprising, therefore, that these are now repeated by consumers as the central principles of healthy eating.

However, people eat foods and not nutrients. Foods (with a very few exceptions) are not simply a source of one nutrient and, therefore, reducing the intake of a certain group of nutrients by excluding particular foods from the diet may have consequences for other nutrients also found in those foods. For example, if milk and dairy products are excluded because of their fat content, this can have serious implications for intakes of calcium and riboflavin.

The corollary of this is that some foods contain a nutrient in quite large amounts. If this is not made explicit, the intake of that particular food may not be altered. For example, ordinary hard cheese (such as Cheddar cheese) is recognized by most people as a source of protein and calcium, important for growing children and for bones. However, it is also very rich in fat. In listing sources of fat, many people would omit to mention cheese, and will continue to eat it often in quite large amounts. If changes are made only to the most obvious sources of fat, such as the spreading fats, cooking oils and full-fat milk, but other sources including cheese, pastries, biscuits and cakes are not reduced, then the overall impact on total fat intakes will be small.

As a consequence, more recent dietary guidelines have moved away from this focus on nutrients and have reverted to giving advice on foods that should be included in the diet, together with advice about quantities.

Eating specific foods that are believed to have 'health-promoting' properties

There is a perception that only certain foods are healthy, and they should be included in the diet. Linked to this is the belief that, when these foods are present, it does not matter what else the diet contains. Thus, in practice, an individual might be eating all the wrong proportions of macronutrients, but believes the diet is healthy because it includes a high-fibre breakfast cereal and semi-skimmed milk. Clearly there is some confusion here. A single food or two cannot make a diet healthy, although they can begin to redress an unbalanced diet.

Another example in this category is the inclusion of nutritional supplements to correct deficiencies in the food consumed. Although the nutritional content may well be improved by the supplements, especially in terms of the micronutrients commonly found in supplements, the balance of macronutrients may still be unhealthy. Again the consumer has a mistaken perception that they are eating healthily.

Including 'organically' grown products in the diet may reduce the level of chemical additives and contaminants consumed, but again does not necessarily make the diet nutritionally better balanced.

The remedy for an unbalanced diet that contains unhealthy proportions of the macronutrients and perhaps inadequate amounts of the micronutrients lies in a change in the foods consumed, and an alteration in the proportions of the different food groups. Improving an imperfect diet can be likened to dealing with a plumbing problem in the house, such as a leaking pipe. It can be dealt with by putting a bucket underneath, and living with the problem; this parallels the taking of supplements or adding one or two 'healthy foods' to the diet. Alternatively, the householder can call in the plumber and have the pipe mended. Similarly, an individual can obtain nutritional advice, either from a dietitian or nutritionist, or from information booklets, and change their diet for the better. In the long term, the latter will clearly be the more satisfactory solution.

Adopting particular dietary practices or lifestyle changes

A whole range of behaviours may be included here. Some diet-related examples, which are suggested by people as 'healthy eating', might include:

- eating regularly
- having breakfast
- cutting down on convenience or junk foods
- eating home-cooked foods
- drinking water
- losing weight
- planning what to eat
- eating organic food
- eating less meat (especially red meat)
- eating more fish/fruit/vegetables.

(A survey of your friends and family would produce many more.)

Lifestyle changes might include:

- taking exercise
- not eating late at night
- giving up smoking
- reducing alcohol intake
- becoming vegetarian.

Although the latter are not strictly ways of obtaining a healthy diet, they may be perceived as part of the healthy lifestyle, which includes diet. This is most clearly seen amongst people who become vegetarian, who often make changes not only to dietary intake but also to many other aspects of life, frequently adopting a more 'environmentally sensitive' lifestyle.

It is not being suggested here that to eat healthily one should adopt a vegetarian diet, although this is a belief held by some. Diets can be healthy (and also unhealthy) whether they contain meat and animal products, or not.

Eating a 'balanced' diet

Although this can be an appropriate definition of what is meant by healthy eating, it is imprecise and, as such, is open to many interpretations. Over the last 40–50 years, the concept of a balanced diet has changed. Its earlier interpretation was of a diet that provided the macronutrients in sufficient amounts to prevent deficiency, with protein often seen as a priority. There was a belief that, if the macronutrients were adequate, then the micronutrients would 'take care of themselves'. This may have been true when the diet contained mostly food close to its natural state, with few processed and manufactured foods on the market.

More recently, it was realized that simply meeting the requirements for macronutrients does not lead to good health, as evidenced by the high rates of 'Western diseases', such as coronary heart disease, cancer as well as obesity. Clearly, something was wrong with this approach.

It is only in the last decade that the 'balance' concept has been clarified to show suggested proportions of different food groups to be included in the diet. This aims to meet both macronutrient and micronutrient needs, as well as achieving a balance of nutrients that could promote health. This has, therefore, involved a change in the concept of 'a balanced diet', which has perhaps not been recognized by everyone. In addition, levels of energy expenditure have fallen, so that energy intakes need to be less. It then becomes even more important to make sure that what is eaten has the appropriate balance of other nutrients.

In the UK, the Ministry of Agriculture, Fisheries and Food (MAFF) produced *Eight guidelines for a healthy diet* in 1990. These were intended to be an update on diet and health for people with some knowledge of nutrition, to give guidance on the balanced diet. The guidelines were as follows.

1. Enjoy your food.
2. Eat a variety of different foods.
3. Eat the right amount to be a healthy weight.
4. Eat plenty of foods rich in starch and fibre.
5. Don't eat too much fat.
6. Don't eat sugary foods too often.
7. Look after the vitamins and minerals in your food.
8. If you drink, keep within sensible limits.

These were supported by a number of additional information leaflets about food labelling and food safety. These guidelines are now still current in the UK, following their re-issue in 1998.

Similar dietary guidelines exist in other countries and are reviewed regularly. In the USA, there is a 5-yearly review. The most recent in-depth scientific review resulted in an expansion of the guidelines from seven to ten. These are intended for children from age 2 years and healthy adults. The new 2000 Dietary Guidelines for Americans are as follows (Johnson, 2000).

- Aim for a healthy weight.
- Be physically active each day.
- Let the pyramid guide your food choices.
- Eat a variety of grains daily, especially whole grains.
- Eat a variety of fruits and vegetables daily.
- Keep foods safe to eat.
- Choose a diet that is low in saturated fat and cholesterol and moderate in total fat.
- Choose beverages and foods that moderate your intake of sugars.
- Choose and prepare foods with less salt.
- If you drink alcoholic beverages, do so in moderation.

A comparison with the UK guidelines shows a great deal of common ground, as would be expected, as both derive from the scientific base that supports advice on healthy eating.

WHAT NUTRIENTS ARE NEEDED, AND IN WHAT AMOUNTS?

In practice, the majority of people have no idea about the actual quantities of nutrients they require each day, and yet most manage to obtain approximately sufficient amounts to maintain adequate health. Whether their health is as good as it could be (i.e. 'optimal') is a matter for debate.

Nutritionists require more specific information on which to base scientific and reasonable advice. The starting point for these figures is the nutritional requirement.

Nutritional requirement

Each individual uses or loses a certain amount of each nutrient daily; this amount must, therefore, be made available to the tissues either from the daily diet or from the body stores of that nutrient. If the nutrient is taken from body stores, it must be replaced at a later stage, otherwise the stores will gradually become depleted and the person will be totally reliant on their daily intake. Eventually, a deficiency state might develop, if the intake is insufficient.

The amount of each nutrient used daily is the physiological requirement. It is defined as the amount of a nutrient required by an individual to prevent signs of clinical deficiency. This amount varies between individuals; it could differ from day to day due to different levels of energy expenditure. It may also alter with the composition of the diet owing to changes in efficiency of absorption or utilization of nutrients.

There are, however, a number of inherent problems with this definition. First, it is argued that this approach, based as it is on the very least amount needed to survive without developing a deficiency, leaves no margin of safety. Consideration could be given to the provision of a nutrient store to act as a reserve in time of physiological stress or reduced intake. Second, it gives no guidance on how to determine the requirement for nutrients for which there is currently no recognized clinical deficiency. This applies to fats (except essential fatty acids) and sugars. Third, there are no universally agreed criteria of when clinical deficiency exists. This is because a clinical deficiency reflects one end of a continuum, making it difficult to define precisely, as indicated in Figure 3.1.

It is cumbersome to obtain individual values for each nutrient requirement. One solution is to look at the average requirements of groups of similar people and to define a reasonable

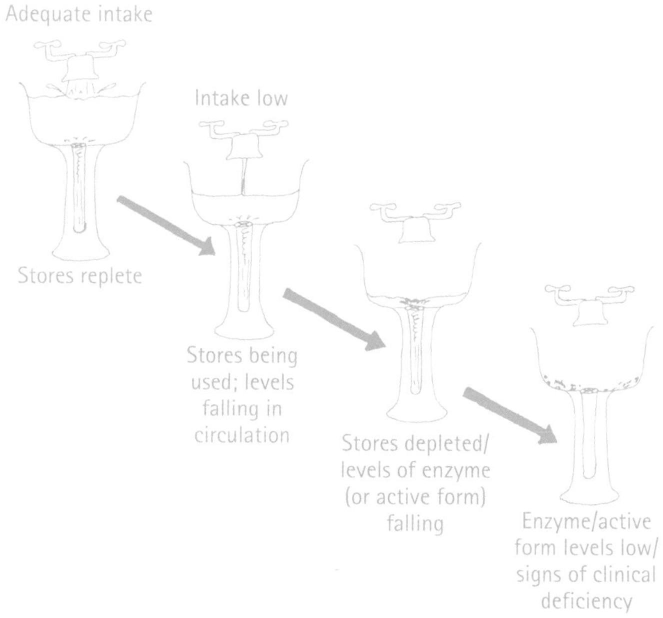

Figure 3.1 The stages of development of a clinical deficiency. This is a general guide to the progression from adequacy to deficiency. In some cases, the biochemical end-point may be very difficult to identify or there may be no specific signs associated with deficiency.

minimum level. The age of the child is taken as a basis for defining 'similar' children; for pregnant women, the stage of pregnancy is taken as the common basis; for other groups of the population, age and gender are common criteria. This is the approach used by the Panel on Dietary Reference Values of the Committee on Medical Aspects of Food Policy, which produced the most recent set of data for the UK in 1991 (DoH, 1991). This Panel derived information about nutritional requirements in a number of ways. These included:

- measures of the actual intakes of particular nutrients in populations that are apparently healthy;
- the intakes of nutrients that are required to maintain balance in the body;
- amounts of a nutrient needed to reverse a deficiency state;
- amounts needed for tissue saturation, normal biochemical function or an appropriate level of a specific biological marker.

The appropriate method has to be selected for each nutrient, taking into account its metabolic activity, mode of excretion, storage in the body and the availability of suitable biochemical indicators. None of the criteria used in determining the level of requirement is deemed perfect, but is the best available with the current state of knowledge.

DISTRIBUTION OF NUTRITIONAL REQUIREMENTS IN A POPULATION

When measurements of requirements are obtained from a sufficiently large population, the results are assumed to follow a typical 'normal' distribution curve. This indicates that, for the majority, the requirement is around the mean for the group, but some have higher requirements and some lower values. If the group is sufficiently large, then half will fall above the sample mean and half below it; this is simply a property of the distribution and not something peculiar to nutrition or requirements.

FROM REQUIREMENTS TO DIETARY REFERENCE VALUES

Having established the range of nutritional requirements for a particular nutrient, it is

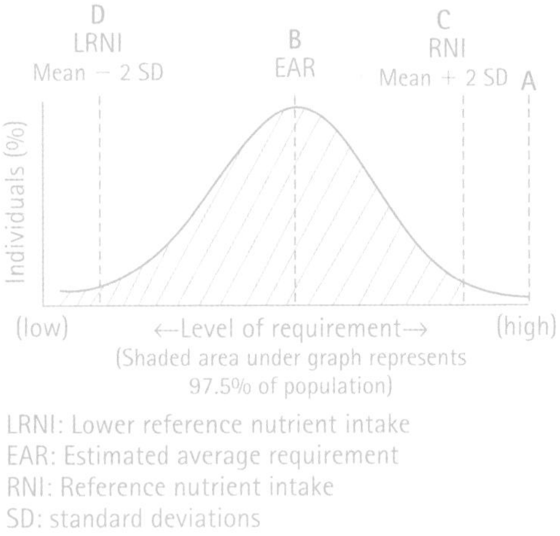

Figure 3.2 The normal distribution curve of nutrient requirements in a population and levels used for setting dietary recommendations.

necessary to define more precisely what would be an adequate level of intake to meet these requirements. Several options might be available (Figure 3.2). Setting the level at a point A, which is above the range of individual requirements, would ensure that everyone's needs were met but might pose a risk in terms of excessive intakes, if the nutrient was harmful in large amounts. There would also be cost implications – should people be encouraged to buy so much food to meet this high level? An alternative might be to set the level at point B, which is the mean. By definition, this would imply that this level of intake would be sufficient for half of the population, but would be inadequate for the other half. This would not be satisfactory for most nutrients. However, point B, which is defined as the estimated average requirement (EAR), is used as the reference value for energy intakes. This is because it would clearly be undesirable to advise people to consume a level of energy that was above the needs of most of the population. In addition, the reference values are actually intended for use by groups. Within a group, there will be some whose energy needs are above and some below the EAR. If the food provided, or consumed, contains an amount of energy that reaches the EAR, and the individuals eat to appetite, then one can assume that their energy needs are being met. If the mean energy provided or consumed lies below the EAR, this suggests that some of the group may not be reaching their EAR and, conversely, a mean intake above the EAR implies an excessive intake of energy amongst some members of the group. However, judgements about individuals cannot be made by comparison with the EAR figure, as this is a group mean.

In practice, for the majority of nutrients, the Panel followed the pattern of previous committees and used a point that is towards the upper end of the distribution curve of nutritional requirements, at the mean + 2 standard deviations. Because of the particular properties of this type of distribution curve, this point (C) covers the requirement figures for 97.5 per cent of the population. It could be argued that this leaves 2.5 per cent of the population outside the limits and, therefore, at risk of an inadequate intake. However, in practice, it was felt that an individual would not have extremely high requirements for all nutrients, and it was thus unlikely that anyone would consistently fail to meet requirements across the range. Eating to satisfy appetite would be likely to ensure adequate intake.

Therefore, to summarize, point C was identified as the reference nutrient intake (RNI). In addition, the Panel identified point D, at the lower end of the requirement range. This represents the mean − 2 standard deviations, and covers the requirements of only 2.5 per cent of the population, who fall below this level. Again, it is possible that there are some people who have nutritional requirements consistently below this point and who may, therefore, meet their needs at this level of intake. However, it is more probable that, if someone is consuming an intake as low as this, they are not meeting their nutritional requirement. This point has been called the lower reference nutrient intake (LRNI). It effectively represents the lowest level that might be compatible with an adequate intake.

The dietary reference value (DRV) tables (published by the UK Department of Health as Report 41; DoH, 1991), therefore, provide three distinct figures for the majority of nutrients: the LRNI, EAR and RNI, which can be used as a yardstick to give a guide on the adequacy of diets. The Panel chose a new name for these figures, moving from the recommended daily amount (RDA), which was used previously. It was felt that this name had been too prescriptive, suggesting that the amounts given referred to what individuals must consume. The corollary of this was that intakes that fell below the RDA were deemed to be deficient.

In setting the dietary reference values with a range of figures, the Panel intend the range to be used and, therefore, to provide more flexibility in assessing dietary adequacy. In addition, the DRV tables contain other data on dietary requirements for fats and carbohydrates, and some micronutrients for which little information was available.

Fats and carbohydrates

The approach to dietary requirements based on deficiency is not appropriate for nutrients having no specific clinical deficiency. Consequently, in the past, no RDA figures were set for fats and carbohydrates. There is now considerable public health interest in fat and carbohydrate intakes, and a desire for guidance on intake levels. The DRV Panel used their judgement, therefore, based on research evidence of health risks at particular levels of intake, to arrive at population average figures for the components of dietary fats and carbohydrates as well as non-starch polysaccharides. Rather than giving absolute figures, the DRV values are expressed in terms of the percentage of total energy, which ideally should come from the various components (Table 3.1). To provide further guidance, individual minimum and maximum values are cited for some of the components.

Some micronutrients

In the case of some of the micronutrients, insufficient data were available to establish a normal distribution of requirements and thence derive values for LRNI and RNI. In these cases, the Panel, wishing to give guidance, have provided a 'safe intake' figure, which is considered to be sufficient to fulfil needs, but is not so high that there is a risk of undesirable effects.

In the USA, a similar approach has been adopted in the revision of the Recommended Daily Allowances that had been set in 1989. Since 1998, the National Academy of Sciences has constituted a number of expert panels to prepare a comprehensive set of reference values

TABLE 3.1 Dietary reference values for fat and carbohydrate for adults, as a percentage of daily total food energy intake (excluding alcohol)

	Individual minimum	Population average	Individual maximum
Saturated fatty acids		11	
Cis-polyunsaturated fatty acids		6.5	10
n-3	0.2		
n-6	1.0		
Cis-monounsaturated fatty acids		13	
Trans-fatty acids		2	
Total fatty acids		32.5	
Total fat		35	
Non-milk extrinsic sugars	0	11	
Intrinsic and milk sugars		39	
Total carbohydrate		50	
Non-starch polysaccharides (g/day)	12	18	24

for nutrient intakes for healthy US and Canadian populations. A number of reports have presented Dietary Reference Intakes (DRI) for vitamins and some minerals. These parallel the DRV figures published by DoH (1991) in the UK. The DRI includes a number of values as follows.

- Recommended dietary allowance (RDA), which covers the needs of most individuals in a particular life stage and gender group.
- Estimated average requirement (EAR), which represents the mean requirement of the individuals in a population.
- Adequate intake (AI) represents an amount for a nutrient that is believed to satisfy needs, but for which there is insufficient evidence to describe the full range of reference intakes.
- Tolerable upper intake level (UL) – the highest level of a nutrient intake that is likely to pose no risk of adverse health effects for almost all individuals in the general population. As intake increases above UL, the risk of adverse effects increases.

Although the figures presented in the US tables are not always the same as those in the UK, they provide similar guidance on the range of nutrient intakes compatible with health.

If the UK tables are compared with those produced by the Food and Agriculture Organization/World Health Organization (FAO/WHO) or by other countries, differences both in the range of nutrients listed and the amounts advised are found. This implies two things. First, there are differences in needs between peoples of certain countries, as a result of differing lifestyles and perhaps different genetic make-up of the population. Therefore, when tables of reference values are used, they should be those relating to the country in question. Second, opinions differ between the committees drawing up the tables in different countries as to the safety margins that should be added to the figures. As a result, final figures also differ. This does not mean that some are more 'correct' than others; it reflects differences in emphasis and serves to underline the uncertainty surrounding such figures. It is important to remember that these figures are never an 'absolute' when their uses are considered. They are basically the 'best judgement' based on the physiological and nutritional data available at the time.

Practical applications

For individuals

It is important to remember that the DRV tables are not designed for use to judge individual nutritional intakes for their adequacy. They should rather be applied to groups of healthy individuals. However, since in practice they are used to assess individual diets, some words of caution are necessary.

Figure 3.3 shows the results of a riboflavin intake study in a large group of boys. Three boys in this group (boys A, B and C) were found to have intakes of A, B and C mg respectively.

The following conclusions can be drawn from the results:

- With an intake of A mg, we can be fairly sure that boy A is not reaching his nutritional requirement for riboflavin, since it falls at the level of the LRNI. He may already be showing signs of clinical deficiency, such as dermatitis. If not, he should be investigated, and given advice on increasing his riboflavin intake.
- Boy B's riboflavin intake, of B mg, is below the EAR for the group. However, this does not necessarily imply that he is receiving an inadequate intake. He may simply be a child with a low individual requirement. On the other hand, if he is not growing normally or showing signs of ill-health, his needs are probably not being met and his intake should be increased.
- At first sight, boy C's intake of C mg seems to be quite adequate, as it almost reaches the RNI; it is quite likely that this is the case. However, the possibility could exist that he has a very high requirement, which is not being met by the current intake, even though it appears quite high. It can only be assumed that his intake is sufficient, if there is no evidence of inadequacy.

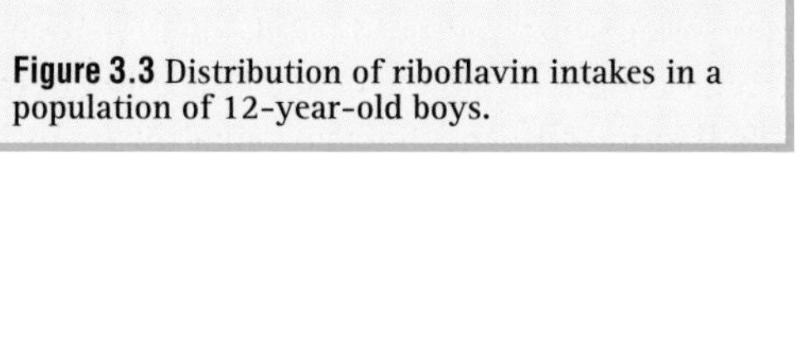

Figure 3.3 Distribution of riboflavin intakes in a population of 12-year-old boys.

Most people are unlikely to consume an amount of each nutrient to match the requirement exactly. However, it is probable that those with higher needs consume more than those whose needs are lower. The higher the correlation of intake and needs, the lower the risk of deficiency there is in any one individual. Unfortunately, the information about individual needs is not available and judgement must be used. The higher the intake level (i.e. the closer it is to the RNI), the lower the risk that it is inadequate. On the other hand, levels approaching the LRNI level are likely to carry a high risk of being inadequate.

Thus, a firm statement about an individual diet is only possible when the intake falls outside the range of RNI to LRNI. Nevertheless, the DRV Panel estimated that the risk of deficiency is about 15 per cent with an intake at the EAR, and falls to negligible levels when the intake approaches the RNI. However, it rises sharply at low levels of intake, approaching 100 per cent at the LRNI.

For groups of individuals

Group mean intakes eliminate the intra-individual variability and, therefore, allow more confident interpretation of results. When a group mean exceeds the RNI, the likelihood of many members of the group having intakes substantially below the RNI is small. Means around or below the RNI suggest that there are some members of the group whose intake may be inadequate. The lower the mean with respect to the RNI, the greater the chance that some members have an inadequate intake. This use is particularly important in evaluating dietary survey data.

For dietary planning

DRVs are used, for example, in institutions in planning diets for groups of individuals. In these cases, the RNI should be taken as the target (except for energy). Similarly, if a dietary prescription for an individual is being planned, then the RNI should be the target, since there is no other information about the actual needs of the individual.

Food labelling

Traditionally, food labelling has used the RDA value previously published in the UK. This corresponds to the current RNI level and is, therefore, sufficient or more than sufficient for 97.5 per cent of the population. In using this figure on food labels, the manufacturer may underestimate how much of the requirement for an individual is actually being supplied.

For example, suppose a food label claims that the food product provides, in a typical serving, 100 per cent of the RNI (or RDA) for vitamin C. Using the DRV figure, we can discover that it, therefore, supplies 40 mg. However, for an adult woman, the LRNI is only 10 mg, and the EAR is 25 mg. Therefore, for an individual whose needs are low, say 15 mg, this food product will actually supply 260 per cent of the actual needs. This is quite different from the claim of 100 per cent. As a result of such discrepancies, the Panel suggested that it would be better if EAR values were used in food labelling. However, the DRV figure does provide a reference point for the fortification of foods, and for the development of new food products.

The Institute of Grocery Distribution (IGD) in the UK has proposed a set of Guideline Daily Amounts (GDA) for use in food labelling. These are based on the predicted daily consumption of an average consumer eating a diet conforming to UK DRV (DoH, 1991) recommendations. The agreed GDA are as follows.

	Men	Women
Calories	2500	2000
Fat (g)	95	70
Saturated fat (g)	30	20

These figures are being used in some labelling in the UK, and help the consumer to see more simply how much fat and saturated fat the food contains as a part of the target daily intake.

Additional labelling directives operate in the UK, related to EU rulings, which use RDA as the basis for guidance. The RDA figures are EU agreed, and are not necessarily the same as the UK RNI or EAR figures. Thus, several yardsticks are in operation, each providing somewhat different information to the consumer.

DIETARY PLANNING

It is important that those who use figures from the dietary reference value tables should understand how they have been derived and, therefore, what are their uses and limitations. In practice, however, this is not always possible and, therefore, a means to translate the scientific information contained in the DRV tables into more accessible format is needed.

Meal planning tools

Many countries in the West have used meal selection guides for a number of years to help their consumers with healthy eating. Food guides provide a framework to show how foods can be combined together in a day's eating to provide an overall intake, which contains the appropriate range of nutrients. They achieve this by:

- grouping together foods that provide (generally) similar nutrients, and that may be interchangeable in the diet;
- making a quantitative statement about the number of 'servings' of foods from each group to be taken daily.

Food guides were first devised in the USA. They first appeared in 1916 and consisted of five food groups – milk and meat, cereals, vegetables and fruits, fats and fat foods, sugars and sugary foods. Further developments occurred between the 1940s and 1970s, with changes to the number and components of the groups used. Such changes reflected an increase in the understanding of the role of diet in health and disease prevention. In particular, more guidance was given about the consumption of fat, sugar and alcohol in the later guides than their earlier counterparts.

Most countries that have developed such a food guide use either the concept of a pyramid or a circle to illustrate that there are various components making up a whole diet. The most recent version of the USA Food Guide is a pyramid (Figure 3.4). This indicates that the foods in

Figure 3.4 The USA Food Guide pyramid: a guide to daily food choices. (Adapted from The Food Guide Pyramid. US Department of Agriculture/US Department of Health and Human Services.)

the groups at the base of the pyramid should be present in the greatest amounts and 'support' the diet. Progressive layers above this should be consumed in smaller amounts. By implication, those at the top (fats, oils and sweets) should be used sparingly, and are the least important components of the diet. The Guide indicates the numbers of servings as a range; individuals with lower nutritional needs (e.g. children) should take the lower number of servings. The Guide also does not apply to infant feeding.

Note also that the Guide does not imply that any single food is essential in the diet, no food alone provides all the necessary nutrients. What is important, however, is to include variety in the diet. In this way, shortcomings in one food are likely to be compensated by an adequate intake in another food. In 1999, a Food Guide adapted for children aged 2–6 years was published in the USA. The nutritional messages are the same as those in the original Food Guide Pyramid. However, the foods pictured are those commonly eaten by children in this age group. In addition, the words used are shorter and the illustrations show active children, in an attempt to promote the importance of physical activity. Most children in the USA have been found not to meet the guidelines depicted in the Pyramid, especially with respect to the grains, fruit and dairy groups. This is resulting in concern about nutritional intakes, especially of sugars, saturated fats and very low calcium intakes. In addition, the rising prevalence (i.e. the numbers of people affected in the population) of overweight and obesity, that now affects over 20 per cent of children in the USA has led to this initiative, in an attempt to influence eating habits at a young age.

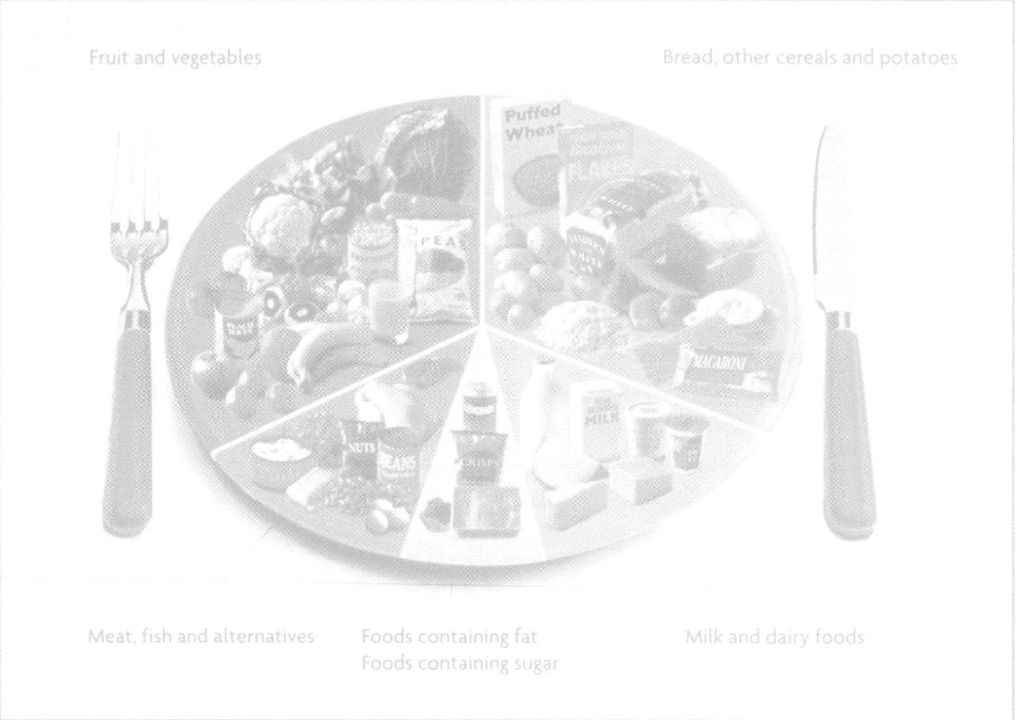

Figure 3.5 The UK National Food Guide: the Balance of Good Health. (From Food Standards Agency 2001: *Balance of good health: information for educators and communicators.* London: Food Standards Agency.) Reproduced by kind permission of the Food Standards Agency.

In the UK, a National Food Guide (the Balance of Good Health) was launched for the first time in 1994 (Figure 3.5). The design is a tilted plate incorporating five food groups in the following proportions.

Segment size as per cent of whole plate	
Bread, other cereals and potatoes	33
Fruit and vegetables	33
Meat, fish and alternatives	12
Milk and dairy foods	15
Fatty and sugary foods	8

The nutritional details of the groups used in the Balance of Good Health are presented in Table 3.2.

The emphasis in the UK Guide is on foods, rather than nutrients, and shows the importance of considering the diet as a whole rather than concentrating on specific foods that may be 'good' or 'bad'. The format was selected after extensive consumer research, which considered a number of possible designs and tested preference for them amongst consumers and their performance as nutrition education tools.

The purpose of the Balance of Good Health is to allow all nutrition educators to provide a consistent message and thereby to reduce the confusion about the creation of a balanced diet. It is, therefore, intended that the Guide should be used widely to provide simple messages of balance and proportion of the food groups in a practical way. In addition, the Guide is intended to be sufficiently flexible to allow choices based on personal preferences and dietary habits, and to take into account availability, costs, cultural norms and ethnic diets. It is, therefore, not intended to be prescriptive.

As with any other food planning guide, the Balance of Good Health does not take into account the needs of those on special diets, infants and children under 5 years, or frail elderly people. Individuals in these groups may need to

TABLE 3.2 Nutritional details of the five groups in the UK National Food Guide (the Balance of Good Health)

Name of food group	Composition of food group	Key nutrients found in group
Bread, other cereals and potatoes	All breads made with yeast and other breads Cereals, including wheat, oats, barley, rice, maize, millet and rye together with products made from them, including breakfast cereals and pasta Potatoes in the form usually eaten as part of a meal (but not as a snack, e.g. crisps)	Carbohydrate NSP Vitamin B complex Calcium Iron (Recommend: ▪ low-fat methods of cooking, and sauces/dressings, spreads ▪ high-fibre varieties to maximize micronutrients)
Fruit and vegetables	Fresh, frozen, chilled and canned fruit and vegetables Fruit juices Dried fruit *Not included*: potatoes, pulses, nuts	Vitamins C, E and carotenes (antioxidant vitamins), folate Minerals: potassium, magnesium, trace minerals Carbohydrate NSP Majority are low in energy
Meat, fish and alternatives	Carcass meats, meat products (but not pastries and pies) Fish and fish products Poultry Eggs Pulses and nuts	Protein B vitamins (especially B_{12}) Minerals: phosphorus, iron, zinc, magnesium NSP (from pulses only) Long-chain polyunsaturated fatty acids (in oily fish) Meat and its products may be significant contributors to fat intake (low-fat alternatives available)
Milk and dairy foods	All types of milk Yoghurt Cheese	Protein Calcium Fat-soluble vitamins (except in low-fat varieties) B vitamins (riboflavin, B_{12}) *Not included*: butter and eggs
Fatty and sugary foods	Butter, margarine, fat spreads, oils and other fats Cream Crisps and fried savoury snacks Cakes, pastries, biscuits Chocolate and sugar confectionery Sugars and preserves Ice cream Soft drinks	Energy Fat Sugar Essential fatty acids Fat-soluble vitamins

NB: The Guide does not include composite dishes: these should be allocated to groups according to their main ingredients.

pay greater attention to the nutrient density of the foods consumed if their intakes are small.

The Guide also aims to help in achieving the dietary guidelines originally published by the UK Government in 1990 in the form of the *Eight guidelines for a healthy diet* (MAFF, 1990). The re-issue of these incorporates the Balance of Good Health as an illustration of how the two can be used in conjunction.

HOW TO USE THE BALANCE OF GOOD HEALTH

The Guide is concerned with the proportions of the foods in the diet. The simplest way to use the Guide, therefore, is to calculate the proportion of the total daily diet provided by foods from the different food groups in terms of numbers of servings eaten during the day. Some concern has been expressed that the definition of a 'serving' or 'portion' is not made explicit. However, it should be remembered that for any one individual, servings of particular foods are consistent over time; it is the contribution of each of these servings to the whole diet that is important.

Figure 3.6 illustrates how the Guide can be applied to assess an individual diet. It is also possible to identify the shortcomings of the diet in this way, and use it as the basis for remedial advice. Adding together the numbers of servings gives the following percentages of the total:

Bread/cereal group	6 servings = 30 per cent
Fruit and vegetables	4 servings = 20 per cent
Meat and alternatives	4 servings = 20 per cent
Dairy foods	2 servings = 10 per cent
Fats and sugars	4 servings = 20 per cent

It is, therefore, possible to see how this day's intake complies with the Balance of Good Health. Clearly, there is not quite enough of the bread and cereals group, far too little fruit and vegetables and rather too much of the remaining

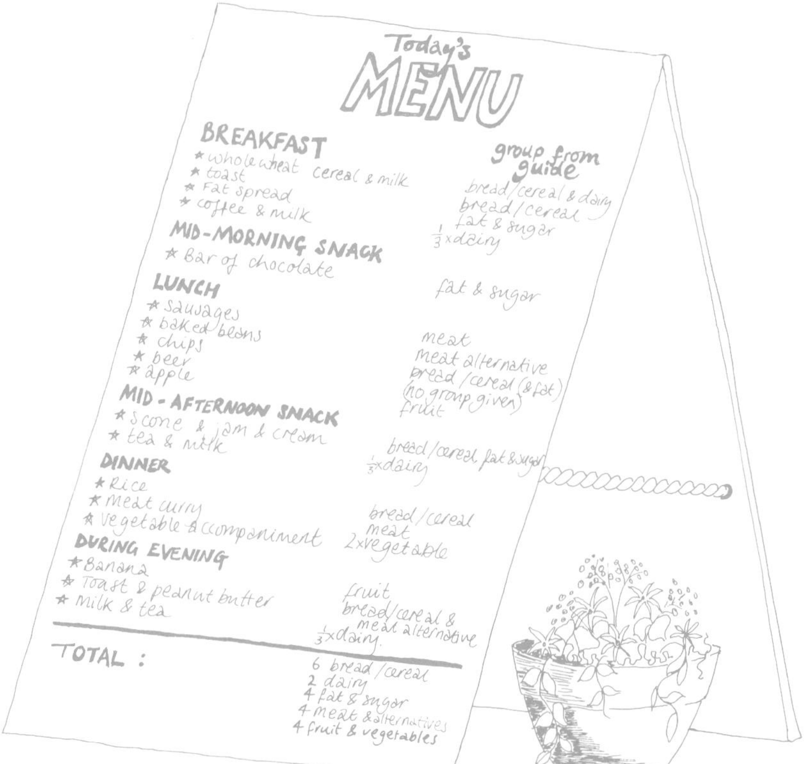

Figure 3.6 Example of a day's food intake and the numbers of servings from the Balance of Good Health.

Activity 3.3

Now carry out a similar exercise on your own food intake. You may have already kept a record of a typical day, or several days' food intake. Make an assessment of the proportions of your diet coming from the various groups.

- What groups are overrepresented?
- Are some underrepresented?

Use the Balance of Good Health to suggest alternatives in the diet that could make the balance better.

three groups. In this way, it is possible to focus on which parts of the diet need attention and make suggestions for replacing foods.

A CONSISTENT MESSAGE

One of the main objectives of the Balance of Good Health is to provide a consistent message for all consumers about a balanced diet. There is evidence of confusion about a number of issues related to healthy eating. These can be found among many consumers as well as in the media, advertising and the catering industry. In particular, confusion exists in relation to intakes of specific nutrients or groups of nutrients. These include fat, complex carbohydrates and sugars, salt, alcohol and antioxidant nutrients. In addition, specific constituents of food, such as additives, or techniques used in food processing, for example, irradiation, cause concern and are linked to 'healthy eating'. Organic foods are generally perceived as being 'healthy', even when their nutrient composition is similar to that of non-organically produced foods. Exotic ingredients or foods are sometimes credited with exceptional nutritional properties; and (often unfounded) claims about 'live' yoghurt, honey, herb drinks and new 'functional foods' all add to the confusion of the consumer.

NUTRITION INFORMATION

There are numerous booklets and leaflets now available to the consumer produced by food companies, retailers, hospital trusts and many other organizations. How should these be viewed and what is the quality of the information they contain? Many of them are sound and very informative. Some, however, can be misleading, often not by what they actually include, but by judicious omission of key points.

When reading nutrition information leaflets, ask yourself the following questions.

- Is the dietary advice being offered compatible with a balanced diet, as described by the Balance of Good Health?
- Is the advice stressing the importance of one nutrient or food, to the exclusion of or in preference to others?
- Is a particular product or brand being promoted?
- Is there bias in the advice being given because of other interests that the sponsor of the leaflet may have?
- Does the leaflet promise unrealistic outcomes?
- Does the advice suggest that you buy products that you have never used before?
- Is the advice being given appropriate to you and your lifestyle?
- Is the leaflet written by a registered nutritionist or dietitian?
- Is scientific evidence being quoted, including references to reputable sources of information?
- Is there an address from which further information can be obtained?

If you can be satisfied that the evidence is balanced and unbiased, then the leaflet is likely to be worthwhile and can be a useful source of information. However, biased leaflets should not be used, as these simply add to the confusion.

It is simply not true that nutrition professionals are continuously changing their views and advice, as the media claim. Scientific debate is an important way of moving knowledge forward, and without it a subject stagnates and becomes dated. New ideas and fresh approaches are essential to continually check that our theories can be supported and that the advice we give is based on sound empirical evidence. The majority of nutrition experts do agree on the basic advice about healthy eating. Where there may be disagreement, it may reflect particular interests of the parties involved or relate to issues where the literature also conflicts.

THE QUESTION OF ALCOHOL

The consumption of alcohol is not discussed in the basic guidance on a balanced diet, as it is not an essential component of the diet and does not feature in all diets. Yet the consumption of alcohol is prevalent, with estimates suggesting that almost 90 per cent of the population in the UK consume alcohol at some time each year. Alcoholic beverages are consumed as part of many social activities, but consumption can also become excessive and result in physical, psychological and social harm to the individual as well as those around them. Economic estimates suggest that health and other problems related to alcohol consumption, including time away from work, represent a heavy financial burden. However, there is also very substantial revenue to the Government from the taxes levied on alcoholic beverages.

Published recommendations relating to alcohol generally adopt the perspective of limiting the intake rather than actively promoting consumption.

In order to quantify amounts of alcohol drunk from a variety of different sources, a standard 'unit' of alcohol has been developed. In the UK, this is equivalent to 8 g or 10 mL of ethanol. This amount of ethanol is found in the following measures of common drinks:

- ½ pint of standard-strength beer (284 mL)
- 1 measure of spirit (25 mL)
- 1 glass of wine (125 mL).

Many other drinks are on the market that do not fit exactly into these categories and it can be difficult, without adequate labelling, to identify exactly how many units are present in a drink.

The definition of a unit differs between countries, and in the USA, equals 12 g of alcohol.

Benchmarks for safe levels of intake of alcohol have been published, using the concept of a unit. These are that men should not exceed 3–4 units per day and women should not exceed 2–3 units per day. In addition, there should be some drink-free days during the week. These benchmarks were introduced in 1995 to replace older guidelines that stated safe intakes to be 21 units and 14 units per week for men and women, respectively. There has been an increase in binge drinking, especially among young people, and amounts of this order were being consumed in one night. This was clearly not a safe intake, and the advice to spread alcohol consumption over a greater period of time was introduced as a consequence.

With progressively higher intakes, there is a greater risk of harm occurring. Consequences of excessive alcohol consumption include damage to every system of the body, including the liver, digestive system, heart, brain and nervous system. In addition, nutritional intake is likely to be affected and chronic overconsumption is associated with a number of specific nutritional deficiencies. Even at moderate intakes, it is likely that alcohol contributes to the total energy supply and this may result in weight gain. Social consumption of alcohol accompanying meals has been shown to be associated with a larger food intake as well as the consumption of higher levels of fat.

However, moderate alcohol consumption has also been linked to beneficial effects, particularly in protection against coronary heart disease. There is a J-shaped relationship between overall mortality and alcohol consumption, with abstainers and heavier drinkers having higher mortality rates than those seen in moderate drinkers. Maximum health advantage for coronary heart disease lies at levels of intake between 1–2 units per day. The reasons for the shape of this curve are still not agreed. In addition, the J-shaped relationship is now known to apply predominantly to men over the age of 35 years and women after the menopause, with benefits increasing in older age groups. The level at which no harm is caused by alcohol also increases with age, so that the young drinker is most at risk. Mortality risk is increased in young drinkers at levels of alcohol consumption normally considered to be 'safe'; this may be associated with accidents and injury rather than the long-term physical damage caused by alcohol itself.

On a population basis, there is no recommendation to increase alcohol consumption, for although abstainers might benefit from a small amount of alcohol, the extra harm that could ensue from increased drinking among heavier consumers would not translate into an overall improvement in health.

SUMMARY

1. Eating healthily is not a matter of adding specific 'health-giving' foods to the diet, using specific food preparation techniques, avoiding additives or taking nutritional supplements. None of these will make the diet healthy.
2. Choosing a healthy diet involves knowing what mixtures of foods to select and in what quantities.
3. Adequate amounts of food must be consumed to meet nutrient requirements. These are expressed as Dietary Reference Values and cover the needs of most of the population.
4. The Food Guides show how a balanced diet can be created, by choosing from a wide range of foods, in appropriate quantities.
5. Alcohol intake can be beneficial to health when taken in small to moderate amounts. Benefits are more likely in middle-aged and older people.

STUDY QUESTIONS

1. A number of commonly eaten foods are perceived as being 'healthy' or 'unhealthy'.
   a. Compile a list of approximately 20 foods that you consider fulfil these criteria.
   b. Ask a number of friends to define the foods as 'healthy' or 'unhealthy'.
   c. State whether different people choose the same foods or whether there are differences (e.g. by age, gender).
   d. Account for the perceptions about these foods.
2. For what nutritional reasons might a vegetarian diet be considered 'healthier' than an omnivorous diet?
3. Explain why a nutritional deficiency state can be difficult to define precisely. What different end-points are used to delineate deficiency?
4. Distinguish between an individual's nutritional requirement and the reference nutrient intake for a particular nutrient (e.g. vitamin C).
5. Explain why an intake below the level of the RNI may be nutritionally adequate.

REFERENCES AND FURTHER READING

Achterberg, C., McDonnell, E., Bagby, R. 1994: How to put the Food Guide Pyramid into practice. *Journal of the American Dietetic Association* 94, 1030–5.

DoH (UK Department of Health) 1991: *Dietary reference values for food energy and nutrients in the United Kingdom.* Report on Health and Social Subjects No. 41. Report of the Panel on Dietary Reference Values of the Committee on Medical Aspects of Food Policy. London: HMSO.

DoH (UK Department of Health) 1995: *Sensible drinking.* The Report of an Inter-Departmental Working Group. London: HMSO.

Fairweather-Tait, S.J. 1993: Optimal nutrient requirements: important concepts. *Journal of Human Nutrition and Dietetics* 6, 411–17.

Hunt, P., Gatenby, S., Rayner, M. 1995: The format for the National Food Guide: performance and preference studies. *Journal of Human Nutrition and Dietetics* 8, 335–51.

Institute of Grocery Distribution 1995: *Voluntary nutrition labelling guidelines to benefit the consumer.* Watford: Institute of Grocery Distribution.

Johnson, R.K. 2000: The 2000 Dietary Guidelines for Americans: foundation of US nutrition policy. *British Nutrition Foundation Nutrition Bulletin* 25, 241–8.

MAFF (Ministry of Agriculture, Fisheries and Food) 1990: *Eight guidelines for a healthy diet.* London: Food Sense.

Mela, D.J. 1993: Consumer estimates of the percentage energy from fat in common foods. *European Journal of Clinical Nutrition* 47(10), 735–40.

Nestle, M. 1999: Animal v plant foods in human diets and health: is the historical record unequivocal? *Proceedings of the Nutrition Society* 58, 211–18.

THREE

THE APPLICATION OF NUTRITIONAL KNOWLEDGE

11 PREGNANCY AND LACTATION

The aims of this chapter are to:

- ❑ establish the importance of nutrition in preparation for and throughout pregnancy;
- ❑ discuss the nutritional needs during pregnancy;
- ❑ identify specific groups in the population who may be at particular risk in pregnancy;
- ❑ describe the possible links between pregnancy outcome and long-term health;
- ❑ discuss the nutritional needs in lactation;
- ❑ identify some of the influences on the mother in choice of feeding method.

On completing the study of this chapter, you should be able to:

- ❑ explain the importance of good nutritional status at conception;
- ❑ discuss some of the metabolic changes that occur in pregnancy in the mother and how these influence her nutritional needs;
- ❑ explain why certain dietary patterns may be associated with increased vulnerability in pregnancy;
- ❑ devise general dietary advice for optimal pregnancy outcome.

Based on studies of well-fed pregnant women in the 1950s in the UK, the physiological norm for weight gain in a 40-week pregnancy was set at 12.5 kg. This appeared to be associated with optimal outcome of pregnancy and has been used as a reference since then. The 12.5 kg comprises:

Fetus	3.5 kg
Increased maternal tissues (including uterus, mammary glands and blood volume)	5.0 kg
Stored fat	4.0 kg

These increases were also believed to prepare the mother's body for lactation, in the form of stored energy for milk production.

On the basis of such figures, it would seem reasonable to conclude that the mother needs to consume a significantly greater amount of food during the pregnancy in order to provide sufficient nutrients and energy to build these extra tissues. The corollary of this is that pregnancy outcome, both in terms of the mother's health and the well-being of the baby, would be adversely affected if her nutritional intake were not increased.

In recent years, a better understanding has emerged of the relationship between nutrition of the mother and pregnancy outcome. This has shown it to be very much more complex than stated here, as well as far from fully understood.

This chapter considers the importance of nutritional status before pregnancy, at the time of conception, and in the presence of major physiological changes, which occur during pregnancy. The indicator of outcome of pregnancy that is widely used is the birthweight of the baby. A favourable outcome is the delivery of a healthy full-term infant, weighing between 3.5 and 4 kg (in the UK; some countries use 4.5 kg as the upper end of the range). This is associated with the lowest risk of infant and perinatal morbidity and mortality. Above this birthweight there is an increased likelihood of obstetric complications as well as neonatal mortality and morbidity. Babies born weighing less than 2.5 kg (termed 'low birthweight') have a 40-fold greater risk of neonatal mortality than those born at optimal weight, and the survivors have an increased risk of neurological disorders and handicap, as well as infection. Work by Barker (1998) and others indicates that infants who experience growth restriction in the womb or in early life may be more susceptible to later degenerative disease. It is, therefore, important to minimize these risks wherever possible. It is, however, also important that the mother herself arrives at the end of pregnancy in a healthy state and well enough to be able to care for her newly born infant.

NUTRITION BEFORE PREGNANCY

The nutritional status of a woman at the time of conception reflects her diet and lifestyle over a number of years, even perhaps going back to her own infancy and childhood. These are dependent on many environmental and social factors, which must be taken into account.

Several features of the pre-pregnancy diet may affect the chances of conception or the success of pregnancy. For example:

- vitamin D deficiency in adolescence may have resulted in rickets with pelvic malformations, making a normal delivery impossible;
- a dietary deficiency of vitamin B_{12} may cause infertility; and
- a history of dieting, or in its extreme form anorexia nervosa, can result in poor nutritional status, with low reserves of many nutrients.

Research on underweight women has found that low body fat stores are associated with amenorrhoea and infertility. Evidence of this association comes from records obtained in wartime from places where food supplies were critical, such as Holland and Leningrad, as well as from more recent studies in infertility clinics and on women with anorexia. These indicate that a body mass index (BMI) of 20.8 appears to be a threshold for normal pregnancy, and that there is a minimum ratio of fat:lean body mass needed to support pregnancy.

Women who are obese (BMI above 30) may also experience infertility, as the associated changes in insulin activity and sex hormones may reduce the viability of the ovum.

It would, therefore, appear to be desirable that a woman planning to become pregnant should aim to achieve a BMI within the range of 20–26. If this is achieved by adopting healthy nutritional practices, then the reserves of micronutrients will also be maximized.

Research on primates and human volunteers suggests that the most crucial phase is the 14 days prior to conception, when the follicle in the ovary is growing rapidly before it extrudes the ovum at ovulation. The environment for the developing ovum in the ovary requires appropriate hormone levels. These are crucially dependent on the maternal state of nutrition both in terms of protein as well as other nutrients. These may include iodine to ensure normal thyroid hormone function, magnesium and zinc for the binding of hormones at their receptor sites, and folic acid for the normal growth of the follicle.

It is clear that nutrition prior to pregnancy has long-term implications and that, for an optimum outcome, diets should be adequate and well-balanced before conception.

NUTRITION AT THE TIME OF CONCEPTION

The embryo at conception and in the first weeks afterwards is extremely vulnerable. The majority of the organs and systems develop in the first 8 weeks after conception. The essential energy and nutrients for this are derived from the mother's circulation and from the lining of the womb. It is, therefore, critical that these can provide the necessary nutrients in appropriate amounts. At this stage in the pregnancy, the placenta has not yet formed, so there is no mechanism to protect the embryo from deficiencies in the maternal circulation. It is, therefore, not surprising that nutritional status and nutritional reserves at this time are vital. Studies from the Dutch hunger winter (1944–45) showed that, among the women who did bear children, it was the ones who had experienced the full duration of hunger (8 months) prior to conception who had the most severely affected infants with respect to malformations.

Trials on the prevention of neural tube defects (NTDs) have shown that supplementing the diet of 'at risk' women with folic acid (4 mg/day) for 3 months before conception and up to the 12th week of pregnancy significantly reduced the risk of NTD in the fetus. Since folate is needed for cell division, it is suggested that these levels override a metabolic abnormality linked to neural tube closure. In the majority of cases, it is impossible to predict which women might be at risk and only those who have already had one affected fetus can be identified as requiring particular supplementation. As a result of these studies, women who might become pregnant are now advised in the UK by the Department of Health (HEA, 1996) to increase their intake of folate by at least 400 μg daily. This is more than the typical diet provides and, therefore, foods fortified with folic acid, or folic acid supplements, are needed. The Folic Acid Campaign is further discussed in Chapter 18. Foods that are a good source of folate are listed in Figure 11.1.

Retinol has also received particular attention in recent years. Reports have suggested that extreme intakes of retinol (doses from 8000 to 10 000 μg/day) are teratogenic (i.e. cause fetal malformations). Such a level of intake is likely to be taken regularly only in the form of supplements. The main dietary source of retinol that might contain these levels is liver. A 100 g serving of liver might contain up to 10 000 μg of retinol; it is unlikely, however, that this would be eaten on a daily basis. Nevertheless, women who may be trying to become pregnant are advised to avoid liver and liver products, as well as supplements that contain megadoses of retinol, as there is a very small risk of harm. No cases of fetal damage attributable to liver intakes have been reported in Britain.

Alcohol is also a potential teratogenic agent, particularly if taken in large amounts, for example, in binge drinking. Women who are

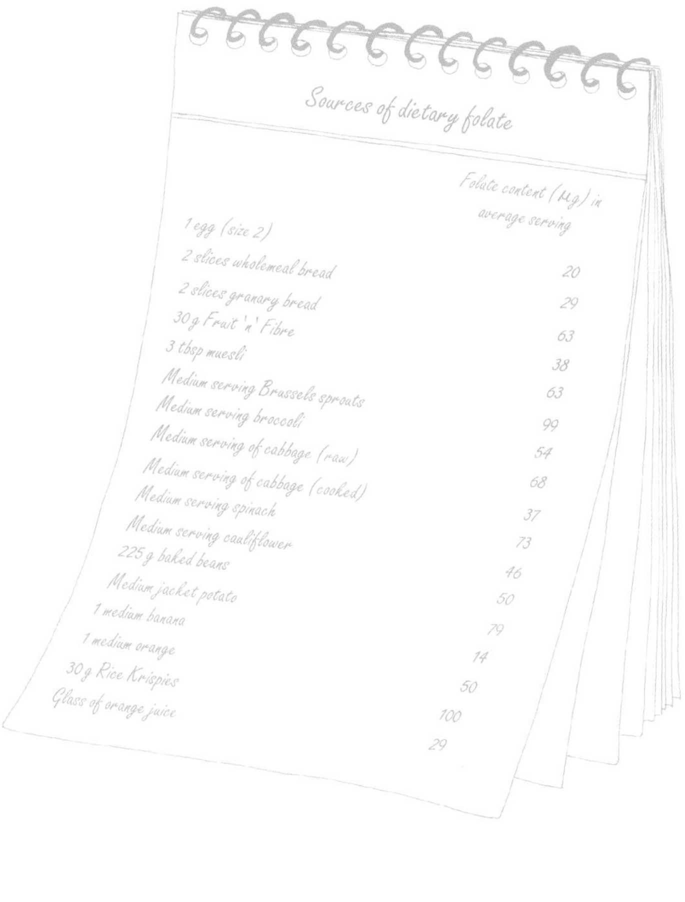

Figure 11.1 Sources of dietary folate.

considering becoming pregnant should, therefore, avoid consuming large amounts of alcohol. This is important in view of the likelihood that damage may be done in the first weeks after conception, before the woman realizes she is pregnant. Later in pregnancy, alcohol taken in moderate to large amounts may result in growth retardation, or more seriously in fetal alcohol syndrome. This includes a series of characteristic malformations and defects affecting the face, heart, brain and nervous system, and is generally associated with reduced mental capacity. For this reason, general advice in the UK is to limit alcohol intake in pregnancy to no more than one standard drink per day and, in any case, to avoid consuming more than 15 units per week. In men who drink heavily, there is likely to be a reduced sperm count, which may be a contributory factor in reproductive failure in a couple.

The weight of the woman and, in particular, her body fat content at the time of conception is also an important determinant of the metabolic changes that occur during pregnancy. Research suggests that a low fat content at conception is a signal to the body to conserve energy so that the metabolism during the pregnancy becomes very efficient and the total energy costs of the pregnancy are low. This is mediated by altered leptin levels. Conversely, in women with high fat stores at conception, there is little energy conservation and the cost of pregnancy is high. Nevertheless, even with this adaptability, mothers with low fat stores give birth to lower birthweight babies than do those with higher fat stores.

Research also suggests that there are nutrients that may be protective at this stage of pregnancy, having an antimutagenic effect. These include riboflavin, vitamins C and E, and monounsaturated and polyunsaturated fats. Foods that are particularly rich in antimutagens are fruit and vegetables, although their activity is likely to be destroyed by cooking.

NUTRITION DURING PREGNANCY

Considerable changes occur in the mother's body during pregnancy. In addition to the developing fetus, there are changes in her own tissues, with an expansion of the plasma volume and red cell mass, increase in the size of the uterus and mammary glands and deposition of fat.

In the 1970s, incremental calculations of the amount of extra protein and fat laid down during pregnancy were performed, which gave an estimate of the energy and protein needs of these 'capital gains'. In addition, an allowance was added for the extra 'running costs' of the heavier maternal body. Such calculations produced a figure for the total additional energy cost of pregnancy of about 335 MJ (80 000 Calories). These figures were used in many countries as the basis for setting recommended intake levels for pregnant women.

Recent findings have shown that energy metabolism exhibits considerable variation, with pregnancy being maintained successfully at an additional energy cost of 523 MJ (125 000 Calories) in well-nourished women in Sweden, and with an energy deficit of 30 MJ (7150 Calories) in women in the Gambia not receiving nutritional supplementation. A woman's adaptive mechanisms to pregnancy can include:

- an increase in food intake to meet energy needs;
- laying down of fat stores/mobilizing fat stores;
- an increase or reduction in the basal metabolic rate (including the costs of synthesis and maintenance of new tissues);
- a reduction in physical activity costs (see Figure 11.2).

Activity 11.1

Think about what you have just read, and answer the following question.

How would the following cases cope with the metabolic demands of pregnancy?

- A rural peasant woman in a food-deficient, poor country.
- A normal-weight woman living in an industrialized Western country.
- An overweight woman, living in a Western country.
- A 14-year-old girl, living in a Western country.

In this way, the energy costs of supporting a developing fetus can be maintained at very different levels of energy intake.

In addition to metabolic adaptations in terms of energy, the body also undergoes other physiological changes to increase the efficiency of nutrient utilization and to optimize the supply to the fetus. Many of these changes commence in the early weeks of pregnancy while the fetus is still very small and its nutritional demands low. At this time, the mother may conserve nutrients in her tissues. Evidence suggests that this applies to protein in particular, with reduced amino acid oxidation occurring in the liver. In the later stages of pregnancy, as the fetus enters a rapid growth phase, this protein can be made available from the mother's tissues to supplement that consumed in the diet. In this way, the needs can be met without a major increase in intake being necessary.

The mother also makes greater use of lipids as a source of energy for her own needs, thus sparing glucose for the needs of the fetus. This change is brought about by alterations in hormone levels, particularly insulin. There are adaptations also in the muscular activity of the intestines, so that food spends a longer time being digested and absorbed. This increases the efficiency of absorption, particularly for minerals such as calcium and iron. In addition, both of these may be better absorbed in response to the physiological regulation, which occurs as a result of the increased need for the minerals.

The slowed activity of the intestines may cause heartburn and constipation. Heartburn arises because the muscles at the top of the

Figure 11.2 Adaptive mechanisms in pregnancy to conserve energy.

stomach are more relaxed, which allows reflux of the acidic stomach contents into the lower part of the oesophagus, causing irritation and pain. Some practical suggestions for relieving heartburn include:

- eating small, frequent meals;
- taking liquids separately from meals;
- avoiding spicy or fatty foods;
- sitting upright while eating;
- waiting 1 hour after eating before lying down;
- not exercising for at least 2 hours after eating.

Constipation occurs because of the longer time available for absorption of water from the digestive tract. Increasing both fluid and non-starch polysaccharide (NSP) intakes can help to relieve this problem, as will maintaining a moderate level of activity.

WHAT ARE THE DIETARY GOALS IN PREGNANCY?

Generally, pregnant women do not eat a diet substantially different from that eaten by the rest of the female population. Studies around the world of pregnant women in different cultures and at different levels of income show that pregnancy can occur successfully at varying levels of nutritional intake, although there are limits to the protection afforded the fetus at low intake levels. Whether the baby that is born is as healthy as possible may not necessarily be apparent in the first instance, since current research suggests that the intrauterine environment is crucial to long-term health (this is discussed later in the chapter).

Birthweights are lower in babies born to women who have lower energy and nutrient intakes, with particularly strong relationships seen with intakes of the minerals magnesium, iron, phosphorus, zinc and potassium, and the vitamins thiamin, niacin, pantothenic acid, riboflavin, folic acid, pyridoxine and biotin. Increasing the food intake does not result in progressively larger and larger infants. Studies by Doyle and colleagues (1990) show that there is a threshold birthweight (of 3.27 kg) above which extra food intake makes little difference, but below which there is a progressively lower birthweight as intakes are reduced.

TABLE 11.1 Guidelines on weight gain in pregnancy

Pre-pregnancy BMI (w/h^2)	Recommended weight gain (kg)
<19.8	12.5–18
19.8–26.0	11.5–16
26–29.0	7–11.5
>29.0	6 (minimum)

Institute of Medicine 1990. *Part I, Weight gain.* Committee on nutritional status and weight gain during pregnancy. Food and Nutrition Board. Washington DC: National Academy Press. Reproduced with permission.

For optimal outcome measured in terms of lowest perinatal mortality, women who are underweight before pregnancy need to increase their food intake more and gain more weight than those of normal weight. The converse is true of overweight women. Various guidelines are now available for the recommended weight to be gained in relation to pre-pregnancy BMI (see Table 11.1 for figures recommended in the USA).

THE DIET IN PREGNANCY

From what has already been said, it is clear that a pregnant woman does not need to 'eat for two'. The mother's appetite should be a good guide to her overall needs for energy.

In the first three months of pregnancy, up to 70 per cent of women suffer from nausea and vomiting. Although this is commonly termed 'morning sickness', probably only 10–15 per cent of women experience sickness in the morning. In the remainder, it can actually occur at any time of day or night – and in some women occurs continuously. Nausea and vomiting of pregnancy (NVP) is a better name for this syndrome. It may range from a mild nausea to quite severe, frequent vomiting. The condition appears to be more prevalent in societies that consume animal products and it has been suggested that NVP is a protective mechanism against potential parasites and pathogens that may be ingested at a critical time in early pregnancy and threaten the embryo. Paradoxically, NVP appears to be associated with a favourable outcome of pregnancy, including higher birthweight and longer gestation. It has

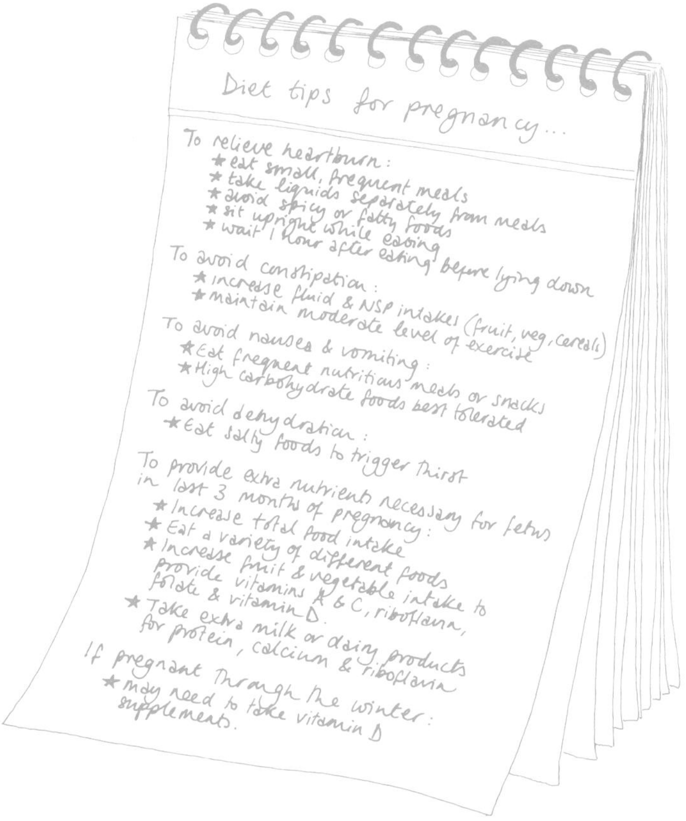

Figure 11.3 Some general diet tips for pregnancy.

been proposed that this may be the result of the adaptation of the placenta to a reduced food intake in the first trimester, which then favours fetal growth once NVP resolves. Frequent meals or snacks are recommended, even if the woman has little appetite for them. It is important that the food eaten is as nutritious as possible and often it is high carbohydrate foods that are best tolerated. Dehydration is also a risk and salty foods that trigger thirst mechanisms may also be useful. An improved quality of the diet may be important to compensate for the period when food intake is low (see Figure 11.3 for general diet tips in pregnancy).

Appetite is usually good in the middle part of pregnancy, so that food intake is at or a little above normal pre-pregnant levels. This ensures an adequate provision of energy and nutrients to form a reserve for the greater needs of the last months.

In the last 3 months, the needs of the fetus are high and the mother's appetite may increase. She is limited in her capacity for food, however, because of the pressure of the enlarged womb on her stomach. The diet chosen should contain a variety of foods to supply the necessary nutrients. Report 41 (DoH, 1991) recommends a small increase in energy intake of 0.8 MJ (200 Calories) per day during the last trimester of pregnancy. This should be provided by increasing total food intake. Together with the adaptations to absorption efficiency and the metabolic changes already mentioned, this will ensure that the additional needs for many other nutrients will be covered.

Particular attention should be paid to certain nutrients for which the increase recommended is greater than can be achieved from a diet designed to just meet the energy requirement. These nutrients are vitamins A and C, riboflavin, folate and vitamin D. Increasing fruit and vegetable intake should provide extra amounts of folate, vitamins A and C. Taking extra milk or dairy products, which can contribute to the extra energy intake and also supplies protein and calcium, will also contribute to meeting the riboflavin needs. Vitamin D requirements may be a problem, especially in women who are pregnant through the winter and are, therefore, unable to synthesize skin vitamin D. If stores have not been accumulated during the previous summer, a supplement of vitamin D is advisable to ensure adequate calcium metabolism. A particular problem may arise in strictly vegetarian women of Asian origin, whose vitamin D status may be precarious, and in whom supplementation with vitamin D has been shown to be of positive benefit for the birthweight and subsequent growth of the baby.

The NSP content of the diet is important in pregnancy because of the tendency for constipation. Including fruit and vegetables and cereal fibre in bread or breakfast cereals can provide sufficient NSP to relieve problems of constipation.

A summary of the dietary reference values for pregnancy is given in Table 11.2.

It should be noted that many of the recommendations made by the UK Department of Health (DoH, 1991) assume an adequate pre-pregnancy diet, resulting in good nutritional status and stores at the outset of pregnancy. Where these are not present, extra intakes will be necessary during pregnancy.

This is a particular problem with iron because it is recognized that a substantial proportion of women have a chronically low intake resulting in poor stores. An early check on haemoglobin and circulating ferritin will confirm if iron status is adequate or whether supplementation is required.

Moreover, where there is a short interval between pregnancies, levels of some nutrients, such as calcium, iron and folate, may be insufficiently restored. It may take 2 years to return levels to their original values. Attention to a nutrient-rich diet is, therefore, important in this situation.

Teenage girls who become pregnant are also particularly at risk, as their own growth needs are high and stores may be insufficient.

Other advice on dietary intake includes food safety issues. The presence of *Listeria monocytogenes* can cause a series of symptoms from mild to severe, but can also result in premature birth or miscarriage and meningitis in a newborn baby. This is a relatively rare condition (estimates are 1 in 30 000 in the UK), but pregnant women are advised to avoid potentially

TABLE 11.2 Summary of dietary reference values for pregnancy

Nutrient	Recommendation
Energy	Increase by 200 kcal (0.8 MJ)/day in last trimester only
Protein	Extra 6 g/day; total recommended 51 g/day
Thiamin	Increase in line with energy: extra 0.1 mg/day; total recommended 0.9 mg/day
Riboflavin	Needed for tissue growth: extra 0.3 mg/day; total recommended 1.4 mg/day
Nicotinic acid	Metabolism becomes more efficient: no increase needed
Pyridoxine	No evidence that increase needed
Vitamin B_{12}	Little information available about needs: no increase
Folate	Increased usage in pregnancy, maintain plasma levels with extra 100 μg/day; total recommended 300 μg/day
Vitamin C	Drain on maternal stores in late pregnancy: extra 10 mg/day; total recommended 50 mg/day
Vitamin D	Seasonal variation in plasma levels of vitamin; 10 μg/day as supplement
Calcium	Maternal store drawn upon in early pregnancy and enhanced absorption: no increase
Iron	Iron stores, cessation of menstruation and increased absorption should cover needs: no increase
Magnesium, zinc and copper	Increased needs, but assumed to be met from increased absorption

From DoH, 1991. Crown copyright is reproduced with the permission of Her Majesty's Stationery Office.

contaminated foods. These include certain cheeses, such as Brie, Camembert and blue-veined cheeses, and meat-based pate. Cooked chilled meats and ready to eat poultry may also be a source of contamination. Other microbiological contaminants include *Salmonella* and toxoplasmosis (mainly from cat litter).

However, there is little evidence to show that education of pregnant women to improve their diet has significant effects. Targeted interventions may make some impact in specific groups and these are considered below. In general, encouragement of healthy eating and increase in nutritional knowledge for the future benefit of the family are useful targets.

SHOULD SUPPLEMENTS BE GIVEN?

There have been many studies of the effects of various supplements on pregnancy outcome. In general, the effects of supplementation during pregnancy are small.

The provision of a balanced energy and protein supplement to undernourished women results in birthweight increases of less than 100 g. High-protein supplements may actually result in reductions in birthweight, possibly associated with development of a larger placenta rather than increasing the size of the fetus. A better understanding of the metabolic adaptations that occur in pregnant women suggests that the result of supplementation is a decrease in the efficiency of energy saving by the mother, with a resulting higher cost of the pregnancy. It is also unclear how much of the supplement the women consume; it may be used to replace intakes rather than add to existing nutrient levels.

Evidence suggests that the greatest effects of supplementation occur when this is given either in the first 3 months of pregnancy or, preferably, before conception. In the latter case, identifying mothers who have already given birth to a low-weight baby and providing supplements in the inter-pregnancy period has proved to be effective in avoiding a subsequent low weight birth. The Women, Infants and Children Program in the USA, which provides food or voucher support to women in low-income groups has demonstrated a consistent benefit in terms of better health of the baby, and reduced need for health and welfare support in the future. This is a cost-effective scheme with greater savings than costs.

In London, supplementation with multivitamins and minerals, of women who had borne a low birthweight infant and who were found to have a poor diet (not meeting the majority of dietary reference values), resulted in a favourable improvement in folate and iron levels up to 9 months after delivery. However, control subjects who did not receive the supplements continued to have low blood levels of these nutrients. This would be an unfavourable start for a subsequent pregnancy and indicates how poor nutrient intakes can be insufficient to restore blood levels of nutrients in the inter-pregnancy period.

Similarly, supplementation with specific nutrients, such as folate or iron, may be most effective if given pre-conceptionally, or in the very early weeks of pregnancy. Although it occurs routinely in much obstetric care, there is controversy about the desirability of supplementation with iron during pregnancy. Some evidence suggests that pregnancy outcome is optimal at haemoglobin concentrations between 96 and 105 g/L, indicating that this level may be the most desirable. Haemoglobin levels above this value can be achieved by supplementation, but this may be counterproductive.

It could be argued that a low iron status is merely a marker of a generally inadequate diet, which may be low in other, less frequently measured nutrients. It would, therefore, appear to be preferable to improve the whole diet, rather than to focus on specific nutrients, which might result in an unbalanced intake.

The need to supplement with long-chain fatty acids has also been debated, particularly for women whose diet is low in dietary sources. Infant growth and development, especially of the brain and retina, is dependent on an adequate supply of docosahexaenoic acid. Poor status in the mother will mean low levels in the infant. Supplementation of the mother in late pregnancy with fish oil has been shown to increase levels of n-3 fatty acids in cord blood of the newborn infant. Supplementation can also increase concentrations of n-3 acids in breast milk.

Supplementation with calcium has been used effectively to reduce blood pressure in women at risk of hypertension in pregnancy. The greatest benefits have been seen in women with low dietary calcium levels. The amount used is at least 1 g of calcium per day. Longer term studies of the offspring from these pregnancies have shown lower blood pressures in the children.

WHO IS MOST AT RISK IN PREGNANCY?

A number of groups in the population are particularly vulnerable to poor pregnancy outcome.

Teenage girls

The nutritional status at conception may be poor for a number of reasons. Adolescents are less likely to be eating a well-balanced diet. This applies particularly to girls, who may be chronic dieters as a result of the current fashion for slimness. Low intakes of vitamins A and C, folic acid, calcium, iron and zinc have been reported.

Furthermore, if the girl is still growing, her own nutritional needs may be high and, if she continues to grow during the pregnancy, the baby's development will be compromised. A teenage mother may have social problems, including eating very little to conceal the pregnancy, having little money, perhaps smoking and living in poor-quality housing. All of these factors will contribute to a poorer pregnancy outcome with a higher incidence of low birthweight, perinatal mortality, premature delivery and maternal problems of difficult labour, anaemia and hypertension being reported.

Low income

Women comprise the majority of those existing on low income. The cost of a diet appropriate to meet the needs of a pregnant woman has been calculated to be between 40 and 65 per cent of the state benefits payable in the UK. For most women in this situation, it is unrealistic to spend this amount on food for themselves, and a nutritionally inferior diet is eaten, containing insufficient amounts of nutrients to meet the needs. This leads to a high incidence of low birthweight. Of particular concern is the fatty acid profile of the diet, which may include few long-chain polyunsaturated fatty acids (such as arachidonic and docosahexaenoic acids) that are crucial for development of the neural and vascular systems, and are particularly important in the last 3 months of pregnancy when brain growth is at its most rapid. These essential fatty acids are found in vegetable oils, green vegetables and oily fish, which occur less frequently in the diets of the poor. This deficit may have long-term consequences for the growth and development of their children.

Underweight and overweight women

The importance of adequate but not excessive weight gain has already been discussed. Infants born to underweight women may exhibit inadequate patterns of growth at 12 months, suggesting delays in development. Overweight women also have increased pregnancy risks, both for themselves and the outcome for the baby. In overweight women, dieting during pregnancy is never recommended; a low energy intake during pregnancy may result in ketosis and pose a threat for the developing fetus. However, maintaining a reasonable level of activity during pregnancy is desirable to avoid excessive weight gain and benefit the mother's physiological fitness. Aerobic exercise may be particularly beneficial for women with a predisposition to gestational diabetes, as it enhances insulin sensitivity.

Other situations

Other at-risk situations that may occur are summarized in Table 11.3.

LONG-TERM CONSEQUENCES OF INTRAUTERINE EVENTS

Studies on animals have over many years shown that the tissues and organs of the fetus go through critical periods in their development, at specific times in uterine life. It has also been clear that a positive or negative stimulus occurring during a critical period can have permanent,

TABLE 11.3 Possible indicators of nutritional vulnerability in pregnancy

Indicator	Possible causes
Low nutrient stores at conception	Adolescent growth spurt Closely spaced pregnancies Low BMI Intake affected by poverty History of dieting/disordered eating
Poor intake during pregnancy (evidenced by poor weight gain)	Poor-quality diet due to: poverty; lack of interest in food; smoking; use of drugs or alcohol Previous low-weight birth Illness/sickness of pregnancy Negative attitude to pregnancy Cultural taboos on diet in pregnancy
Pre-existing or gestational disease/condition	Requires special diet/monitoring of food and drug balance during pregnancy Weight gain/weight loss

lifelong consequences, even after that stimulus has been removed or cancelled. This phenomenon is known as 'programming', and in evolutionary terms is probably an adaptation to improve the chances of short-term survival, while having longer term consequences that may be detrimental. These are less important from the evolutionary perspective, if the consequence is delayed until post-reproductive life. The relevance of programming to humans has only been recognized from the mid-1980s, and since then an enormous amount of research has been published that shows the fundamental impact of events in fetal life on subsequent health of individuals.

Early clues to the need for this research came from observations that the distribution of coronary heart disease in the 1970s in the UK mirrored patterns of infant mortality at the start of the twentieth century. This suggested that events in early life that caused a high rate of infant deaths might in some way contribute to a higher risk of coronary heart disease in survivors. Following improvements in living standards in the middle of the twentieth century, coronary heart disease rates began to show a decrease in the later decades of the century. This fall could not be attributed to any major changes in adult lifestyle factors. Furthermore, as developing countries are becoming more Westernized, so prevalence of coronary heart disease and other Western diseases is rising there, in much the same way as they did in the UK in the middle of the twentieth century.

Evidence in support of a link came initially from data contained in birth and development records of babies born in the early decades of the twentieth century, together with mortality records of those who have since died and measurements made on the survivors. A strong negative correlation between weight at birth and the incidence of coronary heart disease later in life was found (Barker, 1998). This did not apply only to babies that could be classified as 'low birthweight', but was true across the whole range of normal birthweights at full term. This negative association between weight at birth and coronary heart disease has since been demonstrated in several different study cohorts, in the USA, India and Norway.

Furthermore, relationships have been demonstrated between weight at birth and the presence of some of the accepted risk factors for coronary heart disease. The evidence suggests that restricted growth during uterine life programmes the fetus in a way that increases subsequent risk of coronary heart disease and other degenerative diseases. As the mechanisms underlying these findings are explored, it has become clear that birthweight alone is a crude indicator of changes that have occurred during uterine life. Changes in body proportions, including thinness, length, head and abdominal circumference are able to give more information about possible organs that may have been advantaged or disadvantaged in utero. The ratio of the placental to birthweight has also shown to be a useful indicator. At either extreme, an imbalance between these suggests that either the placenta was too small to provide adequate nutrients for the fetus, or it was excessively large and, therefore, took a greater share of nutrients for its own development.

At the cellular level, it is understood that programming may:

- alter gene expression, for example, resulting in different levels of enzyme activity;
- affect cell division, resulting in fewer cell numbers within a particular organ;
- influence levels of hormone secretion, or sensitivity of receptor sites to hormones.

Examples of these changes have been demonstrated in animal studies, but application of modern experimental techniques will allow more to be studied in humans to further the understanding of processes that happened in the womb.

Lower birthweight has been associated with the following conditions.

Higher blood pressure

A systematic review of 34 studies by Law and Shiell (1996) has shown a consistent decrease in blood pressure for each 1 kg increment in birthweight. The relationship is less clear during adolescence but is consistent at other ages. The relationship with blood pressure is also found when the ratio of placental to birthweight is considered. A disproportion between these weights, in either direction from the normal ratio of 1:6, is associated with a higher blood pressure. A number of mechanisms have been postulated to explain these findings. Poor nutrient supply may compromise renal development, with reduced numbers of nephrons that become more susceptible to raised glomerular pressure, leading to hypertension. The involvement of the hypothalamus, pituitary and adrenals is considered as a probable mechanism. The model proposes that the fetus is exposed to higher levels of cortisol. These may originate from the mother, as a result of physiological stress, and are insufficiently blocked by low activity of 11-beta-hydroxysteroid dehydrogenase in the placenta and thus reach the fetus. Downregulation of this enzyme has been demonstrated in the placenta in the animal model. Alternatively, the fetus itself experiences stress and generates high levels of cortisol. The raised cortisol levels have multiple effects on the development and sensitivity of blood vessels as well as the response of the hypothalamus to signals from blood pressure receptors.

Insulin resistance and diabetes mellitus

Many studies have confirmed the relationship between low weight or thinness at birth with a greater risk of impaired glucose tolerance, insulin resistance or Type 2 diabetes in the adult. Raised plasma insulin concentrations and slower glucose clearance after challenge with glucose have both been demonstrated in children who were thin at birth. In adults who were thin at birth, lower rates of energy production from glucose in skeletal muscle during exercise have been shown. These findings have led to the hypothesis that the fetal metabolism responds to a reduced nutrient supply by reducing its utilization of glucose. This is achieved by a reduction in levels of insulin and insulin-like growth factor I and increased cortisol levels. Skeletal muscle growth and glucose uptake are both reduced, and amino acids and lactate are used for energy. Thus, there is reduced muscle bulk, resulting in a thinner baby, and a relatively lower glucose utilization accompanied by less responsiveness to insulin. If this metabolic pattern persists into adulthood, it predisposes to the insulin resistance syndrome and Type 2 diabetes.

A further consequence of programming that may determine glucose metabolism affects the size and function of the pancreatic cells that secrete insulin. Animal studies have shown that rats fed protein deficient diets produced offspring with fewer pancreatic islet cells and a reduced ability to regulate glucose. Such a situation will result in insulin deficiency in adult life.

Cholesterol metabolism and blood clotting

Animal studies have demonstrated that impaired nutrient supply to the fetus in the latter stages of gestation results in diversion of more oxygenated blood flow to the cranial region to protect development there. As a result, the trunk and particularly the liver becomes relatively deprived of nutrients, with the potential for permanent changes to be programmed at this stage. Studies on rats fed low-protein diets have identified changes in levels of enzymes associated with lipid metabolism and blood clotting in the liver. Studies in humans have indicated that infants born with a relatively larger head and either a shorter trunk or smaller abdominal circumference, have raised levels of factors produced by the liver. These include blood-clotting factors, such as fibrinogen, and cholesterol fractions. Both of these may contribute to a higher risk of coronary heart disease in later life.

Other conditions

Other possible conditions that may have fetal origins have been investigated. For many, there is still only emerging evidence and more research is needed. These include associations of fetal development with: various cancers, intelligence, obesity, atopy and food allergies, immune status, polycystic ovary syndrome and osteoporosis. In addition, ageing processes appear to be associated with growth and nutrition in early life; lower weight at 1 year has been found to be associated with increased lens opacity, thinner skin, poorer hearing and reduced muscle strength in old age. Figure 11.4 summarizes the fetal influences on later health.

It should be stressed here that not every small baby is destined to have a lifetime of ill-health. The effects of programming are inevitably modified by lifestyle factors. However, it is clear from the research to date that the greatest risk of developing degenerative diseases occurs in those who had been small at birth, or small at 1 year of age and who are then exposed to adverse conditions in adult life (such as weight gain, smoking, a high saturated fat diet, lack of exercise). The largest babies, or the ones who had grown well in the first year of life, were found to have the lowest risk of developing these degenerative diseases.

These correlations are strong and show up to three-fold differences in risk between those with the highest and lowest birthweights, for example, in the development of impaired glucose tolerance and diabetes. If adult BMI is taken into account, the risk increases to almost seven-fold in those who also become overweight.

The most tantalizing aspect of this research is to discover what aspects of maternal diet are the keys that determine fetal nutrition and development. There is strong evidence that the uterine environment is a major determinant of the size of the fetus. Research from embryo implantation studies shows that the recipient mother has a much stronger influence on the size of the baby than the donor mother, even though the baby has the donor's genes.

A fetus whose rate of growth is rapid is much more susceptible than one growing more slowly to a change in the nutrient supply. The latter appears to be better adapted to withstand a faltering nutrient supply. A key question, therefore, is what determines the setting of the growth trajectory. It is suggested, although human evidence is lacking, that the nutrient availability around the time of conception is critical in determining the partitioning of embryonic cells between fetus and placenta, and sets the rates of growth for both. The availability of nutrients within the mother's womb may itself be determined by her own development as a fetus, when her ovary and uterus were developing. Thus, there is a strong possibility of cross-generational effects that determine the growth of a fetus. There is some evidence to support this proposal, both from studies on rats, where effects of deficiency may take up to three generations to be normalized, as well as from human studies following periods of famine in wartime, where effects have been observed in the following generation.

Many populations have lived for generations in an environment where food supply was poor and the workload heavy; these have been associated with slow fetal growth and small babies. Degenerative disease was relatively rare in these

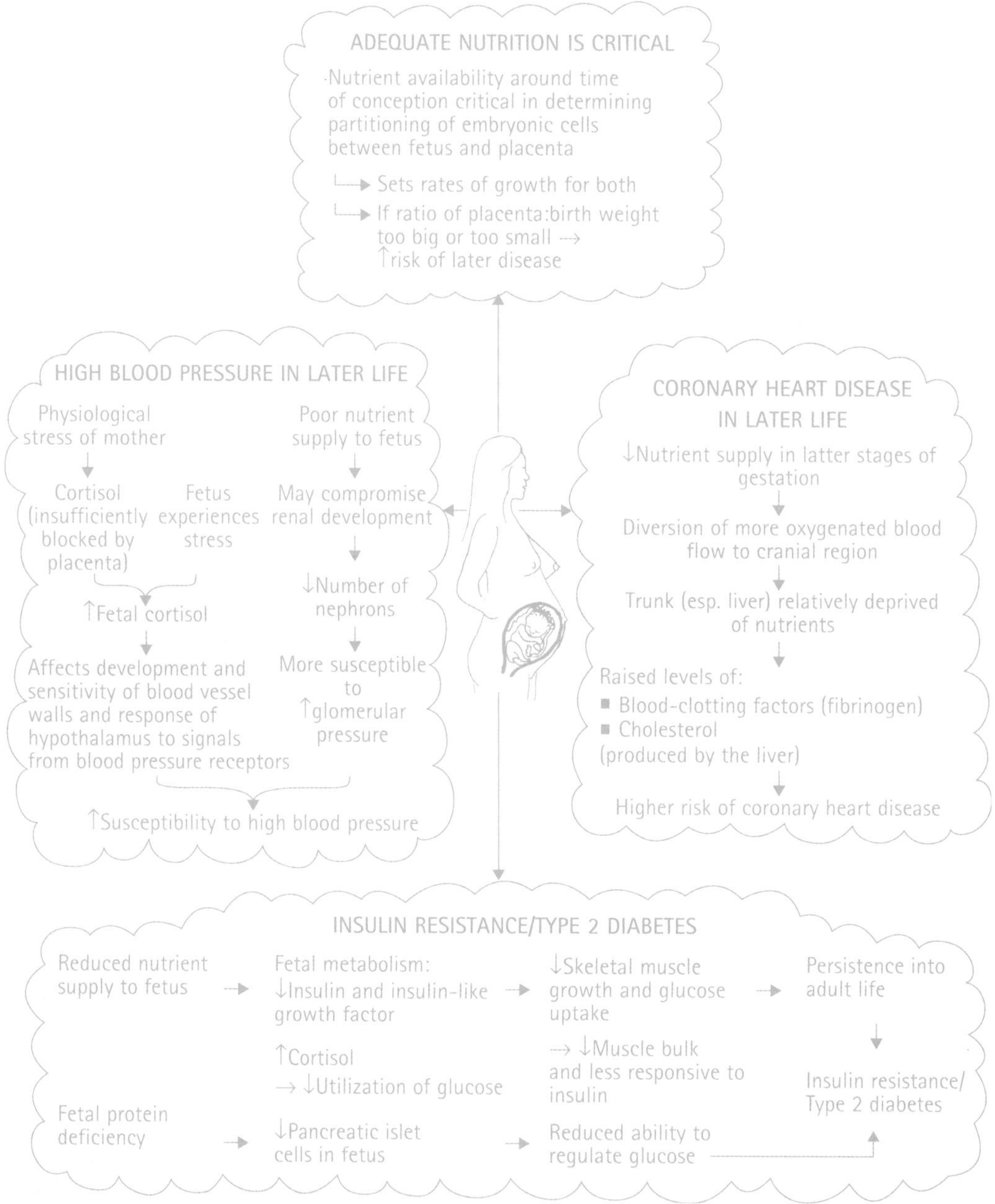

Figure 11.4 Summary of fetal influences on later health.

populations. As Western lifestyles and food habits spread across the world, there is likely to be a transition phase, where maternal capacity to nourish a fetus may still be hampered by a poor uterine environment. Babies will continue to be born small, until the effects of better nutrition improve the overall health of mothers. Thus, there is likely to be an increase in degenerative disease, as small babies become overweight adults, poorly adapted to the plentiful food supplies and lower workloads. This transition phase occurred in the West in the middle of the twentieth century, with a high prevalence of degenerative diseases, but may now be nearing its end, with a decline in some of these diseases. However, developing countries may still be facing the upsurge of diseases, such as coronary heart disease, as they enter the transition phase, especially in urban areas.

Translating this research into practical advice for pregnant women, or those intending to become pregnant is still very difficult. There is insufficient evidence to pinpoint dietary changes that should be made, but overall advice to prepare nutritionally for pregnancy and to maintain healthy eating throughout must remain as the guiding principle. The practice of supplementing the diet during pregnancy may not be beneficial, as the determinants of growth are set very early, before the pregnancy is confirmed. Small babies need to be monitored and the importance of healthy weight and lifestyle stressed in this group, as they have greater vulnerability to disease than those whose weight at birth was higher. The next decade may bring more detailed information about this fascinating area of study.

THE NURSING OR LACTATING MOTHER

Breastfeeding a newborn infant is the natural sequel to pregnancy. The process of lactation (or milk production) does not occur in isolation since the mother's breasts become prepared for lactation throughout pregnancy. By no means all mothers choose to breastfeed their babies. In the UK, prevalence of breastfeeding at birth is around 64 per cent, although there are great differences between middle-class mothers, of whom over 80 per cent may start breastfeeding, and lower social class mothers, where the prevalence is in the order of 25 per cent. For mothers who choose to breastfeed, it is usually a special and enjoyable experience. Those mothers who decide not to breastfeed can provide adequate nutrition for their babies using the many formula feeds available. However, certain aspects of human milk will not be present in the formula. These are discussed further in Chapter 12.

If a woman decides not to breastfeed her child, the breasts return to their normal pre-pregnant size within a fairly short period of time.

THE PROCESS OF LACTATION

There are two stages involved in lactation: milk production and milk ejection (see Figure 11.5).

Milk production or lactogenesis

Milk is made in the mammary glands of the breast, which contain cells arranged in lobules. The synthesis of milk is stimulated by the hormone prolactin released from the anterior pituitary gland, which in turn is stimulated by the process of suckling by the infant at the breast. Thus, the more the infant suckles, the more milk is synthesized and milk production parallels demand.

Some proteins found in milk, such as the immune factors, enter from the maternal circulation, but the majority of the protein content is synthesized by the mammary glands. The fats that contain short-chain fatty acids are synthesized in the breast, but the long-chain fats are derived from the maternal diet. A mother who consumes a high level of long-chain fats will, therefore, have higher levels of them in her milk. The galactose part of the lactose molecule is synthesized in the breast, the glucose part is derived from the maternal circulation.

Milk ejection or let-down

The milk that is formed is not released from the breast until the baby suckles. This initiates a reflex in the mother, involving signals to the hypothalamus, which in turn cause the release of the hormone oxytocin from the posterior pituitary gland. It is this hormone that causes the specialized cells in the mammary gland to contract and eject the milk into the mouth of the infant. The reflex can be inhibited by the mother's mental state: if she is apprehensive, tense or tired, the reflex can fail and milk is not released. An understanding of the nature of the reflex, which allows sufficient relaxation and preparation for feeding, can prevent a great deal of frustration. After about 2 weeks of breastfeeding, the reflex becomes automatic and can be triggered simply by hearing the baby crying.

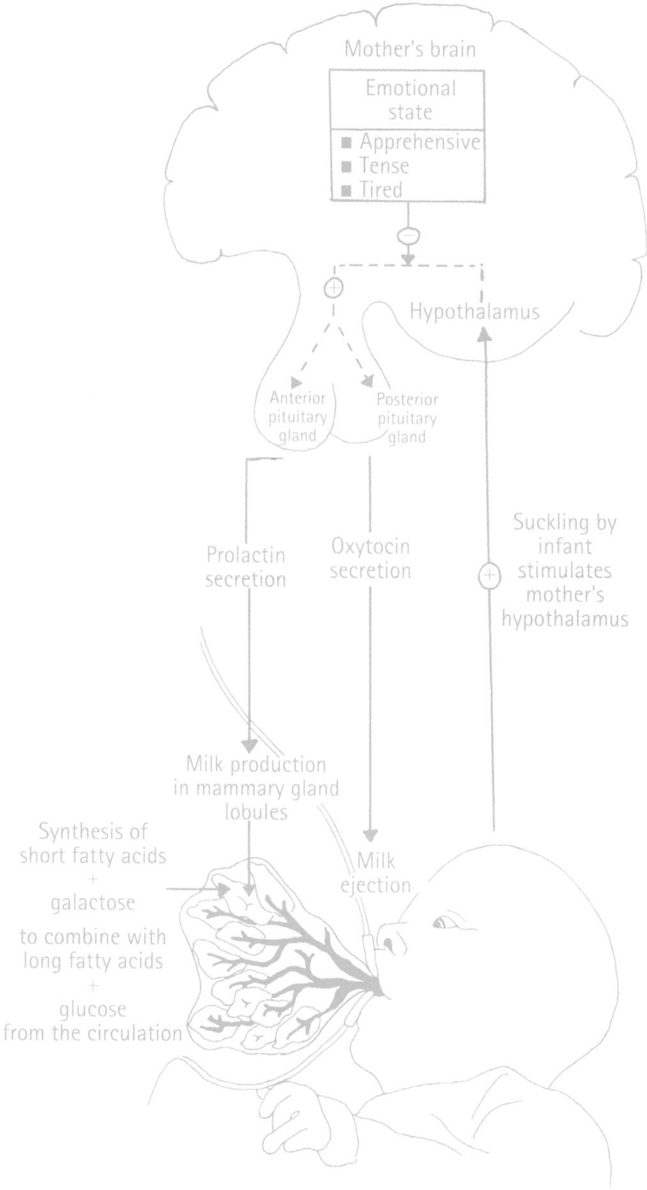

Figure 11.5 The process of lactation.

DIET IN LACTATION

As with pregnancy, no special diet is needed in lactation. It must be remembered, however, that the food eaten by the mother in the first 4–6 months of breastfeeding (before weaning takes place) has to meet all of her own needs as well as those of the baby, which are considerably greater than its needs while in the womb. These increased requirements are reflected in the higher dietary reference values published by the UK Department of Health (DoH, 1991) and summarized in Table 11.4.

Energy

The average daily volume of milk produced varies from mother to mother. Data from the UK and Sweden indicate that the average volume of milk produced in the first 3 months of lactation ranges from 680 to 820 mL/day. The energy cost

TABLE 11.4 Dietary reference values for lactation

Nutrient	Recommended level
Energy	Additional 450–570 kcal (1.9–2.4 MJ)/day at 1–3 months Additional 480 kcal (2.0 MJ)/day between 3 and 6 months
Protein	To cover protein content of milk, increase by 11 g/day; total recommended 56 g/day
Vitamin A	To cover content in milk, increase by 350 μg/day; total recommended 950 μg/day
Thiamin	Increase only in line with increased energy requirement
Riboflavin	To cover extra content in milk, and its secretion, increase by 0.5 mg/day; total recommended 1.6 mg/day
Niacin	To cover extra content in milk, increase by 2.3 mg/day; total recommended 8.9 mg/day
Pyridoxine	No evidence exists of a need to increase intake
Vitamin B_{12}	To cover the content in milk, increase by 0.5 mg/day; total recommended 2.0 mg/day
Folate	To cover the content in milk, and absorption and utilization by the mother, increase by 60 μg/day; total recommended 260 μg/day
Vitamin C	To cover content in milk and maintain maternal stores, increase by 30 mg/day; total recommended 70 mg/day
Vitamin D	To maintain plasma vitamin D levels: recommend a supplement of 10 μg/day
Calcium	To cover content in milk and allow for efficiency of absorption by mother, increase by 550 mg/day; total recommended 1250 mg/day
Magnesium	To cover content in milk, and allow for absorption, increase by 50 mg/day; total recommended 320 mg/day
Iron	Extra content in milk can be met by lactational amenorrhoea; thus, no extra increment
Zinc	To cover zinc content of milk; no information about enhanced absorption is available; thus increase by 6 mg/day; total recommended 13 mg/day

From DoH, 1991.

of producing this milk, assuming an 80 per cent efficiency of energy conversion, has been calculated as 2.38–2.87 MJ (570–690 Calories) per day in the first 3 months. After 3 months, and assuming that weaning begins at around 4 months, the output of milk falls to 700 mL/day, with an energy cost to the mother of 2.45 MJ (590 Calories) per day.

Some of this extra energy can be met from fat stores laid down in pregnancy, although the extent to which this is mobilized appears to vary between women. It is assumed that, on average, 0.5 kg of stored fat is used per month, although women have been recorded as losing between 0.6 and 0.8 kg/month during the first 4–6 months after delivery. In overweight women, a loss of 2 kg/month may be possible, but feeding on demand should continue to ensure that adequate milk production is maintained. Undertaking intense exercise to speed up weight loss can raise lactic acid levels in the blood, which will pass into the milk and affect the taste. However, moderate exercise is beneficial and should be encouraged, as long as energy needs continue to be met.

Dietary energy restriction may affect milk output, particularly in the first weeks before lactation is fully established. However, it is also possible that milk output is only compromised when body fat stores are below a particular threshold level. It is also important to recognize that restricting energy intake to a low level will have consequences for the quality of the diet, and may result in other nutrient requirements not being met. There is a concern that toxic chemical residues, which may be present in maternal body fat, will be mobilized and secreted in the milk, if fat stores are used as a source of energy. There is little evidence, however, on which a judgement can be based.

In women who are chronically undernourished and, therefore, have very low body fat reserves, lactation can still occur satisfactorily even in these apparently adverse circumstances.

Studies suggest that the greater efficiency of metabolism seen in pregnancy carries through into lactation, so that costs of maintaining the mother's body remain low, thus providing extra energy for milk production. However, the nutritional content of the milk probably starts to fall from the third or fourth month of lactation.

Protein

The protein content of milk supplies the amino acids necessary for the growth of the baby, and the additional amount should be provided in the mother's diet. If the diet contains sufficient extra energy to satisfy those needs, then the protein content will also be adequate. On a poor diet, where the total food supply is inadequate, it is not possible to provide additional protein, but protein levels in the milk are maintained for several months even under these circumstances.

GENERAL CONSIDERATIONS

It can be seen from Table 11.4 that nutritional needs in lactation are greater than those in pregnancy. However, if a mother satisfies her need for additional energy, then the increased needs for all the other nutrients should be met, assuming the extra food eaten is well-balanced.

Nutrients that warrant special attention are calcium, and vitamins A and D. If it is not possible to increase food intake, then the nutritional quality of the milk may suffer. The water-soluble vitamins, B complex and C, will be present in smaller amounts. The other constituents, namely fats, lactose, protein and fat-soluble vitamins, may remain at an adequate level for 3–4 months, but will then decline. The weight gain of the baby may slow down or stop at this point, and alternative sources of food will be needed for the baby.

THE DECISION TO BREASTFEED

Human milk is ideally suited to the needs of the human infant. Nevertheless, a significant number of mothers do not take advantage of the process of lactation for a number of reasons. The arguments for and against breastfeeding from the mother's perspective are briefly reviewed and summarized in Figure 11.6. An additional

Figure 11.6 Arguments for and against breastfeeding.

advantage of breastfeeding is that it has been shown to protect women against breast cancer; this may explain the higher rates of breast cancer in developed than in the less developed countries.

The benefits of breastfeeding are discussed further with respect to the infant in Chapter 12.

Because the decision to breastfeed or not is based on so many deeply held beliefs, it should be respected, and mothers who choose not to breastfeed should not be made to feel that they are failing their baby in any way. What matters for the mother and infant is that the mother is confident with what she is doing and can provide all of the nutritional needs that her child requires. She can achieve this with formula milk or by ensuring that her own nutrition is adequate to provide good-quality milk for as long as she wishes to feed her infant.

Activity 11.2

1 Carry out a small survey among your colleagues. Ask whether they have opinions about breastfeeding and try to relate these to their own experience of breastfeeding. This may include seeing siblings breastfed, having breastfeed an infant themselves or having seen friends breastfeeding.
- Is there a gender difference in opinion?
- Is there an age difference?
- Do the opinions you collect match those given in Figure 11.6?
- Can you add others to the list?

2 In what ways do you think health promotion could persuade people to breastfeed their children?

SUMMARY

1 The outcome of pregnancy for both the mother and infant depends on nutritional status of the mother.
2 Nutritional status prior to pregnancy may determine fertility and the early development of the embryo.
3 During pregnancy, the first 3 months are the most critical from the nutritional perspective, as the placenta is not fully developed and the fetus depends entirely on the concentrations of nutrients in the mother's circulation.
4 The needs for some nutrients increase more than others. All nutritional needs can be met from a balanced diet, eaten in sufficient amounts. Many adaptations occur in the mother's body to ensure adequate nutrient supplies.
5 The nutrient supply to the fetus may not only determine the birthweight but also set up the programme for potential health in future years.
6 Lactation is a sequel to pregnancy and also requires adequate nutrition.
7 The quality of the milk is largely protected from shortcomings in the mother's diet for the first 3 months of lactation by increased efficiency in maternal metabolism.

STUDY QUESTIONS

1 Why is it important for a woman to be nutritionally fit at the time of conception?
2 Metabolic adjustments occur in a woman during pregnancy. In the following cases, state what the adjustments are and their consequences for nutritional intake or needs:
   a appetite
   b digestive tract function
   c metabolic rate.
3 Design a poster or leaflet giving practical dietary advice for pregnancy.
4 Why might the following be particularly nutritionally vulnerable while pregnant:
   a vegetarians
   b women on a low income
   c young adolescent girls (aged 13–15)?
5 Identify five reasons commonly cited by women against breastfeeding and consider how you might offer a positive view to counter each reason.

REFERENCES AND FURTHER READING

Allen, L.H. (ed.) 1994: Recent developments in maternal nutrition and their implications for practitioners. *American Journal of Clinical Nutrition* 59(2) (suppl.), 439–541.

Anderson, A.S. 2001: Pregnancy as a time for dietary change? *Proceedings of the Nutrition Society* 60, 497–504.

Barker, D.J.P. 1998: *Mothers, babies and health in later life*. Edinburgh: Churchill Livingstone.

Czeizel, A.E. 1993: Prevention of congenital abnormalities by periconceptional multivitamin supplementation. *British Medical Journal* 306, 1645–8.

DoH (UK Department of Health) 1991: *Dietary reference values for food energy and nutrients for the United Kingdom*. Report on Health and Social Subjects No. 41. Report of the Panel on Dietary Reference Values of the Committee on Medical Aspects of Food Policy. London: HMSO.

Doyle, W., Crawford, M.A., Wynn, A.H.A. et al. 1990: The association between maternal diet and birth dimensions. *Journal of Nutritional Medicine* 1, 9–17.

Food Standards Agency 2002a: *Food portion sizes*, 3rd edn. London: The Stationery Office.

Food Standards Agency 2002b: *McCance and Widdowson's The composition of foods*, 6th summary edn. Cambridge: The Royal Society of Chemistry.

Frisch, R.E. 1994: The right weight: body fat, menarche and fertility. *Proceedings of the Nutrition Society* 53, 113–29.

Godfrey, K.M., Barker, D.J.P. 2001: Fetal programming and adult health. *Public Health Nutrition* 4 (2B), 611–24.

Goldberg, G. 1994: Human pregnancy and lactation: physiological metabolic and behavioural strategies to maintain energy balance. *British Nutrition Foundation Nutrition Bulletin* 19(Suppl.), 37–52.

Goldberg, G., Prentice, A.M. 1994: Maternal and fetal determinants of adult diseases. *Nutrition Reviews* 52(6), 191–200.

HEA (Health Education Authority) 1996: *Folic acid – what all women should know* (leaflet). London: HEA.

Jackson, A.A., Robinson, S.M. 2000: Dietary guidelines for pregnancy: a review of current evidence. *Public Health Nutrition* 4(2B), 625–30.

Langley-Evans, S.C. 2001: Fetal programming of cardiovascular function through exposure to maternal undernutrition. *Proceedings of the Nutrition Society* 60, 505–13.

Law, C.M., Shiell, A.W. 1996: Is blood pressure inversely related to birth weight? The strength of evidence from a systematic review of the literature. *Journal of Hypertension* 14, 935–41.

Livingstone, V. 1995: Breastfeeding kinetics: a problem-solving approach to breastfeeding difficulties. *World Review of Nutrition and Dietetics* 78, 28–54.

Marabou Symposium 1996: Early nutrition and lifelong health. *Nutrition Reviews* 54(2), 1–73.

Rasmussen, K.M. 1992: The influence of maternal nutrition on lactation. *Annual Review of Nutrition* 12, 103–17.

Sayer, A.A., Cooper, C. 2002: Early diet and growth: impact on ageing. *Proceedings of the Nutrition Society* 61, 79–85.

Yajnik, C. 2000: Interactions of perturbations in intrauterine growth and growth during childhood on the risk of adult-onset disease. *Proceedings of the Nutrition Society* 59, 257–65.

12 INFANTS, CHILDREN AND ADOLESCENTS

The aims of this chapter are to:

- ❑ describe the nutritional needs of the normal infant and how these are met by human and formula milks;
- ❑ discuss the process and objectives of weaning and consider the problems that might arise;
- ❑ consider the diets of pre-school children and the key nutritional principles to be addressed in this group;
- ❑ discuss the diets of school-age children, including adolescents;
- ❑ consider the special nutritional dilemmas encountered by teenagers.

On completing the study of this chapter, you should be able to:

- ❑ explain the relative merits of human and formula milks in feeding normal infants and how these may need to be modified for infants with particular needs;
- ❑ relate nutritional needs and intakes to the development of the child;
- ❑ explain some of the reasons why intakes may not be nutritionally sound in school age children;
- ❑ suggest ways in which nutritional intakes in adolescents could be improved.

Adequate dietary intake and nutritional status among children are important for their own growth and development and function. However, there is now also evidence that childhood nutrition influences adult health. Research has shown that intrauterine nutrition influences adult morbidity and mortality, but childhood diet and nutritional status can modify the consequences of being born small. Diet in all the stages of childhood needs to be taken seriously because of its potential for producing normally developed children as well as determining their lifelong health and thus having an impact on a nation's health. With many diets in transition owing to changing social, economic and environmental conditions, consideration of the impact of these changes on the diets of children is important. Particular issues of concern include the establishment of good dietary habits, together with adequate physical activity to prevent the development of overweight, adequate intakes of calcium to promote bone health, and sufficient intakes of minerals and vitamins in the face of a culture often centred on fast food. There are many gaps in our current understanding of children's food habits and influences on these. It is difficult to obtain good-quality information about these and, therefore, health promotion inputs may be missing their target.

INFANTS

Infants are totally dependent on other people for their food supply. During the first year of life, there is very rapid growth, so for its age and size the infant has very high nutritional needs. Neither of these situations normally occur again in a healthy individual. The main aim of infant feeding is to satisfy nutritional needs in the best possible way, and to achieve a healthy infant who is growing at the appropriate rate and developing normally. Although the main emphasis here is on the principles of feeding normal infants, it must be remembered that infants who are premature, ill, disabled or with any other special needs can also be fed successfully, often by only minor adjustment of the normal practice.

Growth

Babies grow faster in their early months and more slowly in the latter part of the first year. An infant's birthweight is doubled within 4–6 months and trebles within the first year.

Growth is slower thereafter, and the weight at 5 years is on average twice that of the weight at 1 year. Standard growth curves (see Figure 12.1) are used to monitor a child's development in terms of height and weight. They are based on percentiles, which represent the range of expected normal results in a group of children. The position of any one child represents their rank if 100 children had been measured. Monitoring weight and height at intervals allows a child's progress to be followed. Deviations over time from the child's usual curve may indicate faulty nutrition, perhaps as a result of concurrent illness. This may be seen frequently in children in developing countries, who may experience periods of infection, possibly often in addition to chronic poor nutrition, resulting in slowed growth.

As in uterine life, post-natal growth may be slowed owing to insufficient cell multiplication or cell growth. The timing of poor nutrition will determine which aspect of growth is affected more. If fewer cells are made, then it is impossible for this to be remedied later by better nutrition. However, failure of cells to grow may be compensated by 'catch up' growth, if nutrition improves. Key periods of cell multiplication occur at different times for different organs. Brain development, for example, occurs very rapidly in the first months after birth and cell multiplication stops by the age of 12–15 months. Although growth continues, the brain is almost at adult size by the age of 5 years. Thus, infancy and childhood are critical periods for nutrient supply to the brain. There has been considerable debate about critical periods for fat cell formation and some evidence suggests that overfeeding in infancy may encourage multiplication of fat cells. These may be associated with higher leptin levels and possible leptin resistance in later life. However, this requires further study.

Growth may also be affected by emotional factors and stress. Where possible, the cause should be investigated and rectified as quickly as possible to prevent long-term consequences.

Nutrition and development

An infant born at full term is able to suck, but is not able to bite or chew pieces of food, so that its diet of necessity is a liquid one. The liquid designed by nature as food for the newborn is milk produced by its mother. This provides not only nourishment, but also immune protection and developmental stimuli.

Alternative milks have been developed; these are highly modified to make them suitable for infants. In Britain, two types of milks derived from cows' milk are available: whey-dominant types based on the dialysed whey protein, and casein-dominant types based on the entire protein fraction. Modern milks are as similar in composition to human milk as is possible, however, they lack the immunological and hormonal factors. Modified soya milks and other hydrolysed protein formulas have also been developed to meet the needs of children with diagnoses of allergy.

From about the end of the third month of life, the baby can cope with a rusk or cereal mixed with milk, by sucking it or swallowing it with saliva. The ability to bite and chew lumps of food begins at 5–6 months, and it is at this stage that an increasing variety of tastes and textures can begin to be introduced into the baby's diet. An ability to chew lumpy food by 6–7 months is an important developmental step and chewing is best learned at this age. If it is delayed, the child may have difficulty in learning to chew later. The ability to chew is also related to early speech development. Early feeding is thus an important preparation for verbal communication.

By the age of 1 year, the infant has progressed from a newborn only able to suck liquids from a nipple or teat, to increasing independence of eating, and attempting to feed itself. By this age, a child may have up to eight teeth, which help in the biting and tearing of food. Molar teeth for proper grinding of food develop late in the second year, when chewing ability becomes more fully developed.

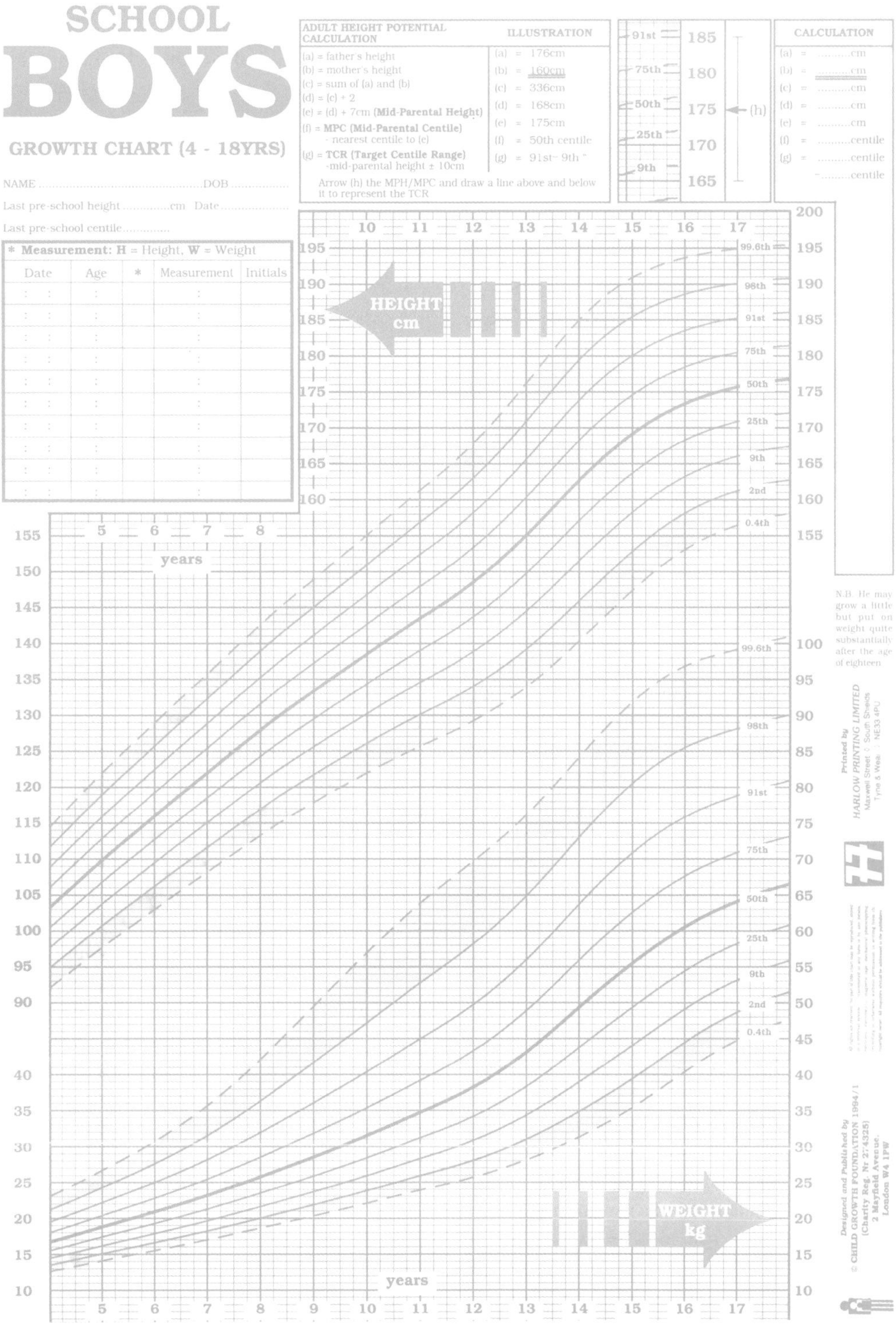

Figure 12.1 Example of a standard growth curve used to monitor child development. (©Child Growth Foundation. Copies of the chart may be purchased from Harlow Printing, Maxwell Street, South Shields NE33 4PU, UK.)

TABLE 12.1 Reference nutrient intakes for selected nutrients for infants

Nutrient	0–3 months	4–6 months	7–9 months	10–12 months
Protein (g/day)	12.5	12.7	13.7	14.9
Thiamin (mg/day)	0.2	0.2	0.2	0.3
Riboflavin (mg/day)	0.4	0.4	0.4	0.4
Niacin (nicotinic acid equivalents) (mg/day)	3	3	4	5
Folate (μg/day)	50	50	50	50
Vitamin C (mg/day)	25	25	25	25
Vitamin A (μg/day)	350	350	350	350
Vitamin D (μg/day)	8.5	8.5	7	7
Calcium (mg/day)	525	525	525	525
Iron (mg/day)	1.7	4.3	7.8	7.8
Zinc (mg/day)	4.0	4.0	5.0	5.0

From DoH, 1991. Crown copyright is reproduced with the permission of the Controller of Her Majesty's Stationery Office.

Development of the digestive tract

In the young infant, digestive enzymes are not fully developed and certain dietary components may not be readily digested. Only small amounts of lipase are produced by the pancreas during the first 3 months, and pancreatic amylase increases only after 6 months. Breastfeeding is believed to promote the release of gastrin and cholecystokinin in the infant, and may promote both the digestive process and the development of the gut. A young infant has the ability to absorb some undigested protein. This is particularly important for the absorption of antibodies present in maternal milk or colostrum during the first days of breastfeeding. However, it may also result in the absorption of proteins, such as egg albumen or lactoglobulin from cows' milk, if these are consumed in the early part of infancy. These proteins will generate antibodies within the infant and may lay the foundations of future allergic reactions. There is concern about early exposure of infants and children to peanuts in some weaning foods. A rapid increase in the incidence of peanut allergy, which can be life threatening, is believed to be linked to this early sensitization.

Nutritional needs

It must be assumed that the nutritional needs of the infant are ideally met by breast milk, when this is produced in sufficient quantity by a fully breastfeeding mother. For this reason, the UK Department of Health (DoH, 1991) took the view that no dietary reference values were required for breastfed infants. Values were, therefore, set for formula-fed infants, which are based on the nutritional composition of breast milk and the average amounts consumed. In addition, some allowance is made in certain cases for poorer efficiency of digestion and absorption of the nutrients in formula milks.

Dietary reference values for infants are shown in Table 12.1.

Energy

Energy needs are determined primarily by body size and composition, physical activity and rate of growth. Infants have a high basal metabolic rate owing to the large proportion of metabolically active tissue and the large loss of body heat over a relatively great surface area. In the second half of the first year, the growth rate slows, but the level of activity increases as the child starts to crawl and then learns to walk around the age of 1 year. Total energy expenditure in infants has recently been measured using the doubly labelled water technique, which has produced lower results than had been previously reported. Results from studies of energy intakes confirm these results.

TABLE 12.2 The estimated average requirement (EAR) for energy for children up to the age of 12 months

Age (months)	Average weight (kg)		Requirement/kg body weight (kJ (Cal))	EAR (kJ (Cal))	
	Boys	Girls		Boys	Girls
1	4.15	4.00	480 (115)	1990 (480)	1920 (460)
3	6.12	5.70	420 (100)	2570 (610)	2390 (570)
6	8.00	7.44	400 (95)	3200 (760)	2980 (710)
9	9.20	8.55	400 (95)	3680 (880)	3420 (820)
12	10.04	9.50	400 (95)	4020 (960)	3800 (910)

From DoH, 1991. Crown copyright is reproduced with the permission of the Controller of Her Majesty's Stationery Office.

Activity 12.1

Using the information in Table 7.6, calculate the equivalent energy needs per kilogram body weight for adults. Assume that the average adult male weighs 75 kg and the adult female 60 kg.

- Compare your figures for adults with those for infants, shown in Table 12.2.
- What is your own energy need per kilogram of body weight?
- Calculate the protein need per kilogram for both infants and adults (use the information in Table 4.5).

Tables 7.6 and 4.5 have been reproduced in the appendix on page 402.

Table 12.2 shows the gradual reduction in the energy requirement per kilogram of body weight as growth rates slow down; however, as body size increases, the total energy needs become greater. The energy requirement for children is up to four times greater than that of the adult, when expressed per unit of body weight. This emphasizes the special need for adequate energy and explains why a shortfall of energy may have such serious consequences for growth.

Protein

In infants, the role of protein is almost entirely to support growth. The infant requires more protein per unit weight than the adult, and has a particular requirement for the essential amino acids histidine and taurine. Human milk provides a relative excess of some of the amino acids (glutamine, leucine and isoleucine) needed for tissue synthesis, and relatively lower levels of others (arginine, alanine and glycine). This means that the neonate has to be very efficient in transforming some amino acids into others to fulfil needs for tissue synthesis. Adequate amounts of feed should be provided to allow the protein to be used for growth, rather than to meet the energy needs. Excessive amounts of protein are undesirable and may be harmful to the infant, as they increase the amounts of waste material to be excreted in the urine, and might result in dehydration. In addition, immature kidneys cannot adequately filter high molecular weight proteins.

Fats

Fat should comprise 30–50 per cent of an infant's energy intake and, above this level, it may be digested poorly. In breast milk, fats supply 50 per cent of the energy. Fats are an important part of an infant's diet because of their energy density, that is, they provide a substantial amount of energy in a relatively small volume. The essential fatty acids found in milk, and particularly the long-chain *n*-3 acids, are important for development of the brain, vascular systems and retina in early months of life. In particular, docosahexaenoic acid may not be synthesized in sufficient amounts by the infant from precursors in the diet to meet the needs of tissue development.

Carbohydrates

Carbohydrate, predominantly in the form of lactose, supplies 40 per cent of the energy in an infant's diet. Lactose yields glucose and galactose on digestion; the latter is essential in the development of the brain and nervous system. Undigested lactose is fermented in the digestive tract to lactic acid and lowers the pH. This is beneficial as many of the pathogenic organisms that can cause gastroenteritis do not thrive in an acidic environment. Infants can also digest and utilize sucrose, although this sugar is sweeter tasting than lactose and can induce a preference for sweet foods in the infant. The ability to digest starch is limited.

Fluid

Because of their relatively small total body water content, babies have a vital need for fluids. Their small body weight/surface area ratio makes them susceptible to dehydration, for example, in hot weather and illness. As an absolute minimum, the normal infant requires daily between 75 and 100 mL of fluid per kilogram body weight, and should be provided with 150 mL/kg, to ensure that all needs are met. Under normal circumstances, this amount of fluid is provided by the milk feed and no additional water is required.

The infant loses water through the skin and respiratory tract, through sweating in warm environments and through the urine and faeces. The volume of urine produced is dependent on the fluid intake and on the amount of solutes to be excreted. An adult kidney is able to concentrate solutes and reduce water loss, if fluid intake is low, but a baby's kidneys initially lack this ability. Thus, feeding a diet with a high 'solute load', in particular with high protein and sodium contents, results in increased water loss via the kidney. Under normal circumstances, fluid intake should be sufficient to cope with this. However, difficulties may arise if:

- a baby is given an overconcentrated feed (unmodified cows' milk is inappropriate for this reason);
- amounts of feed are very small (due to illness);
- there is fluid loss via other routes (vomiting, diarrhoea, sweating);
- solids are given at a very young age (below 2 months).

In each of these cases, additional water should be given to avoid dehydration.

Minerals

Babies require a wide range of minerals in their diet. These include calcium, phosphorus and magnesium for bone development, iron and copper for red blood cell formation, zinc for cell division and growth, together with other trace elements. The iron content present at birth has usually been used in red blood cell formation by 4–6 months, and an additional source of iron is needed at this stage. Calcium and phosphorus are present in equimolar quantities in human milk, which matches the ratio in the body. An excessive intake of phosphorus can dangerously lower calcium levels. This is a particular problem in premature infants and those fed on unmodified formula. The minerals in human milk are associated with the protein or fat fractions of the milk, which probably facilitates their availability.

Vitamins

The vitamin content of milk is generally adequate, with the exception of vitamins D and K. Human milk is low in vitamin D and the UK Department of Health (DoH, 1991) recommends that breastfeeding mothers should take a vitamin D supplement of 10 μg/day to ensure adequate levels in their milk, especially in the winter months. Formula-fed infants receive adequate levels of the vitamin.

Breastfed infants are also at risk of low vitamin K intakes. It has been routine practice to give newborn infants a dose of the vitamin in the first days of life by intramuscular injection. Although the evidence is not clear-cut, there has been concern that this may increase the risk of childhood cancer and oral administration of the vitamin is now recommended until the issue has been clarified.

Meeting nutritional needs

A baby's nutritional needs are generally met either by the use of human milk from the breast or formula derived from cows' milk, modified to a composition resembling that of human milk. The continued development of formula milks ensures that they come closer to the content of human milk than ever before. In Western societies, mothers are free to make the choice between breastfeeding and bottle-feeding, without fear that their baby will be disadvantaged in any way as a result of their decision. The professional consensus is that breastfeeding is better for the baby, and possibly confers benefits to the mother. In many poor areas of the world, the use of infant formula may increase health problems rather than solving them. Where standards of hygiene are poor, with inadequate water supplies and non-existent or poor sanitary facilities, it is almost impossible to prepare artificial feeds with the degree of cleanliness necessary to prevent infection. In addition, poverty may tempt the mother to prepare excessively dilute feeds in an attempt to extend the supply of the milk powder. This can and does lead to serious malnutrition in the infant. In such a situation, the only safe choice for infant feeding is with human milk from the breast. The spread of formula milk throughout poor regions of the world has resulted not only in greatly increased deaths from infection in infants, but has also removed the birth-spacing benefits of breastfeeding.

BREASTFEEDING OR BOTTLE-FEEDING?

Across the world there are programmes and activities to promote breastfeeding, since it is recognized as nutritionally the best way of feeding the newborn infant. The World Health Organisation (WHO) and the United Nations Childrens Fund (UNICEF) jointly promote the Babyfriendly Hospital Initiative (BFHI), which encourages hospitals to put in place a number of measures that will facilitate the initiation and continuation of breastfeeding. Some 15 000 hospitals have been certified as Babyfriendly around the world, with around 260 in industrialized countries.

A series of studies on behalf of the Department of Health in the UK has taken place since 1975 to provide national statistics on the incidence, prevalence and duration of breastfeeding and other feeding practices adopted in the early weeks and months after birth. The most recently reported of these was carried out in 2000 (Hamlyn et al., 2002). The survey identified the reasons given by mothers for the choice of infant feeding method. Most women decide before the birth how they will feed the baby. The decision is based on the mother's own attitude to the idea of breastfeeding, but is also influenced by the views of her mother, friends and partner. Previous experience of feeding is also a strong influence.

Breastfeeding is more likely in mothers from social class 1, compared with social class 5. However, there have been marked increases in prevalence among women in social class 5 since the earlier surveys. There is also a higher prevalence among older mothers, ranging from 46 per cent in teenage to 78 per cent in mothers over 30 years. Improvements have also been noted in prevalence among mothers educated to age 16 (to 54 per cent), where the rates had been lowest, compared with rates in those educated beyond the age of 19 years (88 per cent prevalence reported).

Reasons cited for choosing breastfeeding are generally very positive, including that it is the best and most natural way of feeding the baby (79 per cent of respondents said this) and that it is convenient (37 per cent said this). Other reasons mentioned included that it develops a closer bond with the baby, is cheaper and more natural. Those who choose to bottle-feed have more negative views about breastfeeding, considering that they would be tied to the baby and wanted others to be able to feed it (25 per cent), worrying about how much milk the baby receives and generally finding the idea distasteful (19 per cent).

The attitude of society in general is important in helping women make the choice, and in supporting and helping breastfeeding mothers. Unfortunately, many people have negative attitudes to breastfeeding, considering it inappropriate and even shameful behaviour, especially if carried out, however discreetly, in public; this can affect the new mother. The ambivalent view of society about the function of breasts can make it difficult for some women to consider feeding their baby themselves.

There has been an increase since 1990 in the number of women attempting to breastfeed their baby, with 71 per cent starting to breastfeed in England and Wales (and 63 per cent in Scotland, 54 per cent in Northern Ireland). The overall figure for the UK is 69 per cent. However, the numbers who continue to breastfeed decrease quite rapidly, falling to 52 per cent by 2 weeks, 42 per cent by 6 weeks and 28 per cent by 4 months. However, 13 per cent of mothers were still breastfeeding at 9 months. These rates are lower than in most other north European countries.

The most common reasons for stopping in the early weeks were given as rejection of the breast by the baby and painful nipples. However, when feeding continued for more than a week, but had stopped by 4 months, insufficient milk was the most commonly cited reason for stopping. In reality, this should rarely be a reason for failure to breastfeed, and probably represents inadequate support and information being made available in the first days of breastfeeding while the process is becoming established. More help for new breastfeeding mothers could increase success rates. An additional reason for stopping breastfeeding between 4 and 6 months was that the mother was returning to work (mentioned by 39 per cent of respondents).

Overall, this survey shows an encouraging improvement in incidence and prevalence of breastfeeding. In particular, improvements have occurred in those groups where previous levels of breastfeeding had been lowest.

Formula milk and breast milk compared

The composition of formula milks available in Britain is governed by a directive from the European Commission (EEC, 1991), and Statutory Instrument 77 (MAFF, 1995). Derived from cows' milk, they are classified as 'casein-dominant', based on the entire protein fraction, or 'whey-dominant', containing the dialysed whey protein. Modifications include the addition of lactose, maltodextrins, vegetable oils, various vitamins and trace elements, and reductions in the level of protein, electrolytes and some minerals, such as calcium.

Bottle-feeding, if carried out correctly, with due attention to hygiene, appropriate concentrations and closeness during the feeding, can provide most of what the infant needs. However, the unique composition of human milk, with over 200 constituents and with a varying content, will probably never be matched by a manufactured formula feed. The composition of breast milk is not constant between women and within the same woman for different lactations and even during the day. The milk secreted towards the end of a feed (hind milk) is richer in fat and, therefore, higher in energy value than the fore milk, at the start of the feed. This may play a part in appetite control, with the richer hind milk providing a feeling of satiety. Obviously, this cannot happen with a formula feed.

Proteins in milk

The proteins in human milk are predominantly whey proteins, including alpha-lactalbumin, lactoferrin and various immunoglobulins; casein forms only 30–40 per cent of the total protein. Although the lactalbumin is a major source of amino acids, the other whey proteins have a non-nutritional role, in particular, as protective agents (see below for their role in immunity).

In cows' milk, casein comprises 80 per cent of total protein, which can form tough, leathery curds in the stomach and be more difficult to digest. In the formula milks based on whey, the casein content is reduced (from 27 g/L in cows' milk, to 6.0 g/L). Beta-lactoglobulin, which is normally found in cows' milk and is a potential allergen, is also absent from these formula milks.

Human milk also contains non-protein nitrogen compounds, including taurine, urea, and a number of hormones and growth factors. Their functions are still uncertain but may well help with the normal development of the infant. Until their function is clearly defined, it is unlikely that these substances will be included in formula milks.

Carbohydrates in milk

Lactose concentrations in human milk are greater than in cows' milk, although levels in formula are similar. Formula milks may also contain maltodextrin as a source of carbohydrate. Lactose enhances the absorption of calcium as a result of the lower pH resulting from fermentation to lactic acid, which makes the calcium more soluble.

Fats in milk

Although the total fat contents of human and cows' milks are similar, the fatty acid compositions are quite different. Modified milks contain added oils to increase the unsaturated fatty acid content towards that of human milk. Nevertheless, there remains a much greater diversity of lipids in human milk, which contains cholesterol, phospholipids and essential fatty acids. Digestion and absorption of fat from human milk is aided by the presence of lipase within the milk secretion, which starts the process of digestion before the small intestine is reached. Some milks have been reformulated to include more essential and long-chain fatty acids.

Vitamins

The levels of the water-soluble vitamins in milk reflect the maternal levels, and thus rely on a sufficient intake by the mother. In the West, it is rare for vitamin levels to be deficient in milk due to maternal undernutrition. Human milk also contains binding factors for folate and vitamin B_{12}, which facilitate their absorption. Most formula milks contain levels of the vitamins greater than those found in human milk. However, apart from vitamins D and K, for which intake may be too low from human milk, there appears to be no advantage in this.

Minerals

Levels of many minerals are modified in the manufacture of formula from cows' milk. This is because their concentrations would generally be too high for the human infant to cope with. In particular, this applies to calcium, phosphorus and the electrolytes. Many of the minerals are associated either with proteins or fat globules, and this appears to facilitate their absorption. Specific binding factors have been identified for iron and zinc, which make the absorption of these minerals from human milk much greater than that from formula.

Immunological factors

Apart from the nutrients and water, human milk contains a number of other constituents. Most importantly, it contains a range of substances that enhance the immune system of the baby. Among these are:

- white blood cells – T and B lymphocytes, neutrophils and macrophages;
- immunoglobulins, which are the circulating antibodies;
- lysozyme, which has specific antibacterial action;
- lactoferrin, which binds iron to prevent its uptake by bacteria that need it for growth and replication, and also promotes growth of *Lactobacillus* sp.;
- bifidus factor, which promotes growth of *Bifidobacteria* that prevent the growth of potentially pathogenic bacteria;
- cytokines and growth factors.

The overall effect of these constituents is to promote the development of the baby's own immune system and reduce the risk of infection, while it is still immature. Immune factors specific to the environment are produced by the mother's gastrointestinal and respiratory tracts, which then stimulate the mammary glands to synthesize similar compounds. Thus, the immunity provided is 'tailor made'. Evidence from around the world, including both industrialized and developing countries, indicates that there are lower infection rates in breastfed compared with bottle-fed infants.

Other factors

Human milk may also contain substances passed through the mother, such as drugs, alcohol, nicotine and pollutants. This causes some concern to mothers and, where possible, such agents should be avoided when feeding the baby. However, environmental pollutants may be stored in maternal body fat and be released during the lactation process. At present, there is insufficient evidence to decide the risk from these.

HIV infection may be transmitted through breastfeeding. However, whether a woman who is infected chooses to breastfeed is largely dependent on the alternatives available to her and her baby. If these are safe, it is probably better to feed with formula; if not, then the recommendation of the WHO is that breastfeeding is the better option. The advantages of breastfeeding in these situations still outweigh the risk of infection from HIV.

Other milks available

Alternative milks are available for infants who are allergic to cows' milk or lactose. The most widely available are those based on modified soya protein. These milks contain glucose and carry a possible risk to teeth. Their use should be carefully monitored. Hydrolysed protein formulas are available for highly allergic children and these should be used under supervision.

Special milks for babies born pre-term are also available, although their use is still controversial. It has been recognized that mothers giving birth to pre-term infants, produce milk that has a higher content of fat, protein and sodium, and less carbohydrate. This would appear to be necessary to sustain the rapid growth of the baby and to compensate for the lack of reserves with which it is born. A combination of breast milk and pre-term formula is considered the best compromise for these infants.

Future health

It has been claimed that breastfeeding confers advantages in terms of the later health of the baby. Some studies have shown more advanced development during childhood in those children who received breast milk, even for a short period in infancy. A meta-analysis by Anderson et al. (1999) showed that breastfeeding conferred an advantage of 3.2 point increments in cognitive function by adolescence. A study of adults aged 53 (from the British 1946 birth cohort) confirmed that breastfeeding was significantly and positively associated with educational attainment, but this was largely accounted for by the cognitive effect at 15 years.

Other possible advantages that have been proposed include less allergic disease, lower cholesterol levels, less obesity, heart disease and multiple sclerosis. Breastfed infants have higher levels of low-density lipoprotein (LDL) and very low density lipoprotein (VLDL) as infants; this may be linked to lower cholesterol levels in later life, through adaptation of enzyme levels.

Some of these advantages are difficult to show and require long-term studies. However, using records from the early years of the twentieth century, Barker (1994) has shown that men who were breastfed beyond the age of 1 year actually experienced higher mortality rates. It is suggested that this is a reflection of inadequate nutrition and possibly restricted growth, since breast milk is not a complete food beyond about 5–6 months. On the other hand, other work by Barker shows that infants who gained weight well and had highest weights at the age of 1 year had the lowest incidence of impaired glucose tolerance and cardiovascular disease. Clearly, nutrition in the first year of life has to be good enough to promote growth and development for long-term health. However, more information is needed.

WEANING

The process of weaning an infant literally means 'to accustom' the baby to new foods, and in so doing to diversify the diet from milk to one containing solid foods. The age at which this occurs and the foods used vary between different cultures and communities, and may be as early as 2 months or as late as 12 months. Neither of these extremes is nutritionally ideal. The optimal age of weaning is between 4 and 6 months.

In the UK, the Infant Feeding Survey 2000 (Hamlyn et al., 2002) has shown that there had been a move to slightly later introduction of solids. Although 24 per cent of mothers had introduced solids by the age of 3 months, this was less than half the number recorded in 1995. By the age of 4 months, 85 per cent had introduced solids and almost all the babies in the survey were receiving some solids by the age of 6 months.

Early weaning is more common in social classes 4 and 5, in the north of England and Scotland, among bottle-fed babies and by mothers who smoke.

Why should a baby be weaned?

Developmental advantages ensuing from weaning have already been mentioned. Further, from the age of 4 months onwards the physiological development of the baby allows more varied foods to be ingested and digested, and their waste products to be excreted. Early weaning tends to result in faster weight gain but, by the age of 1 year, differences between infants weaned before 8 weeks and those weaned after 12 weeks have disappeared. In addition, there is a small tendency for infants weaned early to experience more respiratory illnesses and cough in the first year of life. Early weaning may precipitate an allergic response, and in infants who are at high risk of developing allergies, weaning as late as possible is advised.

Weaning has important developmental advantages. The ability to manipulate a bolus of food in the mouth and swallow it, to coordinate a utensil and bring food to the mouth and to drink from a cup all help in the development of muscles in the face. These are important in the acquisition of speech.

From the nutritional point of view, weaning is required to provide certain nutrients that can no longer be supplied in sufficient amounts by breast or formula milk. In particular, this applies to energy, protein, iron, zinc, vitamins A and D.

There is particular concern about iron status in infants, with low stores and the possibility of anaemia in 12 per cent of young children. The low iron status may result in delayed psychomotor development and defects in cellular immunity.

An infant's stomach capacity is considerably smaller than an adult's, which makes it very important to ensure that the foods offered contain enough energy in a compact form. Commonly, the first food introduced to the infant is the local staple cereal. In the West, this may be specially formulated, designed for weaning and enriched with a number of nutrients. Rice (or other non-wheat cereals) is preferred to wheat, which may cause gluten allergy to develop. In developing countries, the local staple is used, prepared as a gruel or porridge.

Other purées may then be introduced, for example, potato, vegetable, pulse or fruit purées, dairy products such as custard or yoghurt. These are all smooth with a relatively bland taste, with which the infant can gradually become familiar. As the child becomes accustomed to the novelty of solid foods, minced meat, fish and other sources of protein, such as sieved soft cheese can be included, together with vegetables and fruit that have been minced or mashed to retain more texture.

As chewing ability develops, the pieces of food offered become more distinct, allowing chewing to be practised. 'Finger foods' held in the hand allow the child some independence and help to develop coordination, as well as providing some nutritional value. These can include rusks, fingers of toast or pieces of hard cheese.

The diet should aim to provide a variety of different food groups, to ensure that a range of nutrients is consumed (Table 12.3). Particular attention may need to be paid to iron and vitamin D sources; vitamin C will help the absorption of iron and should also be provided. Some examples of suitable foods to provide these nutrients are shown in Table 12.4.

Milk should remain the cornerstone of the infant's diet, as it contains important amounts of protein, calcium and vitamins, as well as providing energy. Amounts of milk offered should be 600 mL at 4 months when weaning starts, but still 350 mL in the 1-year-old. The type of milk offered to the infant is also important. The UK Department

TABLE 12.3 Suggested food groups to be included in the diet at 6–9 months and 12 months

	Number of servings/day	
Food group	**6–9 months**	**12 months**
Bread, cereals, potatoes	2–3	At least 4
Fruit and vegetables	2	At least 4
Milk and dairy products	500–600 mL milk	2–3 servings + 350 mL milk
Meat, fish and alternatives	1	1–2
Fatty and sugary foods	Avoid	Limit

TABLE 12.4 Sources of iron, vitamin C and vitamin D suitable for weaning

Sources of iron	Sources of vitamin C	Sources of vitamin D
Red meat (beef, lamb), pork poultry	Unsweetened fruit juice: diluted	Oily fish, e.g. sardines
Liver, liver sausage	Citrus fruits, e.g. oranges, satsumas	Eggs and egg dishes
Oily fish, e.g. sardines	Summer fruits: strawberries, peaches, nectarines	Fortified margarine
Eggs and egg dishes	Green leafy vegetables	Breakfast cereals fortified with vitamin D
Beans and lentils	Tomatoes, green pepper, peas	Baby cereals fortified with vitamin D
Baby foods fortified with iron	Potatoes	Evaporated milk
Breakfast cereals with added iron		Some yogurts
Green leafy vegetables		
Dried fruits, e.g. apricots, prunes		
Fish fingers		

of Health (DoH, 1994) recommends that infants should continue to receive breast milk, formula or a 'follow-on' milk up to the age of 1 year. 'Follow-on' milks have been introduced in recent years, as suitable for infants from 6 months of age. They are less modified than infant formula, but still contain added nutrients to provide a valuable source of nutrition. Drinks should be offered in a cup, and the practice of leaving a child with a bottle or 'trainer' cup (one with a feeding spout) for periods of time is discouraged as it can lead to pooling of drink in the mouth. This can cause decay of newly erupted milk teeth.

Pasteurized cows' milk should not become the major milk drink until after the age of 1 year. This is because it contains low levels of iron and vitamin D, and may contribute to deficient intakes if taken as the main milk in the diet. However, cows' milk may be used to make dishes containing milk, such as custards and sauces. Infants should not be given low-fat milks, such as skimmed milk or semi-skimmed milk, as these contain insufficient fat and, therefore, have a low energy density.

Throughout the weaning process, it is recommended that:

- the child is always supervised during mealtimes;
- sugar and salt are not added to the infant's food;
- foods should not be heavily spiced;
- nuts should not be included in the diet;
- soft-boiled eggs should be avoided because of possible contamination with *Salmonella*; hard-boiled eggs are safe;
- pâté and mould-ripened soft cheeses (such as Brie) should be avoided because of the risk of *Listeria* contamination;
- drinks other than milk should be offered from a cup from the age of 6 months; they should be dilute and unsweetened.

Special 'infant drinks' may contain large amounts of sugar and should be avoided or only used rarely and with care. Infants should never be left with a sugary drink in a feeding bottle, as newly erupting teeth may be damaged.

Commercial weaning products are of value. They are often fortified with additional nutrients, which is especially useful when the child has a very small intake, when home-prepared foods may provide very few nutrients.

Infants cannot cope with large amounts of foods rich in non-starch polysaccharides (NSPs), such as whole grain cereals and pulses, and these should not be an important part of the weaning diet. However, small amounts can be included, and quantities increased when appetite is bigger.

By the age of 1 year, the infant should be eating solids several times per day, and be included in family meals. The complete process of weaning may take longer than this, however, and full chewing ability will not be attained until the molar teeth have erupted towards the end of the second year.

Figure 12.2 Summary of how to wean a baby.

Supplements of vitamins A, C and D are available; these are recommended for all infants from the age of 1 to 5 years, and for breastfed infants from the age of 6 months. The daily dose of supplement provides 200 μg of vitamin A, 20 mg of vitamin C and 7 μg vitamin D.

It should be remembered throughout that the infant is undergoing a process of learning about food and, to develop a child with a broad appetite for foods, many different tastes should be offered. Variety in the diet helps to ensure an adequate nutritional intake. Nutrients that need attention remain iron, zinc and vitamin D. Refusal of a specific food need not eliminate it completely from the diet. It can be reintroduced later. Important foundations are being laid down at this time and it is essential that the caregiver makes this a pleasurable learning experience for the infant. Sometimes the weaning process falters and a child that has been gaining weight may stop doing so. This has been called 'failure to thrive' and is of multifactorial origin. There is no evidence that it is associated with deprivation and neglect. There appears to be an underlying lack of interest in food in the child, slower eating and diminished appetite. Delayed progression on to solids and a limited variety of foods eaten have also been described. Intervention with dietary advice and practical management of mealtimes can result in rapid improvement, if there is no underlying organic cause. The process of weaning is summarized in Figure 12.2.

THE CHILD FROM 1 TO 5 YEARS OF AGE

These years provide a time to move from the milk-centred diet of the first year of life to the typical diet of the family. In nutritional terms, this represents a change from a diet which contains approximately 50 per cent fat, no NSP and simple sugars rather than starches (as seen in the milk-fed infant), to one meeting or approaching the dietary guidelines, with 35 per cent fat, 11 per cent non-milk extrinsic sugars and plenty of starch and NSPs. Clearly, there needs to be a gradual transition from one to the other.

The food habits developed at this time will be the foundation for the approach to diet and nutrition for the rest of the individual's life. During this period, the child will also develop some independence in relation to food, and this may lead to conflict with the parents. Infants more readily accept new foods and tastes. During early childhood there may be an increasing reluctance to try new foods. This served a protective function in the past, as a young child began to wander off and might have been tempted to try a hazardous food. Exposing children to new foods is, however, important. Perseverance, which may necessitate up to five or ten exposures to the food can pay off. Modelling on others who are eating the food is a helpful way of persuading a young child to accept it. Finally, presenting a novel food together with a familiar taste can be useful, for example, as part of a liked dish. Parents have an important role in determining what food is available for the child in the home. The attitude of parents to food is central, and conscious or subconscious preferences for foods, or attributes attached to a food will be passed on to the child. Foods used as a positive reward ('have some chocolate for being a good boy'), or a hurdle to be overcome to achieve something pleasurable ('eat your vegetables and then you can go out to play') can foster attitudes to these foods that were not necessarily intended. Children need guidance and family food rules are beneficial to provide a framework in which their own food habits can develop. Ideally, these should focus on healthy foods and eating patterns.

Growth is slower than in the first year of life but tends to occur in spurts, often accompanied by surges of appetite. Activity also increases markedly during the second year, as the child becomes increasingly mobile. Full dentition by about the age of 2 also increases the dietary repertoire. Because capacity remains relatively small, between-meal snacks are likely to be needed in addition to the three main meals of the day. It is important to maintain healthy eating guidelines in mind when selecting snack foods, since these should be contributing to total nutritional intake, rather than being additional to it. Unfortunately, poorly selected snacks, often comprising little more than sugar, in drink or solid form, can seriously compromise nutritional intake, as they dull the appetite at mealtimes. Snacks can include:

- fresh or dried fruit (although the latter may stick to the teeth and be cariogenic);
- wholemeal sandwiches with nutritious fillings;
- raw vegetables as 'finger food' to chew;
- dry breakfast cereal;
- low-sugar or savoury biscuits;
- yoghurt or milk;
- popcorn (plain, rather than sugar coated);
- scones or similar plain cakes.

Meals should consist of nutrient-dense foods, with at least 250 mL of milk daily, and cereal and bread used to fill up to appetite. Appetite remains the best guide to overall food needs at this age.

Food refusal can be a major problem, and can cause a great deal of stress to parents. The child needs a consistent and firm response from the parent, so that the association of eating with mealtimes is learned. If the child does not eat at table and is then allowed to snack between meals, disorganized eating habits may develop for the rest of their life. Experimentation with food within limits is important. Given a wide range of foods to experience, we all develop as individuals in our choice of foods with specific likes and dislikes. Ideally, our children should develop with few dislikes, if we give them the appropriate guidance and personal example.

A national study (Gregory et al., 1995) of children aged 1.5–4.5 years, as part of the National Diet and Nutrition Survey in Britain, found that, on the whole, children were eating large amounts of salt and sugar, and insufficient fruit and vegetables. Although the mean intake of energy was found to be lower than the estimated average requirements, the children appeared to be growing well. As a result, it has been suggested that energy requirements may need to be decreased by 10–12 per cent from their current levels. Other findings included the following.

- Those who had the highest energy intakes also consumed the most NSP.
- Total sugar intakes represented 29 per cent of total energy and starches 22 per cent; the intake of non-milk extrinsic sugars comprised 19 per cent of total energy.
- There was a reciprocal relationship between fat and sugar intakes.
- Fat intakes were generally between 34 and 36 per cent of total energy and, therefore, in line with Department of Health recommendations (DoH, 1991). It should be remembered that young children should not be rigorously put on low-fat diets, as this can compromise their total energy intake. Other studies show that low-fat/high-fibre diets are being given to this age group, reflecting confusion about healthy eating guidelines.
- Iron intakes were low in a proportion of children: 24 per cent of those aged 1.5–2.5 years, and 16 per cent of those under 4 years had intakes below the lower reference nutrient intake (LRNI), with low ferritin levels indicative of low stores of iron, and low haemoglobin levels resulting in anaemia in 1 in 12 of the sample. Apart from help with iron-rich foods, parents may need advice about promoters and inhibitors of iron absorption.
- Dental caries was found in 17 per cent of this age group.

In a secondary analysis of these data, it was found that only 1 per cent of children met the reference nutrient intake (RNI) recommendations for iron, zinc, vitamins A and C, and guidelines on non-milk extrinsic sugars (NMES). Two or fewer of the targets were met by 76 per cent of the children. Compliance with the recommended levels of intake was related to socio-economic status, with more children from lower social groups, with a head of household in a manual category and mothers with fewer educational qualifications meeting the least number of RNIs/recommendations.

Overall, it can be concluded that the quantity of the diet of this age group in the UK is currently adequate, although certain aspects of its quality probably need attention. In particular, there needs to be:

- more attention given to iron-containing foods;
- a reduction in both the amount and frequency of consumption of sugars, especially in the form of soft drinks; these could be replaced by milk or water;
- a reduction in the consumption of savoury snacks that are high in salt;
- an increase in the consumption of fruit and vegetables;
- more attention to the impact of socio-economic factors on food choice in families.

SCHOOL-AGE CHILDREN

Influences on nutritional intakes

When children start school, their eating patterns begin to be increasingly influenced by factors other than the home environment. However, it should be remembered that parents remain the 'gatekeepers' of what is consumed at home and can still have a considerable influence by determining what is provided at mealtimes, and what snack foods are available for children to help themselves. They also continue to serve as important role models.

Autonomy

A study of 9-year-old children in the UK reported that this group felt that parents had a great deal of control over their food choices. However, the greatest number (90 per cent) reported control over the content of breakfast, with 2/3 reporting control over snacks and only 1/3 reporting control over the amount of food eaten (Robinson, 2000). This appears to leave children with a reasonable amount of autonomy in various aspects of their diet.

Adolescence itself is a time of transition, associated with progress towards autonomy. This is reflected in all aspects of the teenager's life, but inevitably impacts on food choice and nutritional intake.

Rejection of food selected or prepared by parents is a normal aspect of this developing autonomy. Foods chosen as alternatives may be less healthy, as a gesture of independence and perhaps peer solidarity. There is also likely to be experimentation with foods and adoption of novel dietary practices. At other times, the adolescent may still want to be part of the family and eat what is provided in the home.

Growth

Growth rates are relatively slow during the pre-adolescent years, but growth still occurs non-linearly with surges accompanied by increases of appetite. Periods of slow growth may be accompanied by a relatively small appetite and, at such times, particular attention must be paid to the nutrient density of the diet. In adolescence, periods of rapid growth take place that have profound effects on appetite.

School may also be emotionally taxing for children, which may affect their food intake. In addition, beginning school is often accompanied by exposure to many childhood infections and periods of (often minor) illness. These can have an impact on food intake and, if numerous, may affect growth.

Activity

Apart from growth, activity is the other main influence on appetite in this age group. Starting school may significantly alter a child's activity pattern, the direction of the change depending on how active the child was during pre-school years. Children of primary school age tend to be relatively more active in their play and levels of activity have been shown to decline in a large proportion of adolescents, especially girls. Following the *Health of the nation* report (DoH, 1992), physical activity in children has become a focus of policy in the UK, with recommendations made for an increase in activity in this age group. There is concern that many hours are being spent watching television, playing computer games and staying in the house, rather than being involved in physical activity or even just walking. Estimates from studies in Scotland suggest that teenagers may now expend between 2 and 3 MJ (500–700 Calories) per day less than their peers did 60 years ago. Average time spent watching television has been shown to be positively associated with increased body weight, skinfold, fat mass and prevalence of overweight in pre-pubertal children. The reasons for this association are complex.

Societal pressures

Pressures from friends will increasingly influence food intakes as a child goes through school, and this becomes most notable in adolescence. In addition, societal pressures linked to body image have a major impact on the food intake of some individuals, especially girls at this age. Adolescence is the peak age for dissatisfaction with body image and attempts at dieting are prevalent, more so in girls than boys at this age. Changing food trends are particular influences. In recent years, there has been a major shift from traditional meals, and many children and teenagers consume a series of snacks during the day rather than eating 'normal' meals. The choice of foods available in fast-food outlets can be a limiting factor for making healthy selections.

There is also widespread concern about the impact of advertising on food choices in this group. Food advertising is the single largest category of advertisement shown during children's television programmes. The majority of these are for products that are high in sugar and fat and low in fibre, and include confectionery, snack foods and breakfast cereals. This trend is also seen in other countries, such as the US and Australia. The advertisements for these foods are often humorous, animated and easy to follow, so that they are memorable to children. In contrast, there are no advertisements for foods that should form a substantial part of a healthy diet, such as fruit and vegetables. Although advertisements by themselves do not change food habits, there is concern that the balance of those shown is in conflict with health promotion messages.

Nutritional needs

Steady growth during childhood up to adolescence, increasing per year by 10 cm in height and 2.5 kg in weight, is reflected by a gradual increase in the need for nutrients. There is a certain amount of accumulation of stores during this time, most notably of body fat, which then becomes available to contribute to the fuel required for the pubertal growth spurt. Calcium is also laid down and provides some of the needs for bone growth.

At adolescence, growth rates are greater than at any other time of life, except early infancy. In most girls, the growth spurt begins between the age of 10 and 13, in boys between 12 and 15 years. In both cases, rapid growth takes place over a period of 3 years. Girls gain lean tissue and fat, and increase by 20 cm in height and 20 kg in weight. In boys, there is a loss of fat and a gain in lean tissue, with increases of 30 cm in height and 30 kg in weight. These increases account for approximately 40 per cent of adult weight. It is to be expected, therefore, that the nutritional requirements at this time will reflect this growth.

The timing of the need for additional nutrients varies with the individual, and depends on the onset of growth. In the West, peak appetite occurs around the age of 12 in girls and 14 in boys, apparently corresponding to the most rapid growth period. The demand for new tissue synthesis results in increased nutrient requirements for:

- calcium, phosphorus, magnesium and vitamin D for bone;
- protein, zinc and iron for muscle;
- iron, folate, vitamin B_{12} and copper for the synthesis of extra blood cells to supply it with oxygen;
- adequate energy to sustain this synthesis, and the B vitamins to release it.

If energy needs are not met, the growth spurt may be delayed or reduced. However, energy needs for growth probably do not exceed 10 per cent of total energy requirements at this time.

Once the growth spurt is over, nutrient requirements settle down to adult levels.

Selected dietary reference values are shown in Table 12.5 for the age groups from 4 to 18 years. In addition to these specific guidelines, children's diets should approach the general recommendations on fat and carbohydrates (shown in Table 12.6).

No distinction is made between genders for the majority of nutrient requirements for children up to the age of 10 years. After this age, with the onset of the pubertal growth spurt, different figures are set for male and female adolescents. In part, these reflect the different body weights at these ages. However, special needs for menstrual losses are incorporated in the iron requirement calculations.

TABLE 12.5 Dietary reference values for children from 4 to 18 years

Nutrient	Age 4–6		Age 7–10		Age 11–14		Age 15–18	
	M	F	M	F	M	F	M	F
Energy								
(MJ/day)	7.16	6.46	8.24	7.28	9.27	7.92	11.51	8.83
(Cals/day)	1715	1545	1970	1740	2220	1845	2755	2110
Protein (g/day)	19.7	19.7	28.3	28.3	42.1	41.2	55.2	45.0
Thiamin (mg/day)	0.7	0.7	0.7	0.7	0.9	0.7	1.1	0.8
Riboflavin (mg/day)	0.8	0.8	1.0	1.0	1.2	1.1	1.3	1.1
Niacin (nicotinic acid equiv.) (mg/day)	11	11	12	12	15	12	18	14
Folate (μg/day)	100	100	150	150	200	200	200	200
Vitamin C (mg/day)	30	30	30	30	35	35	40	40
Vitamin A (μg/day)	500	500	500	500	600	600	700	600
Calcium (mg/day)	450	450	550	550	1000	800	1000	800
Iron (mg/day)	6.1	6.1	8.7	8.7	11.3	14.8	11.3	14.8
Zinc (mg/day)	6.5	6.5	7.0	7.0	9.0	9.0	9.5	7.0

From DoH, 1991. Crown copyright is reproduced with the permission of the Controller of Her Majesty's Stationery Office.

There are no dietary reference values (DRVs) given for vitamin D, as it is assumed that sufficient will be synthesized in the skin during everyday activity. However, some children of Asian origin may require a dietary supplement.

These dietary guidelines should be met in the same way as for adults, by eating a diet in line with the Balance of Good Health, which provides an appropriate balance between the five main groups shown. Thus, the diet should provide mainly starchy carbohydrate sources, fruit and vegetables (five servings per day of each of the two groups). In addition, there should be three servings of milk and dairy produce, and two servings of meat and alternatives. Intakes of fatty and sugary foods should be limited; they may be included in the diet when the needs for the other four groups have been met.

TABLE 12.6 General recommendations on fat and carbohydrates

Total fat	35% of food energy
Saturated fatty acids	11%
Polyunsaturated fatty acids	6.5%
Total carbohydrate	50% of food energy
Non-milk extrinsic sugars	11%
Intrinsic and milk sugars + starch	39%
Non-starch polysaccharides	18 g/day

Activity 12.2

Return to Activity 12.1 and perform a similar exercise for children and adolescents for the following body weights:

Age (years)	Male weight (kg)	Female weight (kg)
5	18	17.75
10	31	31.5
14	49	48
18	65	55.5

It is helpful if meals are planned to include items from each of the food groups wherever possible.

WHAT DO CHILDREN AND ADOLESCENTS EAT?

Studies of children's attitudes to healthy eating in recent years have shown that in general children understand the concept of a balanced diet as described in the 'Balance of Good Health' model. They are also aware of the relationship between diet and health, both present and for the future. Children also demonstrate an awareness of the potential risk for heart health of excessive fat intakes, and the desirability of a normal body weight. The health implications of being too thin and the dangers of eating disorders are also recognized. For this age group, however, social pressures are important, and knowledge does not necessarily translate into behaviour.

A number of studies took place during the 1980s and early 1990s on groups of children from 5 to 17 years of age. In general, these studies showed that the health of schoolchildren in Britain is good. There was no widespread evidence of dietary deficiency, and no biochemical or functional improvements were seen with the use of supplementation. However, a European study has reported that the diet of UK children is amongst the worst in Europe, being high in fat and sugar, low in fibre, iron and calcium and possibly folate.

A new survey of young people aged 4 to 18, which is part of the ongoing National Diet and Nutrition Survey programme in the UK was published in 2000 (Gregory et al., 2000). This was a comprehensive study, including 7-day dietary records, anthropometric measurements, biochemical and clinical assessments, and lifestyle and socio-economic characteristics. Over 1700 children responded to the survey and the data provide a valuable picture of this group.

Some of the main findings are summarized here.

Health-related aspects

- The young people in the survey confirmed the secular trend, being both taller and heavier than the cohort studied in 1982–83.

- Blood pressure increased with age; it was significantly higher in those children who used salt at table, for boys who smoked and boys in the oldest group who drank alcohol.
- Physical activity levels were recorded as fairly active in the 4–6-year-old children. After this age, activity decreased with increasing age and girls were less active than boys.

Dietary patterns

- Foods eaten by over 80 per cent of the respondents included: white bread, biscuits, chips, potatoes, savoury snacks and chocolate confectionery.
- Meat consumed most commonly was chicken and turkey (65–79 per cent of respondents); beef and veal were consumed by 43–63 per cent of males and 43–52 per cent of females. Ten per cent of the oldest girls reported that they were vegetarian or vegan.
- Raw and salad vegetables were eaten more by girls than boys (37–53 per cent of boys, 49–66 per cent of girls), but consumption of green leafy vegetables was similar, at around 40 per cent of the groups.
- Apples and pears were the fruit consumed most often, but consumption declined sharply with age (from 70 to 39 per cent in youngest and oldest boys and from 66 to 44 per cent in girls). Bananas were the next most popular fruit (average consumption 40 per cent), and citrus fruits the least popular (average 25 per cent).
- Whole milk was consumed most by the youngest group (75 per cent) and declined sharply with age. Conversely, the consumption of semi-skimmed milk increased with age to approximately 60 per cent in the oldest group.
- The most popular beverages were carbonated soft drinks, consumed by up to 85 per cent of boys and 73 per cent of oldest girls. Low-calorie versions were consumed by more girls than boys. Tea was a more common choice of beverage than coffee.

Nutritional intakes

The survey results were affected by underreporting, as is commonly found.

- Total energy intakes were below the estimated average requirements (EAR) for all age groups. In particular the oldest age group of girls and boys reported intakes of only 77 and 83 per cent of their EAR. As body weight and height show no evidence of inadequate energy intakes, it is assumed that these results are underreported. Cereals and cereal foods provided the main source of energy, as found also in the National Food Surveys.
- The contributions to the total food energy intake of the main macronutrient groups are shown in Table 12.7.

TABLE 12.7 Contributions of the main macronutrient groups to total energy intake for young people aged 4 to 18

Macronutrient	Contribution to food energy	Main contributing food groups
Protein	13.1%	Meat and meat products Cereals and cereal products
Carbohydrate	51.6% (boys) 51.1% (girls)	Cereals and cereal products Sugar and preserves
Fat	35.4% (boys) 35.9% (girls)	Cereals and cereal products (biscuits, buns, cakes and pastries) Meat and meat products
Non-starch polysaccharides	11.2 g (boys) 9.7 g (girls)	Vegetables, potatoes and savoury snacks Cereals and cereal products

- Intakes of non-milk extrinsic sugars provided an average of 16.5 per cent of energy, mainly from carbonated soft drinks and chocolate confectionery.

Micronutrient intakes were generally above the RNI for most nutrients, for most age groups. However, some intakes were below the LRNI, and the prevalence of this increased with increasing age and was more likely in girls than boys.

- Among the vitamin intakes, vitamin A and riboflavin were most likely to fall below the LRNI. Further, in the oldest age group of girls, there were some intakes below the LRNI for all vitamins studied.
- For mineral intakes, levels below the LRNI were found in the youngest age groups mostly for zinc. With increasing age, a greater range of mineral intakes fell below the LRNI. These included iron, calcium, magnesium, potassium, zinc and iodine. In the case of iron, 50 per cent of the oldest group of girls (aged 15–18 years) had intakes that fell below the LRNI. Among the oldest boys, magnesium intakes (18 per cent) and potassium (15 per cent) were the most common minerals to fall below the LRNI.
- Those respondents who took dietary supplements generally had higher intakes from food sources than non-users of supplements. Supplements affected mean intakes for vitamin A and C, iron and zinc, but did not affect the intakes below the LRNI.
- Poor nutritional status identified in blood analyses was shown in some individuals for vitamin D, vitamin C, folate, riboflavin and thiamin. In addition, serum ferritin levels were below the normal range for adults in 13 per cent of boys and 14 per cent of girls. This finding was more common in younger boys (18 per cent affected), but older girls (27 per cent affected).

Other smaller studies confirm these findings. In general, the transition from primary to secondary school is associated with the beginning of greater independence in food choice and is accompanied by an increased consumption of less desirable foods and a reduction in desirable foods, most notably fruit and vegetables.

In addition, socio-economic status results in differences in the nutritional quality of children's diets, with lower intakes of total energy and lower intakes of nutrients when energy intakes had been taken into account. This trend corresponds to that reported in adults.

School meals

A meal in the middle of the school day is important nutritionally, socially and educationally. In terms of academic performance, it is important that children eat in the middle of the day to maximize their learning opportunities.

Nutritional guidelines for school meals that had existed since the 1944 Education Act were abolished in the UK in 1980. Prior to this date, the meal offered at school had to provide one-third of a child's daily requirements of protein, energy and some minerals and vitamins. From 1980, the only obligation that remained was to provide a meal for those who were entitled to free school meals, by reason of low income. Since this date, considerable concern has been expressed about the nutritional adequacy of the diets of schoolchildren.

Following a period of consultation, Minimum Nutritional Standards have been established, taking effect from April 2001. There is once more a duty to provide a paid meals service in schools, and guidance documents have been produced by the Department for Education and Skills. Schools have more autonomy than in the past and at secondary level hold budgets for the provision of meals. This means that many schools are able to adopt whole-school policies on food and nutrition. The School Nutrition Action Group (SNAG) initiative has provided a framework for the formation of school-based alliances between teachers, pupils and caterers together with help from appropriate health professionals. Many of these are in place and they allow the consumers to be involved in the decision-making process and thereby increase their sense of ownership of the school meal provision. School management also needs to be involved to ensure there is an adequate provision for a lunch break in the timetable and that a suitable environment exists to enable meals to be taken in comfortable surroundings.

When aspects of healthy eating are part of the school curriculum, the food service can provide the practical illustration in a positive way as well as contributing to the pastoral welfare of the children.

Some issues about the provision of meals in school remain to be resolved. These include the following.

- Ensuring that cultural diversity is recognized in the meals provided.
- Improving the uptake of free school meals – reports suggest that to achieve this a number of factors, for example, insensitive administration that results in an associated stigma, the quality of the food, eating environment and service, all need to be addressed. Some Local Education Authorities have introduced swipe cards for all children, so that there is no distinction made at the point of purchase between the children receiving free lunches and those who are paying.
- Provision of drinking water to accompany the meals.
- Monitoring of the provision of the meals and maintenance of standards. This is a role for the appropriate government agency.

Minimum nutritional standards

The national nutrition standards are based on the food groups in the Balance of Good Health (see Table 12.8). In terms of defining a healthy diet, they incorporate the following principles:

- a balanced diet with plenty of variety, and enough energy for growth and development;
- plenty of fibre-rich starchy foods, such as bread, rice, pasta, potatoes and yams;
- plenty of fruit and vegetables;
- not eating too many foods containing a lot of fat, especially saturated fat;
- moderate amounts of dairy products;
- moderate amounts of meat, fish or alternatives;
- not having sugary foods and drinks too often.

In addition to these general principles, specific nutrients have been identified as important for children of school age. These are:

- calcium – important for bone health;
- iron – important for preventing anaemia;
- folate – important for adolescent girls and young women, but establishing a good intake in early years forms a sound base;
- zinc – for normal growth and development.

Slightly different nutritional standards have been established for children in primary and secondary schools. In addition, there are separate standards for children of nursery school age.

TABLE 12.8 Minimum nutritional standards for school meals (DfES, 2001)

Food groups	Primary school	Secondary school
Starchy foods such as bread, potatoes, rice and pasta	Provide at least **one** from this group daily. Items cooked in oil or fat should not be served more than **three** times a week	Provide at least **two** from this group daily. At least **one** of these should not be cooked in oil or fat
Fruit and a vegetable	One item of **both** must be available every day. Fruit-based desserts must be available **twice** a week	**Two** items of **both** should be available daily
Milk and dairy foods	Provide at least **one** from this group daily	Provide at least **two** from this group daily
Meat, fish and alternative sources of protein (cheese may be provided as an alternative for primary school children **only**)	Provide at least **one** from this group daily. Red meat to be served **twice** a week; fish to be served **once** a week	Provide at least **two** from this group daily. Red meat must be served at least **three** times a week; fish to be served at least **twice** a week

TABLE 12.9 Summary of Caroline Walker Trust Nutritional Guidelines for School Meals

Nutrient	Guideline
Energy	30% of the estimated average requirement
Fat	Not more than 35% of food energy
Saturated fatty acids	Not more than 11% of food energy
Carbohydrate	Not less than 50% of food energy
Non-milk extrinsic sugars	Not more than 11% of food energy
NSP (fibre)	Not less than 30% of the calculated reference value
Protein	Not less than 30% of the RNI
Iron	Not less than 40% of the RNI
Calcium	Not less than 35% of the RNI
Vitamin A	Not less than 30% of the RNI
Folate	Not less than 40% of the RNI
Vitamin C	Not less than 35% of the RNI
Sodium	Should be reduced in catering practice

NSP, non-starch polysaccharide; RNI, reference nutrient intake. From Sharp, 1993 with permission.

These standards apply to all lunches (hot or cold) provided during term time. There are additional recommendations for the provision of water, free of charge. Milk to drink should also be available every day. It is recommended that some hot food be offered daily, especially in the winter months.

Caterers are also given guidance on good practice, which includes the following key points:

- reflect the likes and dislikes of children;
- work with the school to check that healthy eating principles are being reinforced by both the curriculum and the lunch service;
- actively encourage children to have a balanced diet;
- aim to offer a selection of foods, which, over the week, reflects the proportions in the Balance of Good Health, and make changes gradually;
- offer a variety of foods;
- use a variety of cooking methods that lead to minimum destruction of nutrients.

In addition to the above, guidance is provided on various foods within each food group, portion sizes, special dietary requirements and monitoring of the nutritional standards. Even though the new minimum standards have been expressed in terms of food groups, and servings from these, caterers are encouraged to use the Caroline Walker Trust Guidelines on School Meals to check the nutritional value of the meal provided. These are shown in Table 12.9. This is particularly important where children have a free choice in a cash-cafeteria selection. Throughout, caterers are encouraged to promote healthy eating and encourage children in a variety of ways to eat the food provided.

Where children can leave school at lunchtime, caterers have to compete effectively with local food outlets. Attractive packaging, advertising and promotions can all help keep children in school for lunch.

Alternatives to school lunch

Packed lunches brought in to school may be of variable nutritional content (see Figure 12.3). Confectionery and soft drinks may also be available in school, often as a fund-raising activity, and may tempt the children to eat these items rather than more nutritious foods. In some schools, children can go out of school at lunch time, and foods purchased away from school may include pizzas, chips, burgers or cakes and soft drinks. The UK Department of Health survey (DoH, 1989) found that foods eaten out of school were generally of lower nutrient density, especially among the older schoolchildren. In particular, these meals contained less protein, iron, calcium, retinol, thiamin, riboflavin and vitamin D. A small section of the

Figure 12.3 Example of a healthy packed lunch.

teenage population have no lunch, with 11 per cent of girls and 5 per cent of boys aged 14–16 reporting this.

Overall, a well-balanced lunch can provide between 30 and 40 per cent of the nutrients required in the day. If no food is taken or a very poor-quality snack is eaten, then the likelihood of daily nutritional needs not being met increases because it becomes more difficult to achieve adequate intakes from the remaining meals. Eating is a social activity and having lunch with one's peers can provide an important socialization activity, teaching the individual about food habits and learning from others. A proportion of children come to school without having eaten breakfast, or a snack on the way to school. In some schools, Breakfast Clubs have been established that provide food before the school day begins. The School Fruit Initiative aims to provide all primary school children with a piece of fruit in school each day. This is still being developed, but pilot schemes report a fair measure of success. School milk is also being reintroduced into some primary schools, to try to address some of the potential nutritional problems in this age group.

However, it must be recognized that providing healthier choices for children in school does not necessarily lead to changes in behaviour. One study reports the outcomes of a 2-year programme in secondary schools (Parker and Fox, 2001). This had a number of dietary targets, including increasing intakes of high-fibre bread, fruit and vegetables, non-fried potatoes and non-cream cakes. After 2 years, there was some change in consumption of high-fibre bread, but other changes were not sustained. This study demonstrates the challenge of improving dietary intakes of children in school.

SOME POTENTIAL NUTRITIONAL PROBLEMS

As part of the development of increasing independence, children, and particularly teenagers, may encounter difficulties with their diet, which might result in nutritional problems. These are summarized in Figure 12.4.

Vegetarianism

An increasingly common finding among children and teenagers in the UK is the rejection of the omnivorous diet in favour of a vegetarian (non-meat) diet. In addition to the reasons for choosing to be vegetarian that are discussed in Chapter 16, this age group may be subject to peer pressure or initially make the decision as a bid for independence from parental control.

Unfortunately, many young vegetarians may have an inadequate understanding of the principles of nutrition, so that the traditional 'meat and vegetables' becomes just 'vegetables', or cheese omelette, or baked beans on toast. There may be little attempt to introduce other dietary items, such as pulses, cereals or grains, into the diet to replace the animal foods being avoided. In this way iron, zinc and niacin may become inadequate, as well as calcium, if dairy products are omitted. It has already been mentioned that iron intakes are low in teenagers, particularly girls. A small study in London found that anaemia was three times more common among vegetarian 12–14-years olds, with an incidence of 25 per cent, compared to 9 per cent in omnivores.

There is also concern about low calcium intakes and future health. The majority of bone mass is accrued during the teenage years, with high assimilation rates of dietary calcium. Dietary reference values are high to allow for this. If calcium intakes are low, it is likely that less bone will be made. This may have

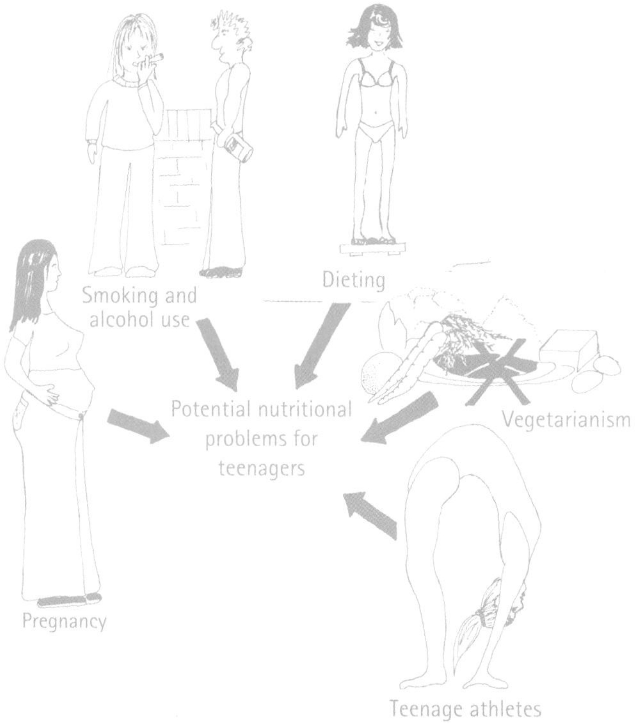

Figure 12.4 A summary of potential nutritional problems encountered by children and teenagers.

repercussions in later life, with an increased risk of osteoporosis.

Many vegetarian meal replacements are now available, based on soya or quorn, which are acceptable and which can help to maintain an adequate nutritional intake, although they can be expensive as an everyday item. It should be remembered that a well-planned vegetarian diet can be nutritionally adequate and may be advantageous in terms of long-term health benefits.

Teenage athletes

Teenage athletes are particularly vulnerable, if they spend a lot of time training and participating in their chosen sport. This is because the energy needs for their physical activity must be met in addition to their needs for growth. Most schoolchildren participate in some sport, which involves no more than 2–3 hours per week; playing in school teams may occupy a further 3–4 hours a week. This amount of extra physical activity increases nutritional needs slightly, but probably not beyond the limits of the usual recommended levels for nutrients with the exception of energy. As with adult athletes, there is a particular need for carbohydrate, preferably in its starchy form, to sustain muscle glycogen levels. School sports teachers should be aware of this.

Where a teenager aspires to be of national class standard, training may take up much more time, often from a very young age. This imposes considerable nutritional needs both for energy and associated nutrients in line with the increase in energy. Energy needs may be 50 per cent greater than those for an average teenager. Meeting these necessitates eating an enormous amount of extra food, which can be quite daunting for a teenager. There may be reluctance to do this for fear of becoming overweight, or appearing greedy. However, full athletic potential and normal growth cannot be achieved without the appropriate nutritional input.

Pregnant teenagers

Pregnancy is associated with changing nutritional requirements. When these are additional to the high needs of adolescence, there is a risk that the intake may not be adequate to meet both. Approximately 1 per cent of all conceptions in England and Wales are in girls under 16; this represents 9400 pregnancies.

In addition to the nutritional needs, there may be social and emotional factors that compound the nutritional difficulties. Dietary habits of pregnant teenagers have been shown to be more erratic than those of pregnant adults and low levels of vitamins A and C, folate, calcium, iron and zinc have been recorded. If the pregnancy is unwanted, as is often the case, the girl may try to limit weight gain or even diet to lose weight. There may be parental rejection and she may leave home, which can reduce her opportunities to obtain a healthy diet.

Attendance at antenatal clinics may be erratic or non-existent, so monitoring of the pregnancy to anticipate problems and obtain advice about diet may be missed. Unsurprisingly, there is an increased risk to both mother and fetus in teenage pregnancies. Maternal mortality may be 2.5 times greater at the age of 15 than between 20 and 24; the infant is likely to be of low birthweight, and is at higher risk of morbidity and mortality from a number of causes.

A teenager who becomes pregnant needs to increase her nutrient intakes and gain sufficient weight to allow the normal development of her baby. She requires foods with high nutrient density and cannot afford to include low nutrient density foods in her diet. She may also require supplements.

Dieting

Dissatisfaction with body image is a prevalent phenomenon in Western societies, affecting more females than males. This is transmitted to children from their parents and inevitably influences attitudes and behaviours in children. The preference for slimness is strongly related to the child's current body weight, but a desire to be thinner is found among those with a normal body weight and also those that are underweight. The desire for a thinner body has increasingly been reported in pre-adolescent children. Over half of teenage girls questioned reported feeling fat and wanting to be thinner; the figure for boys in this study was approximately 20 per cent.

Dieting is a natural corollary to this dissatisfaction, with over 40 per cent of teenage girls reporting past attempts at dieting, and 23 per cent reporting being on a diet at the time of study. A further 6 per cent claim to be dieting all the time. The intensity and duration of dieting is also variable, with some diets lasting only a few days, but other girls reporting continuing their diets for more than 4 weeks.

Dieting practices may be variable. Some may reduce fat, snack or total energy intake, and increase fruit and vegetable intake. However, up to 15 per cent are reported to use extreme weight loss measures, such as fasting, skipping meals (usually breakfast), vomiting and using diet pills. Filling up on diet drinks to prevent hunger is also reported. Dieting can become a habit, establishing a pattern of chaotic eating. The food intake is continually restrained; if the restraint slips, a binge may occur, with large amounts of 'forbidden' foods being eaten. However, restraint is very soon re-established. Changing to a vegetarian diet may be part of a dieting strategy and be perceived as a means of weight management.

This type of dietary intake pattern can lead to inadequate energy and nutrient consumption, with subclinical deficiencies developing and implications for future health. In particular, poor nutritional status at the beginning of pregnancy may harm the fetus. Low iron status may lead to poorer cognitive abilities, and low zinc status may depress immune function and lead to higher rates of infection. Finally, poor status of antioxidant nutrients may facilitate damage at cellular level, which may in years to come result in degenerative diseases. In its most severe form, disordered eating can develop into bulimia nervosa or anorexia nervosa, both of which carry serious health risks. In the extreme, anorexia may result in death. Adolescent girls tending towards thinness should be counselled about the dangers for their future health. A body mass index of 18 or less is a useful criterion for the need to intervene.

Dieting is less of a problem among boys, although anorexia has been reported in up to 5 per cent. In some, an obsessional preoccupation with sport as a means of weight control may replace the vomiting and purging used by girls.

Usually adolescent boys are more concerned about becoming taller and stronger, and concentrate more on body building than restricting their body size.

Nutrition and IQ

In the late 1980s, research was published which suggested that supplementing the diets of schoolchildren with vitamins and minerals could improve results in non-verbal intelligence tests. However, the results of these studies have not been supported by other work. In addition, there is no information about the original nutritional status of the children who were supplemented. It is possible that children who are malnourished could benefit from supplementation and show improved mental functioning. However, there is no persuasive evidence currently available that, in children who have a normal diet, supplementation with minerals and vitamins can improve mental abilities.

Smoking and alcohol use

Both smoking and the use of alcohol are becoming more common among older children and teenagers in the UK. A quarter of 15-year olds are reported to be regular smokers and the rate is higher among girls. Alcohol interferes with the absorption and metabolism of a number of nutrients including amino acids, calcium, folate, thiamin and vitamin C. If the intake is modest, these effects are probably of little concern. However, binge drinking may have a more serious impact on nutrient levels. Among 15–16-year olds, 15 per cent of girls and 26 per cent of boys claim to be drinking more than 10 units per week, often in binges. This sort of drinking may also be accompanied by vomiting, which removes nutrients from the body. Ultimately, nutritional status may be affected. In addition, alcohol itself will have damaging effects on the organs of the body, just as in an adult.

Smoking increases the free-radical load in the body and, therefore, the requirement for vitamin C. This should be provided in greater amounts to those teenagers who smoke. A particularly vulnerable situation exists in those teenagers who are dieting and smoking, to help control their hunger and their weight. In this case, nutrient intakes may be inadequate to offer protection against the harmful free radicals in cigarette smoke.

SUMMARY

1. The transition from infant to teenager and young adult involves enormous changes in body size and composition. The constituents of the new tissues must be obtained from the diet. Thus, at all stages of this process, nutritional requirements are high.
2. Human and formula milk can provide the nutritional needs of the infant, although human milk confers some immunological and developmental advantages.
3. The process of weaning should start at 4 months. It parallels stages of development but is nutritionally important.
4. Between the years of 1 and 5, the child consolidates the early experience with food, and becomes more independent. Growth rates are slower but, because appetite can be small, the nutrient density of the diet is of great importance.
5. The diet of the school-age child is increasingly affected by external influences. It is important that well-balanced diets are provided at home. It must be recognized that children need to exercise choice in their food intake, as part of development. However, a sound foundation of education about food can make these choices healthier.
6. Teenagers are more vulnerable than the other age groups to peer pressure and may pass through phases of experimentation with food. Again, a core of well-balanced food provided at home can ensure that good nutrient intakes are maintained.

STUDY QUESTIONS

1 a Prepare a table summarizing the nutritional and non-nutritional differences between human milk and formula milk.
  b Do you have more points under the nutritional or the non-nutritional heading? Try to account for this.
2 Write a short article for a 'Parenting' magazine in answer to the question 'Why does my 18-month-old child have an erratic appetite?' Include some practical advice.
3 a What are the main nutritional principles underlying the balance of the diet suitable for children aged between 5 and 10 years?
  b What problems might be encountered?
  c Which nutrients might be most at risk?
4 At what ages are teenage boys and girls most nutritionally vulnerable and for what reasons?
5 Suggest some ways in which teenagers could be targeted for nutritional advice.
6 For the 11–16 year age group, how important nutritionally do you consider the following meals to be? Explain your viewpoint:
  a midday meal
  b breakfast
  c snacks.

REFERENCES AND FURTHER READING

Anderson, J.A., Johnstone, B.M., Remley, D.T. 1999: Breast feeding and cognitive development: a meta-analysis. *American Journal of Clinical Nutrition* 70, 525–35.

Barker, D.J.P. 1994: *Mothers, babies and diseases in later life*. London: British Medical Journal.

Child Growth Foundation 1995: *Boys/girls growth charts*. London: Child Growth Foundation.

Decsi, T., Koletzko, B. 1994: Polyunsaturated fatty acids in infant nutrition. *Acta Paediatrica* 83(Suppl. 395), 35–7.

DfES (UK Department for Education and Skills) 2001: *Healthy school lunches for students in secondary schools*. London: DfSE.

DoH (UK Department of Health) 1989: *The diets of British schoolchildren*. Report on Health and Social Subjects 36. London: HMSO.

DoH (UK Department of Health) 1991: *Dietary reference values for food energy and nutrients for the United Kingdom*. Report on Health and Social Subjects No. 41. Report of the Panel on Dietary Reference Values of the Committee on Medical Aspects of Food Policy. London: HMSO.

DoH (UK Department of Health) 1992: *The health of the nation: a strategy for health in England*. London: HMSO.

DoH (UK Department of Health) 1994: *Weaning and the weaning diet*. Report on Health and Social Subjects 45. Report of the Working Group on the Weaning Diet of the Committee on Medical Aspects of Food Policy. London: HMSO.

EEC 1991: Commission Directive on infant formulae and follow-on formulae. *Official Journal of the European Communities* L175, 35–49.

Food Standards Agency 2001: *The balance of good health. Information for educators and communicators*. London: Food Standards Agency.

Gregory, J.R., Collins, D.L., Davies, P.S.W., Hughes, J.M., Clarke P.C. 1995: *National diet and nutrition survey: children aged 1.5 to 4.5 years*. Volume 1: Report of the diet and nutrition survey. London: HMSO.

Gregory, J., Lowe, S., Bates, C.J. et al. 2000: *National Diet and Nutrition Survey: Young people aged 4–18 years*. Volume 1. Report of the Diet and Nutrition Survey. London: The Stationery Office.

Hamlyn, B., Brooker, S., Oleinikova, K., et al. 2002: *Infant feeding 2000*. London: The Stationery Office.

Hill, A.J. 2002: Developmental issues in attitudes to food and diet. *Proceedings of the Nutrition Society* 61, 259–66.

MAFF (Ministry of Agriculture, Fisheries and Food) 1995: *The infant formula and follow-on formula regulations.* Statutory Instrument 77. London: HMSO.

Parker, L., Fox, A. 2001: The Peterborough Schools Nutrition Project: a multiple intervention programme to improve school-based eating in secondary schools. *Public Health Nutrition* 4(6), 1221–8.

Robinson, S. 2000: Children's perceptions of who controls their food. *Journal of Human Nutrition and Dietetics* 13, 163–71.

Ruxton, C.H.S., Kirk, T.R., Belton, N.R. 1996: The contribution of specific dietary patterns to energy and nutrient intakes of 7–8 year old Scottish schoolchildren. *Journal of Human Nutrition and Dietetics* 9, 5–31.

Sharp, I. 1993: *Nutritional guidelines for school meals.* Report of an Expert Working Group. London: The Caroline Walker Trust.

13 ADULTS AND THE ELDERLY POPULATION

The aims of this chapter are to:

- review the dietary guidelines that have been made for adults in the UK;
- identify the particular needs of men and of women;
- review the nutritional aspects of a vegetarian diet;
- consider the effects of alcohol consumption on the achievement of dietary goals;
- discuss some human situations that may influence diet and so affect the attainment of the guidelines, including belonging to an ethnic minority group, having a low income, retirement and ageing.

On completing the study of this chapter, you should be able to:

- discuss the dietary recommendations and guidelines that are in existence in the UK for adults, and explain the reasoning behind them;
- explain the background to the special dietary needs of men, and particular diet-linked diseases, which the guidelines are aiming to prevent;
- discuss why women may be considered a nutritionally vulnerable group at certain stages of their life, and whether the dietary guidelines address their problems;
- discuss the advantages and disadvantages of following a vegetarian diet;
- explain why members of some ethnic minority groups consume different diets and the implications of this for dietary guidelines;
- discuss the implications of living on a low income in meeting dietary recommendations and goals;
- show how social, psychological and emotional circumstances may affect an older person's diet and the implications of these for meeting nutritional guidelines.

Dietary reference values and nutritional guidelines have, of necessity, been devised for the population as a whole. It would be both impractical and confusing to set a great number of different recommendations for various subgroups in the population. The guidelines current in the UK are very much in line with those in other Western countries and are the result of a wide consensus.

As discussed in Chapter 3, the progress towards achieving these guidelines is slow and in some cases trends in consumption appear to be moving contrary to the desired direction. It has been suggested that the guidelines are too ambitious as they set goals that only a very small amount of the population currently meet. An intermediate set of guidelines, closer to the actual patterns of consumption in the population, may be a more realistic target.

It is also important that a 'whole-diet' approach is adopted. Many people at present mistakenly believe that, if they change just one aspect of their diet, they are already eating more healthily. For example, there has been an increase in use of low-fat spread and semi-skimmed milk. These changes are desirable, but they do not go far enough towards a healthier diet. Such changes may result in a lower energy intake from dairy fat, which is then replaced by fats

Activity 13.1

Refer back to Chapter 3 to remind yourself of the basics of a healthy diet.

What are the dietary reference values – what are they based on?

- Are they to be used for assessing the diets of individuals?
- Why are healthy eating guidelines produced?
- What is the difference between dietary reference values and healthy eating guidelines?
- What were the nutritional targets set in the 'Health of the nation' report?
- How are these converted into a practical way of planning diets?
- How does the Balance of Good Health help consumers to achieve a healthy diet?

contained in biscuits or processed convenience foods. More extensive changes to the diet, for example, becoming vegetarian may have a number of positive health effects but, at the same time, increase risks from unforeseen consequences in the diet.

In addition, it should be recognized that there are many groups within the population who, for a diverse number of reasons, cannot achieve the targets. All of these groups will be considered in this chapter, exploring the reasons why they may have different needs, and considering some of the barriers that prevent them achieving dietary guidelines.

ADULT MEN

Many dietary guidelines around the world originated from a concern about morbidity and mortality from coronary heart disease. Consequently, they were based largely on findings from studies of men, since almost all the early studies targeted groups of men. In addition, their primary focus was related to intakes of fat, which for many years has been the major dietary factor linked to coronary heart disease development. Only in more recent years have dietary guidelines widened to include other dietary components, such as starchy carbohydrates, alcohol, salt and other micronutrients, including the antioxidant vitamins.

Do men have problems achieving these guidelines and are they appropriate?

Most men understand that they are at risk of heart disease, although many adopt the attitude that 'it won't happen to me'. Consequently, motivation to change dietary habits may not be very great. This may be sustained by social norms, which, in some cultural subgroups, expect men to have a traditional diet that contains plenty of meat and not to eat the more 'feminine' salad, fruit and vegetables. Some acceptance of a need to change spreading fat was achieved by the initial advertising of a polyunsaturated margarine in the UK as the 'margarine for men'.

Among some men there is also a general reluctance to be concerned about their health, reflected in lower attendance rates to health services by men than by women and a lower uptake of screening services. Exposure to information about healthy eating is generally less among men, as women gain this information from magazines (often in association with articles on cookery or weight loss), from information at health centres and supermarkets. In all cases, men have less access to these sources.

Further, traditional education philosophy excluded boys from learning about food and nutrition at school; the National Curriculum in the UK has introduced some teaching about health and diet to all children.

Concern about body weight is much less amongst men, although current trends in the UK show that more men than women are overweight. In addition, the distribution of body fat in men, with a greater tendency to deposit abdominal fat (apple-shape) means that overweight is a greater health risk.

Traditionally, more men have been smokers and heavy drinkers, although in both cases rates in women have increased in the last two decades. These are lifestyle factors, which may compound risk in several chronic diseases that also have nutritional risk factors. Men, therefore, are at nutritional risk and it is important

Activity 13.2

Work with a partner on this activity. Imagine you are given the brief of tackling one aspect of health promotion for a group of men (it could be reducing alcohol intake, losing weight, taking more exercise or altering the diet). Make some suggestions about:

- which group of men you would like to use as your client group;
- which aspect of health promotion you would like to tackle;
- how you might go about identifying the problem, and trying to suggest solutions.

What do you think are going to be the main barriers to success?

that attempts to change to a healthier diet are made, encompassing whole diet changes.

Studies show that, when changes are made, results are better in the younger age group than in older men. In addition, men in the higher social classes are more likely to make changes. Therefore, greatest benefits are seen here. There is a need to target men to increase their awareness of the importance of dietary change as well as exercise, and other lifestyle factors, such as drinking and smoking, in a more active approach to disease prevention. This will be easier to achieve in some groups than others; regrettably those with the greatest need for change are often the ones who are most difficult to reach. Imaginative approaches on the part of primary health care teams and health promoters are needed. These can include health promotion in the workplace or through social clubs, perhaps related to support of sporting activities.

ADULT WOMEN

There is a dilemma in trying to devise an optimal diet for women, as different stages in a woman's life may require different nutritional priorities.

A very important point to remember is that women generally have a smaller food intake than men, related to their lower energy needs. Within this smaller intake, however, they still need to obtain all of the nutrients essential for good health. Consequently, they have less margin for error in their diet – most of what they eat has to be nutrient rich. Eating too much 'empty energy' will result in an insufficient intake of micronutrients and possible health risks.

Most of the specific health issues for women have been discussed in other parts of this book; they are highlighted here to remind the reader of the vulnerability of the female to poor nutrition at various ages.

A female adolescent requires a certain amount of body fat to be present for normal reproductive activity to begin. Yet, during this time of life, many adolescent girls feel an enormous pressure from society to restrict their weight gain and achieve a slim body shape. These two goals are difficult to reconcile, with the result that some girls do not start to menstruate or, having started, stop again, as their body weight falls. This has implications for bone health in later life, in particular, because adolescence is also the time when the bone assimilates its minerals and achieves most of its final mass. Once into her early twenties, a woman is no longer able to add significant amounts of calcium to her bones, with the result that, if the bone mass is not optimal, she may develop osteoporosis in her early old age.

In early adult years, a woman may want to have children. Research dating back to the Dutch hunger winter in 1944–45 (when the population of Holland suffered severe food shortages for a period of 8 months), but replicated in many studies since then, has shown that an adequate amount of body fat is needed for normal fertility. The normal development of the fetus is threatened if the woman is underweight. More recent work shows that various vitamins and minerals must be present in sufficient amounts from the beginning of the pregnancy to avoid low birthweight and associated risks to the child, both in its early and later life.

Certain diseases are also a particular threat for women. Women experience anaemia much more commonly than men, principally because the iron lost in blood during menstruation is not replaced adequately from the diet. Both cancer of the breast and heart disease cause a large number of deaths, and are believed to have a dietary component. In addition, osteoporosis is a condition that causes disability in many more elderly women than men.

Physical activity, which is beneficial in promoting health, has for many years been more socially acceptable for men than for women. There is now an increase in women taking part in sport, but problems of time and access to sports facilities still bar many women from being more active. There may be a reluctance also to expose a less than perfect body in the gym.

Social research shows that a woman's food choices tend to be dictated more by the likes and dislikes of her partner and children than by her own preferences, even when she is the one with the major responsibility for food provision within the household. Thus, even if a woman might want to eat a healthier diet, she may experience pressure from her family to minimize change.

Finally, it must be recognized that women represent the majority (in the UK, 65 per cent) of those living in poverty, with its associated effects on nutrition. As a result of these conflicts and dilemmas, women generally have more nutritional problems than men.

VEGETARIANS

There has been a steady increase in the UK in the number of people who reject meat from their diet and follow some variant of the vegetarian diet. Surveys suggest that between 5 and 10 per cent of the population may be following some form of vegetarian diet. Numbers tend to be greatest in females and among teenagers and young adults, although people of all ages are represented. The move to vegetarianism may initially include the rejection only of red meat, but might further also exclude white meats, fish and, occasionally, other animal products such as eggs and cheese. Thus, the diet is based on cereals, pulses, nuts, vegetables and fruit. Many vegetarians, but not vegans, also include dairy products and eggs. Various categories of vegetarianism have been defined according to the foods of animal origin that are included in the diet (e.g. a lacto-ovo-vegetarian will eat cheese and eggs, a pescarian will eat fish).

The reasons for adopting a vegetarian diet vary, but may include:

- compassion for animals and concerns about animal welfare;
- rejection on ethical grounds of the intensive production methods used in animal husbandry and food production;
- concern over Western overindulgence in food, and exploitation of poorer countries and world resources;
- dislike of the taste, texture or smell of meat;
- concern over the safety of meat and animal products in the light of 'food scares', such as *Salmonella*, bovine spongiform encephalopathy (BSE) and the use of antibiotics;
- religious or cultural reasons.

From a nutritional perspective, an ideal diet is one that contains a wide variety of foods, providing maxiumum opportunities to meet nutritional requirements. However, it cannot be said that foods of animal origin are an essential part of such a diet, and there are many populations around the world who exist on diets that are exclusively plant based. Problems of deficiency may arise when there is overreliance on a limited number of foods, or foods of limited nutritional value, for example, cassava, yam and maize. Where the quantity of food supplied by such a diet is sufficient, and the diet contains a variety of plant foods, then nutritional adequacy is not a problem. This is generally the case in Western societies and a well-planned vegetarian diet may provide a greater diversity of foods than one based around meat, including more vegetables, pulses and nuts. As a result, many nutrients may be present in greater amounts than in an omnivorous diet. However, meat and animal products are rich in a number of minerals and vitamins that may not be sufficiently replaced in a vegetarian diet.

In general, a well-balanced vegetarian diet containing grains, vegetables and nuts is likely to provide more of the following nutrients: folate, vitamin C, carotene, thiamin, vitamin E and potassium.

Nutrients about which there may be some concern, especially if the diet lacks dairy products, include the following: protein, iron, calcium, iodine and zinc, vitamin B_{12}, vitamins A and D, and n-3 fatty acids.

It is particularly important that attention is paid to these nutrients in the diets of vegetarian infants, children and adolescents (see Chapter 12). For adults, there is little evidence for a deficiency of most of these nutrients; however, a number are discussed below.

Vegetarians are probably more prone to iron deficiency anaemia because of the poorer bioavailability of iron from plant-based diets. Attention should be paid to maximizing absorption by including enhancing factors, such as foods containing vitamin C in the diet. Vitamin B_{12} occurs only in foods of animal origin and, therefore, their strict exclusion will be a risk factor for deficiency. Many foods designed for vegetarian diets, such as meat substitutes, are fortified with the vitamin, but vigilance is needed to ensure an adequate intake.

Vitamin D status may be compromised when the vegetarian diet is also very high in phytate and low in calcium, as has been reported in some macrobiotic diets and among people of Asian origin in the UK.

Lower intakes of the long-chain *n*-3 fatty acids are also a feature of vegetarian diets that exclude fish. Levels of these fatty acids are lower in plasma of adult vegetarians and also in the milk during lactation. These fatty acids have a role in the development of the retina and central nervous system in the infant, and the significance of these lower levels for infant development is being studied.

More interest has been focused on the positive aspects of a vegetarian diet, in relation to some of the chronic diseases prevailing in Western societies. Studies of adult vegetarians show that they have similar energy intakes compared with omnivores. However, the body mass index of vegetarians is on average 1 kg/m^2 lower than in matched omnivores. The reasons for this are unclear, but may be attributable to lower fat or alcohol intakes. One of the reported consequences of the lower body weight is a lower blood pressure, which may confer advantages in terms of stroke and coronary heart disease.

Data from five cohort studies (Key et al., 1998), including 76 000 subjects, has shown that vegetarians had a 24 per cent reduction in mortality from coronary heart disease. Mortality in semi-vegetarians, who ate fish only or meat less than once per week, was intermediate between meat eaters and vegetarians. It is proposed that these differences can be attributed to lower intakes of saturated fat in vegetarians, and related lower plasma total cholesterol concentrations. In addition, vegetarians tend to have higher intakes of polyunsaturated fatty acids, especially linoleic acid and dietary fibre. Both of these will also affect cholesterol levels, and the risk of coronary heart disease.

Higher intakes of dietary fibre are also possibly responsible for lower rates of constipation, diverticular disease, appendicitis and gallstones that have been reported among vegetarians. At present, there is no firm evidence that vegetarian diets protect against cancers.

Overall, a planned vegetarian diet can meet many of the dietary guidelines and contribute to better health. There are a number of possible shortcomings from the exclusion of meat and dairy products, and these nutrients should be replaced from other foods. A badly constructed vegetarian diet will, however, carry no health advantages and may be hazardous to long-term health. The possible advantages and disadvantages of a vegetarian diet are summarized in Figure 13.1.

MINORITY ETHNIC GROUPS

Many people around the world for a variety of political or economic reasons move to and settle in a country that is not their own. In doing so, they become immigrants to that country. If the culture of the host country is similar to that of the immigrant's own mother country, settlement is relatively easy. If there are many cultural, religious and language difficulties, the immigrant may experience alienation in the host country. If the immigrant is a refugee forced to leave the home country, the psychological challenges of adjustment may also create difficulties with the diet.

Food habits are one of the aspects of an immigrant family's culture that may undergo little adjustment, resulting potentially in some nutrition-related problems. These may be the

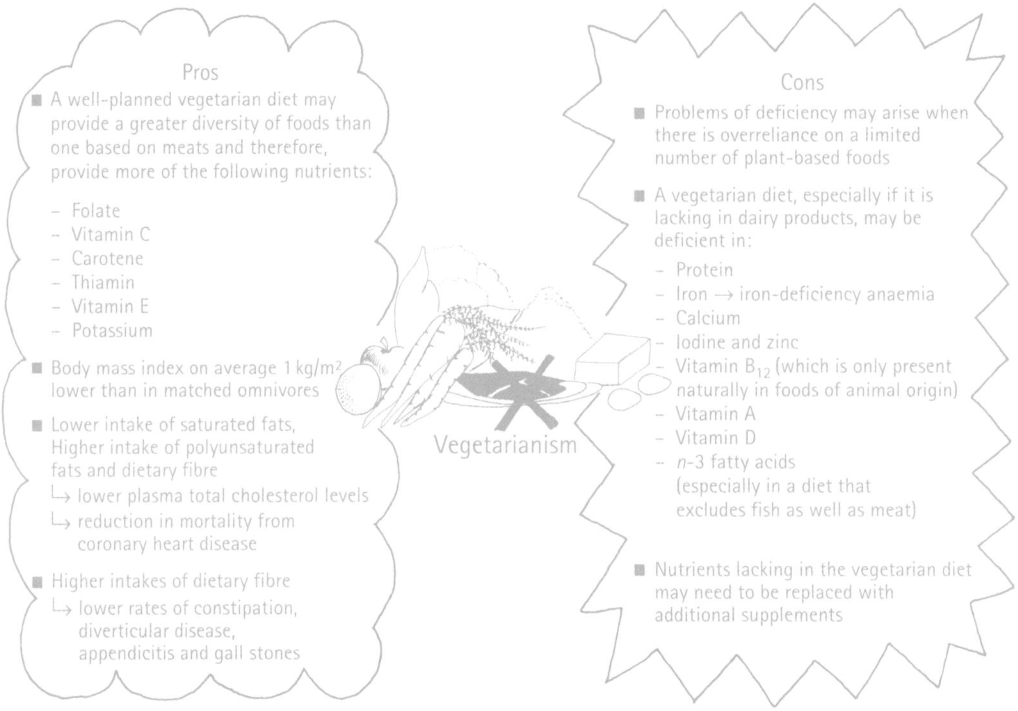

Figure 13.1 The possible advantages and disadvantages of a vegetarian diet.

result of a number of factors that impinge on the diet.

When traditional foods are eaten, the dietary mix may seem quite different from that of the typical host country diet. Consequently, some of the guidelines that have largely been created around a 'British' diet may not be applicable. It is necessary, therefore, to explore two main issues:

- what do some of the larger minority ethnic groups in Britain eat, and what consequences does it have for their health?
- should the dietary guidelines be applied to the traditional diets eaten, and how can this be achieved?

The main groups of immigrants in the UK are Europeans (including people from Southern Ireland and those of Eastern European and Mediterranean origin), Asians from the Indian subcontinent (including Indians, Pakistanis and Bangladeshis), people of Afro-Caribbean origin from Africa or the West Indies, and Chinese people, from Singapore, Hong Kong and Vietnam as well as some from China. There are many other groups that have settled in the UK from every country in the world, but numerically these are much smaller, and have not been studied as an identified group, although it is possible that nutritional issues do exist. People belonging to minority ethnic groups including those of mixed race in the UK represent about 8.8 per cent of the UK population (2001 figures).

The Europeans, together with the small groups of immigrants from various parts of the globe not mentioned above, have not as a group been reported to experience nutritional difficulties or possible deficiencies in Britain. It is possible that, like any other individual, they may experience personal dietary problems, which may be exacerbated by factors related to their ethnic origin.

Features common to many members of ethnic minority immigrant groups

Newly arrived immigrants may share the common feature of belonging to a socially disadvantaged sector of society, even if they were relatively well off in the home country. This may be reflected in various aspects of life, including low income or unemployment, poor housing, poor educational opportunity and less access to health care. All of these may have a bearing on nutrition. In those who maintain the traditional diet, the higher cost of some imported foods and the need to travel to specialist shops may limit the amount of food eaten.

The traditional diet may be modified by the substitution of some 'British' foods to replace unavailable traditional items. Unfortunately, the British foods chosen are often those of poorest nutritional quality, such as highly refined processed items like cakes, biscuits, crisps and soft drinks. These are not nutritionally comparable to the traditional items they may be displacing. In this way, a well-balanced traditional diet, by attempting to become integrated into the British diet, becomes nutritionally poorer. It is important that, where some adaptation to the British diet occurs, the foods chosen should be nutritionally adequate.

For the children of some of these families, especially those new to the UK, school meals may pose a major dilemma. If the child has been brought up from infancy eating only a traditional diet, foods presented in school may be completely unfamiliar both in content, style of presentation and expected way of being eaten. In time, peer pressure may encourage these children to sample British foods and, if they enjoy them, they may eventually request them at home. It should be pointed out, however, that many of the children in British schools who are of minority ethnic group origin are second- or even third-generation children of former migrants, who no longer consider themselves as anything other than British, and have perhaps been eating the typical British diet for the whole of their life. Traditional foods may be something that they eat only in the presence of members of the older generation or occasionally at home.

A different problem exists at the opposite end of the age spectrum, as some of the early migrants into Britain in the late 1950s and 1960s reach retirement and old age. For many of these, life has remained very traditional. This is particularly true for the women who may have never worked, or integrated much with the local population. Services such as meals on wheels or luncheon clubs may not provide appropriate meals. Because of this, the person may be excluded from receiving this provision. In some parts of Britain, special 'ethnic' meals on wheels are provided for the local population, but this service is not widespread. In most cases, the older generation of immigrants rely on their children and grandchildren to provide them with food, if they cannot cope themselves. Welfare services are gradually recognizing the need to encompass the needs of ethnic elders in their provision.

Asian immigrants

Much attention has been focused by nutritionists on the South Asian immigrants from Bangladesh, India and Pakistan. In addition, smaller numbers came to Britain from Africa, in particular Uganda and Kenya.

Religion is an important part of the culture for most of these groups, and many are followers of one of the three major religions found in Asia: Hindu, Islam and Sikh. All three have specific dietary laws, which have an impact on the foods consumed and may result in nutritional consequences. The main features of the religions and their dietary prescriptions are outlined below.

Hindu religion

This is an ancient religion, one of whose main precepts is the sanctity of life and the transmigration of the soul. As a consequence, there is a prohibition on the taking of life, including that of an animal for food. Thus, traditionally Hindus are vegetarian, eating only plant foods, or foods from animals that do not include killing – for example, dairy products. Eggs may be avoided by some Hindus, particularly women, as they are seen as a potential source of life. The cow is deemed sacred, and its products are prized in the diet. Orthodox Hindus will adhere strictly to the dietary laws, but some who are less strict may eat meat, but usually not beef or pork (the pig is considered unclean).

Fasting, which means either total abstinence from food, or alternatively the eating of 'pure' foods – fruit, yoghurt, nuts and potatoes – may be a regular occurrence.

Islam

Followers of Islam are Muslims. The religious teachings in the Koran encompass most aspects of life, including dietary laws, as well as rules on fasting. Muslims are permitted to eat the flesh of ruminant animals (which excludes pork), poultry and fish (some but not all exclude shellfish). The animal must be ritually slaughtered by a registered butcher; the meat is bled and sacrificed to Allah. It is thus made 'halal'. Meat prepared in this way is available in Britain, either fresh or frozen. Milk and dairy products are not a major part of the Muslim diet in the UK, although they are eaten increasingly, as the diet becomes more British. Even though meat is allowed in the Muslim diet, the amount actually eaten may not be very large. This is especially true for women who normally eat last, giving the larger share to the men in the household.

All Muslims over the age of responsibility (early adolescence) are required to fast from sunrise to sunset for a 4-week period each year known as Ramadan. The actual number of hours of fasting depends on the time of year in which Ramadan falls. When it occurs in the summer months, there may be up to 16 hours of fasting a day, but perhaps less than 8 hours in the winter. In the early years of the twenty-first century, the fast falls in October/November/December, and is moving back through the year into the Autumn months. Ramadan is associated with eating during the hours of darkness, with special foods being prepared, many high in fat and sugar. Families rise before dawn to eat; this alleviates the problems of hunger during the day. Ramadan finishes with special celebrations, again involving particular foods prepared only at this time of the year.

Sikhism

This religion developed comparatively recently (in the sixteenth century) and incorporates some features of both the Hindu religion and Islam. Dietary restrictions are less than in either of these religions: eggs or meat are not prohibited, but some Sikhs may believe in the transmigration of the soul and are vegetarian.

Very few eat beef, and pork may be considered unclean, as with the other religions described above. Animals for meat must be killed in a prescribed manner by a single blow to the head; meat produced in this way is known as 'khatka'.

General features

Traditional Asian meals may consist principally of the staple (a rice or wheat dish), together with one or several side dishes, which provide the garnish or flavour part of the meal. Fruit is more likely to be eaten for dessert rather than a sweet cooked dish. Sweets may be prepared for special occasions, rather than everyday. The most Westernized meal may be breakfast, which might include cereals and toast, rather than the traditional leftovers from the previous day. In the Health Survey for England 1999 (DoH, 2001), which considered the health of minority ethnic groups, consumption of red meat and fried foods was reported to be high among Bangladeshi groups, and the diet was also low in fibre. The Indian diet contained least amounts of red meat (for religious reasons), lowest fat levels and had a higher fibre content.

Asian women tend to have a more marked domestic role in the traditional household. Particularly for these women, integration with the British community may be slow. Change occurs most quickly in those communities where the women have roles outside the house: going out to work, or meeting others.

Afro-Caribbean immigrants

Immigrants to Britain from the Caribbean are predominantly of African descent, although some may be of Indian origin. The cultural outlook of these groups has been influenced by life both in the Caribbean and Britain. Several ethnic subcultures exist, linked to the island of origin. Traditional Caribbean food habits may be kept by significant numbers of this population and are likely to be diverse. Generally, they pose few nutritional problems, apart from obesity.

The diet is largely based on cereals, such as corn, rice and wheat, and starchy vegetables including potatoes. These may be served in the form of spicy stews or soups, containing many different vegetables. Many of the traditional foods, such as mangoes, breadfruit, cassava, green bananas, plantain and yams, are available in West Indian specialist shops, indicating that they have remained an important part of the diet. The diet is higher in carbohydrate (50 per cent), lower in fat (32 per cent) and alcohol (2 per cent) than the equivalent white British diet. Food patterns may be different among this population and dietary assessment requires specialist knowledge (see Sharma and Cruickshank, 2001).

One of the subgroups of the West Indian community are the Rastafarians who aspire to return to Ethiopia, which is seen as the African homeland. There is a strong adherence to the Bible, and many of the dietary laws are based on a very strict interpretation of Bible writings. In its strictest form, the diet is vegetarian, containing no meat or animal products. It is based predominantly on fruit, vegetables and cereals. However, because pulses are not a major item in the West Indian diet, the vegetables tend to be starchy roots and leafy vegetables, both of which contain little protein. There can be a lack of vitamin B_{12} in the diet. In other ways, however, the diet may be considered healthy, with a prohibition on alcohol, convenience and processed foods, and a low salt intake. As with all dietary laws, the extent to which the diet is kept will vary between individuals. However, as Rastafarianism is perceived as conferring an identity to the individual, there is a considerable motivation to keep to the dietary laws.

Chinese immigrants

The Chinese have a food culture very different from that of the indigenous British population, which has remained largely unchanged despite long periods of settlement in Britain. Although some British foods are included in the diet, usually being requested by the children, these form only a small part of the daily intake. The diet includes rice as a staple, and meat, fish, fruit and vegetables prepared in many diverse ways.

Food is perceived by older Chinese as not just providing nutrients but contributing to the overall balance of the energy in the body. This is described in terms of hot and cold (or male and female, yin and yang) properties. Foods are ascribed such properties according to the effects they are believed to have on the body (not on the actual temperature of the food). In addition, particular stages of life, such as pregnancy, as well as illness, alter the body's balance. An appropriate selection of foods can restore the balance. For example, if children eat a school meal that is considered 'hot', they will be given a 'cooling' food to restore their balance when they return home. Thus, rather than avoiding British foods, the Chinese simply accommodate them, and adjust other foods eaten accordingly. There are no reports in the British literature of nutritional problems associated with the Chinese diet.

Potential nutritional consequences

Vitamin D deficiency began to appear among children of Asian immigrants in the early 1970s. Initially, it was believed that the cause was linked to the skin pigmentation, which reduced the synthesis of vitamin D on exposure to sunlight. However, this was not supported by results of measurements of vitamin D synthesis after ultraviolet exposure in light- and dark-skinned individuals. A further possibility was that the traditional dress of many Asian immigrants required that the body be covered, allowing little exposure of the skin and minimizing vitamin D synthesis. This may contribute to the deficiency, but is unlikely to be the sole explanation.

Investigation of the diet of affected and unaffected individuals has shown that most vitamin D deficiency occurs in those who follow the most strictly vegetarian diet. Diets that contain no meat, eggs or dairy produce appear to be the most rachitogenic (rickets causing) among the Asian population. It has been suggested that the high content of dietary fibre and phytate reduces the availability of calcium and removes vitamin D from the body in the faeces. In addition, the lack of animal products directly reduces vitamin D intake. A strict vegetarian diet has also been found to lead to rickets among Rastafarian children. Health promotion campaigns among the Asian population have largely reduced the occurrence of rickets among the children, although low plasma vitamin D levels are still recorded. The problem of osteomalacia in adults (women, in particular), however, remains and appears to be difficult to prevent by education.

Anaemia arises in these groups from inadequate intakes of iron, folic acid or vitamin B_{12}, or a combination of these. Iron deficiency arises in infants because of prolonged milk feeding, and inadequate use of iron-rich weaning foods. This has been found in both Asian and Afro-Caribbean families. Pregnant women are also at risk, in particular those who are vegetarian. Language barriers, especially among those newly arrived in the country, may prevent them seeking or accepting medical advice to treat the anaemia.

Folic acid deficiency also occurs in pregnant women, whose needs are increased to support fetal cell division. Prolonged cooking of vegetables and reheating from day to day destroys all potential folate in these foods. This is particularly a problem when the diet is vegetarian.

Vitamin B_{12} deficiency is particularly found in vegetarian immigrants, being seen most in the Hindu population in the UK. It may coexist with iron and folate deficiency, and has also been linked to a higher than average occurrence of tuberculosis.

Studies on the incidence of dental caries show that pre-school children in immigrant groups throughout Europe tend to have a higher prevalence of dental caries than the indigenous population. This is particularly true among the Asian communities and is believed to be associated with a higher intake of sugar-containing drinks, including milk, and a higher frequency of consumption of sugar products.

Obesity, diabetes and heart disease are the newer diseases among the Asian population at present. Central obesity is particularly common among the South Asian groups, especially among women (DoH, 2001). The incidence of both diabetes and heart disease is higher among members of Asian minority groups than the indigenous British population. This may seem surprising, since the traditional diet is rich in starchy carbohydrate and contains large amounts of vegetables, in line with dietary guidelines. Recent work has shown that Asians have higher plasma levels of lipoprotein(a) than Europeans. This increases coronary heart disease risk. In addition, the Westernized diet and lifestyle contribute to increasing body mass index with central fat deposition, insulin resistance and raised blood lipids. These combine to produce an elevated risk for both heart disease and diabetes. A key factor in prevention is physical activity, which can help to reverse many of these trends. However, uptake of physical activity is low in many members of these groups.

For all of the immigrant groups, the traditional diet more closely resembles the dietary guidelines than does the current British diet. It is important that minority ethnic groups are encouraged to retain their traditional dietary practices, perhaps incorporating some of the staple foods available in Britain. They should be discouraged from including the unhealthy British dietary practices into their traditional patterns.

One of the most disadvantaged groups are refugees, who may come from many different countries. There is a high level of food insecurity in these households, particularly within the first two years of arrival in the UK. It is difficult to reach people in these groups, but child hunger is likely to be common, and significantly associated with recent arrival and receipt of fewer benefits.

LOW INCOME AND NUTRITION

People on a low income may be living in poverty. This is a relative term: it can be taken to mean an absolute lack of material possessions but, in Western society, it is more commonly used to reflect disadvantage in relation to the rest of society. In practice, the definition varies between different organizations. Two definitions that are used are:

- people receiving less than half of the average income (whether from employment or state benefits); and
- people having to spend more than 30 per cent of income on food.

Numbers of people in poverty have been increasing in Europe throughout the last decades.

It is documented that people in these situations have poorer health in almost every measure used to assess health, with excess morbidity and mortality at all ages. Various groups are particularly vulnerable to poverty. These include the following.

- Families with children, in particular, where there is a lone parent or where neither parent is in employment.
- Women, owing to the traditional dependence of women on a male breadwinner, their traditional role as carers of children and their poorer pension rights as a result of incomplete employment records. In two-adult households where the woman is the sole wage earner, the income is usually lower than in those with a male wage earner.
- People with a disability, owing to poorer employment prospects and higher than average living costs.
- Members of minority ethnic groups, owing to a higher unemployment rate and a greater representation among the low paid. In addition, there are now many refugees and asylum seekers throughout Europe who are often in severe financial hardship, which also reflects on their nutritional intakes.
- Young people who have left school but have not been able to find work. They have very low entitlements to benefits and may not be supported by their families, leading perhaps to homelessness and a life in poverty.
- Homeless people have major problems in achieving an adequate food intake. They may have additional problems that compromise nutritional status, such as alcohol or drug abuse. Alcohol may provide a substantial proportion of the energy intake. Studies on this group find that they are up to four times more likely to be underweight and have a diet that is low in a wide range of nutrients. Shelters for the homeless and soup kitchens are an important source of nutritional provision and attention to the quality of the food could make a difference to the status of this group.

Income is not the only factor contributing to poorer health experienced by people in these groups. One of the main factors is likely to be their diet, but poorer housing, low self-esteem, poorer educational opportunity and lifestyle habits detrimental to health, such as smoking, all make a contribution.

Characteristics of the diet

Expenditure on food is described as elastic, which means that when income is limited and other, fixed, expenses have to be met, the food budget can be trimmed accordingly. However, those on a limited income may spend up to three times more, proportionately, on food compared with the average UK family.

The expenditure on food is cost efficient; the annual National Food Survey consistently shows that the lowest income groups obtain more nutrients per unit of money spent. Table 13.1 shows some of the foods typically bought by the low-income and high-income groups, and in Table 13.2 the amount bought per 1 pence of expenditure is shown.

Studies such as these of the foods eaten typically show that low-income families rely more heavily on white bread, whole milk, sugar, eggs, meat products and margarine, and consume less reduced fat milk, poultry, carcass meat, fish, fresh vegetables (excluding potatoes), fruit, brown and wholemeal bread. Vegetables and potatoes are more likely to be processed rather than fresh. There is also less variety of foods eaten; for example, among pregnant women in Edinburgh and London, the poorest had only half the number of different foods in their diet compared with the richer women. The diet is, therefore, more likely to be monotonous, with few new additions.

Table 13.2 shows that, for every food group, those households with a lower income buy more (by weight) for their money. This applies to even simple products, such as confectionery or soft drinks. Overall, expenditure is also less, with a mean expenditure of £22.03 by group A and £14.07 by group D recorded by DEFRA (2001).

This cost efficiency often necessitates shopping around to find the best value for money, which may be time consuming. Some poorer residential areas may have limited shopping facilities, and the term 'food deserts' has been coined to describe this situation. Access to the wider choice of foods in larger supermarkets may be limited by

TABLE 13.1 Types of foods eaten by the highest (A) and lowest (D) income groups studied by the National Food Survey 2000 (consumption in g/person per week) (calculated from DEFRA, 2001)

Food	Income group	
	A	D
White bread	175	375
Wholemeal, brown and other bread	258	174
Breakfast cereal	155	110
Biscuits	108	143
Milk	464	833
Cheese	111	88
Meat and meat products	849	971
Fats and oils	149	200
Sugars and preserves	90	142
Potatoes (fresh)	568	776
Fresh green and other vegetables	857	581
Processed potatoes and vegetables	462	581
Fruit	895	573
Fruit juice	483	211

TABLE 13.2 'Value for money' of foods bought by high-income (A) and low-income groups (D) (amount purchased in grams per 1 pence spent) (calculated from DEFRA, 2001)

Food	Income group	
	A	D
Milk, cream and cheese	9.3	13.8
Meat and meat products	1.9	2.8
Fish	1.3	2.0
Fats and oils	3.8	6.0
Sugar and preserves	7.0	12.9
Vegetables and potatoes	6.3	10.4
Fruit	6.8	9.0
Bread	7.8	11.5
Cereals	4.2	6.3
Soft drinks	22.1	31.3
Alcoholic drinks	2.3	3.8
Confectionery	1.6	2.0

lack of transport or insufficient resources to make the trip worthwhile. In general, about 30 per cent of the British population have no access to a car and are, therefore, dependent on public transport for their access to more distant shops. In addition, the temptation of a large variety of foods on offer makes a stark contrast with the amount of money available. Consequently, local and often smaller shops may be used, where both choice and value for money are likely to be less. There may also be a problem of a lack of storage facilities, necessitating frequent purchases of perishable items. Shopping becomes a chore, with little scope for enjoyment. It should also be noted that 'value for money' in terms of quantity of food purchased does not necessarily equate to nutritional value.

TABLE 13.3 Cost of common snack foods, in pence, to supply 420 kJ (100 Calories). Values calculated from Food Standards Agency (FSA, 2002b) and at 2002 supermarket economy prices

Food	Costs to provide 420 kJ (100 Calories) (pence)
Digestive biscuits	2
Wholemeal bread	2
Kit Kat (chocolate wafer)	6
Crisps	7
Milk	7
Banana	10
Chocolate bar	12
Peppermints	13
Coca cola	13
Sponge cake	15
Yogurt	21
Orange/satsuma	35
Apple	42

The cheaper foods bought may have poorer nutritional content; for example, cheaper meat products contain more fat and salt, cheaper vegetables may be less fresh and have lower vitamin contents.

Nevertheless, families try to maintain conventional eating patterns to lessen the impact of low income, often eating cheaper versions of 'mainstream' meals. Also, parents endeavour to protect their children against the effects on the diet of poverty, buying foods that the children prefer. As a consequence, children in low-income families may actually receive more of their favourite foods than children from better-off households. To achieve this, parents in several studies record missing meals. Protecting the children also means that the family meal is focused on what the children prefer and will eat, rather than the likes and dislikes of other family members. Eating may cease to be a pleasure and becomes simply a means to ward off hunger.

Food selection is made from a rational perspective, with a view to the meal it can produce in the most economical way. Therefore, foods that may require preparation and addition of several other ingredients to constitute a meal are less attractive. A ready-made product, such as a meat pie, needs few additional items to make it into a complete meal, in contrast to a leaner meat, which itself contains less energy and requires vegetables, pasta, potatoes, bread, etc. to make a meal. Predictability of portion size and number also helps in meal planning.

As one of the primary concerns is to feel satiated after a meal, foods that provide a large amount of energy for a small financial outlay may be preferred. Consequently, foods high in fat and sugars will be more satisfying than a low-fat, low-sugar food and will provide a cost-efficient source of energy. The cost to supply 420 kJ (100 Calories) from a variety of snack foods is shown in Table 13.3. Not all are nutritionally poor; for example, bread and milk can provide a cheap nutritious snack.

Nutritional implications

Current dietary advice (discussed in Chapter 3) is to eat more fruit, vegetables and starchy carbohydrate, and to reduce the intake of fats, particularly from whole fat dairy products and meats rich in saturated fats. In addition, the consumption of fish is encouraged. The National Food Surveys show that the trend towards a healthier pattern in the diet is more marked in the higher income groups surveyed and, in many cases, is moving in the opposite direction in the poorer groups. Thus, although there is a small downward trend in fat intake in poorer families, more of that fat is still saturated, and fruit and green vegetable consumption in one study was found to be equivalent to two apples and ten Brussels sprouts per person per week.

Evidence collected in many centres around the UK has shown that the costs of a 'healthier basket' of foods are greater than for a 'less healthy' basket. The difference in price varies between regions of the country, but may represent an excess cost of 20 per cent for the 'healthier' basket. In addition, the access to many of the healthier items may be more limited in the areas where the poorer families may shop.

The stresses of living on a low income mean that health concerns are not one of the highest priorities, even though evidence suggests that the desire to eat more healthily exists. Knowledge about what constitutes a healthier diet is also present among poorer families, although it may be fragmentary. Reports have shown that, if there was more money to spend, then this would be used to buy more fruit, vegetables and leaner meats. At present, for such families, the cost of the food takes precedence over issues of taste, cultural acceptability and healthy eating.

Members of these families run the risk of having lower intakes of many of the micronutrients. In particular, these include iron, zinc, calcium, magnesium and potassium, as well as the vitamins, especially vitamin C, folate, riboflavin, niacin, beta-carotene and vitamin E. Many of these are the 'antioxidant nutrients', which are believed to be especially important to health. At the same time, the diet may be low in non-starch polysaccharides (NSPs) and polyunsaturated fats, but contain excessive amounts of saturated fat and sugars. The consequences for health are likely at all ages. Links with nutrition have been discussed also in the relevant sections of the book; a summary is provided here.

- Infants are less likely to be breastfed, although there has been an increase in prevalence reported in the Infant Feeding 2000 Survey (Hamlyn et al., 2002). Breastfeeding is protective against infection in early life, enhances gut development, and may protect against allergy and eczema. It is also associated with better school performance in childhood and a higher IQ for children born pre-term.
- Infants in low-income families have a higher consumption of infant formulae, potatoes, confectionery, squashes and soft drinks, and a lower consumption of milk products and fruit. Nutrient intakes are higher in saturated fats and cholesterol, and lower in carotene and vitamin C.
- Toddlers have slower growth and slower recovery from infection, but also more have a high body mass index (BMI), more dental caries and higher blood lipids. Their diets are higher in saturated fatty acids, sugars, starch and sodium (present in higher amounts in processed foods that form a larger part of the diet). There are lower intakes of NSPs, beta-carotene, vitamin C, iron, zinc, calcium and iodine.
- Older schoolchildren have lower intakes of most vitamins and minerals, lower levels of activity and poorer bone accretion. There are higher rates of anaemia among teenage girls and lower iron status, which probably impacts on cognitive ability. If the poor iron status continues into pregnancy, there are higher risks of stillbirth, low birthweight, and increased risk of hypertension and heart disease in the offspring later in their lives.
- Lone parents have a greater likelihood of falling below the lower reference nutrient intake (LRNI) for many nutrients, the greater their 'poverty index'. (This was assessed on a number of lifestyle factors associated with low income.) Pregnant women have generally lower intakes of energy and nutrients, poorer weight gain and higher occurrence of low birthweight babies. This has implications for their future health and perpetuates the intergenerational effects of deprivation.
- Older adults have lower nutrient intakes, poorer immune status and higher risk from all diet-related diseases.
- Special dietary requirements are more difficult to follow.

Activity 13.3

Keep a record of your expenditure on food for a period of 1 week. Use the Balance of Good Health (FSA, 2001) to break down this expenditure into the main food groups.

- Which of the groups costs you the most and which the least?
- Is it possible for you to change your expenditure on food?
- Could you spend less during the following week?

Prepare a plan of which food groups you could buy less and which more during the next week. How easy do you find this exercise?

Make a list of the constraints that operate for you in trying to be more economical in your food expenditure. Which could you overcome, and which are beyond your control?

Practical help

Attempts have been made to devise sample diets that would be nutritionally sound and at the same time cost no more than a low-income budget could afford. One such was the 'ten pound diet' produced by Ministry of Agriculture, Fisheries and Food (MAFF; see Leather, 1992), which gave precise amounts of 26 different food groups/items, which could be used to plan meals for 1 week within this budget. Many people felt that this diet was socially unacceptable, as it expected people on a low income to eat differently from the rest of society.

More practical help is reported by the National Food Alliance, which brings together many local projects engaged in empowering people on low income and enabling them to work together in low-cost cafes, food cooperatives and other support groups. In this way, access to and education about food are improved, the feelings of isolation are reduced and self-esteem can be enhanced. In association with these more social improvements, there can be a better diet and a greater interest in food and eating healthily.

Further work was undertaken on a strategy on food and low income by the Low Income Project Team (DoH, 1996). This aimed to bring about a better understanding of the costs of healthy eating and facilitate access to healthier foods by involving policy makers and providers of the food. As part of this initiative, ways of mapping price and availability of healthy food have been developed. This can then be used to identify areas that serve their local community poorly in terms of healthy food and attempt to address this. Local projects as part of the Governments initiative on Social Exclusion in the UK are helping local groups around the country to improve their access to better quality food; this may be through, for example, local street markets, 'Get Cooking' clubs or community cafes.

OLDER ADULTS

In this discussion, the term 'elderly' is used to refer to men and women of pensionable age. In the UK, this generally means 65 years or over for men and over 60 years for women. The upper end of this age spectrum is not defined, but there are increasing numbers of people over 100 years old in the UK (the majority are women).

In 2001, 18.3 per cent of the population in the UK or 10.8 million people, was over retirement age (65 in men and 60 in women). The total numbers of the elderly are increasing in most Western countries: by 2030, it is estimated that one in four of the adult population will be aged over 65 years. In the UK, the greatest increase in the early part of the twenty-first century will be particularly in the over-85 age group, with a smaller relative increase in the over-75s. The numbers between 60/65–74 will fall slightly, reflecting the lower birth rates in the 1930s and during the Second World War. The over-85 group are the most vulnerable sector of the retired population, and the most likely to experience nutritional problems. However, it is anticipated that the increased knowledge of nutrition among younger adults, and the consumption by some of a healthier diet, will reduce the occurrence of nutritional problems as they get older. Current statistics suggest that an average of 13 years of disability for men and 16 years for women may be expected at the end of their life. The proposals of the 'Health of the nation' white paper of adding 'years to life and life to years' are particularly relevant in this group.

In making general statements about the vulnerability of the elderly population, it is important to remember that there is considerable variation between individuals, as at any age. Preparation for retirement and a healthy old age should have begun earlier in life, with the acquisition of good eating habits and a healthy lifestyle, involving both physical and mental stimulation. Several studies confirm that health and good nutrition coexist in the elderly, and when one begins to deteriorate, often so does the other.

Why are some elderly persons at risk?

Elderly people are at increasing risk of having marginal nutrition resulting from the ageing process itself and its impact on social factors, as well as an increased incidence of disease. These factors are summarized in Figure 13.2. Ageing is believed to be the result of an increase in oxidative stress and dysregulation of cellular function over time. Supplementation with several antioxidants, most notably vitamins E and C has been associated with a reduced risk of age-associated chronic diseases as well as maintenance of cognitive function.

It is helpful to consider how ageing affects some of the body's systems, which may in turn contribute to poor nutritional status.

Sensory system

Changes to the sensory system will have an impact on both the ability to obtain food as well as its enjoyment. Loss of hearing or visual acuity may restrict shopping as well as social contacts, leading to isolation. Loss of sensitivity to taste and smell, which is a normal feature of ageing, can reduce the attractiveness of food. Elderly people may actually complain that food does not taste 'as it used to'. This is more likely to be a reflection of their failing sense of taste, rather than a change in the food itself. Enhancing flavours with herbs and spices can overcome some of these problems. However, it should also be recognized that a zinc deficiency can contribute to loss of taste acuity.

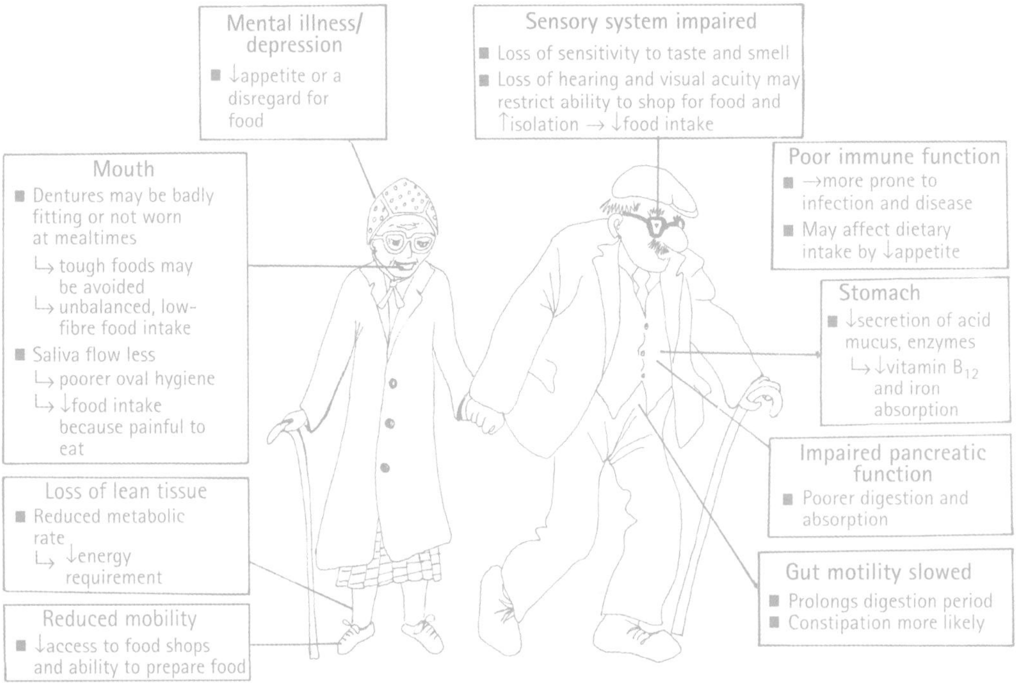

Figure 13.2 Factors resulting in increased risk in older adults.

Gastrointestinal system

The loss of teeth and wearing of dentures should not have a major impact on food intake. It is reported that 57 per cent of the 65–74 age group have none of their own teeth, with 75 per cent of those over 75 similarly affected. Although more elderly people are keeping their teeth for longer, there is still a substantial proportion of this group dependent on dentures. If the dentures are badly fitting, not checked regularly or even not worn at mealtimes because of discomfort, the dietary intake may suffer. Foods that are coarse, tough or require prolonged chewing may be avoided, possibly resulting in unbalanced intakes. Saliva flow is less in an older person, which may result in poorer oral hygiene and associated infections adding to oral discomfort.

There is a reduced secretion of acid, mucus and enzymes in the stomach in old age, and a decrease in pancreatic function. Gut motility is slowed and this may prolong the digestion period to compensate for the poorer enzyme secretions, but a more likely result is constipation. An adequate intake of dietary fibre (NSPs) as well as sufficient fluids is, therefore, desirable. The use of laxatives is to be discouraged, especially those based on mineral oils, which can deplete the body of fat-soluble vitamins. The reduced gastric secretion may produce a lower level of intrinsic factor for vitamin B_{12} absorption, as well as reduced solubilization of iron and its consequent absorption.

Kidney function

The amount of active renal mass declines with age and is on average 30 per cent less at 80 than at 30 years. Consequently, the kidneys may have a poorer ability to concentrate the urine, as well as eliminating waste products more slowly. Therefore, fluid balance will be under less precise control. In addition, thirst mechanisms are less sensitive. Thus, an elderly person runs the risk of dehydration, if fluid intake is not consciously maintained. Sometimes, the added problem of incontinence, or even a reluctance to have to get up in the night to empty the bladder, may discourage an individual from drinking enough. Consequences of dehydration include confusion, dry lips, sunken eyes, increased body temperature, dizziness and low blood pressure. An intake of eight cups (1.5–2 L) of drink per day is recommended.

Lean tissue

There is a progressive loss of lean tissue throughout life, although the actual extent depends on lifestyle factors. On average, 40 per cent of the peak tissue mass may be lost by the age of 70 years. This results in reduced basal metabolism and, consequently, a reduced energy requirement. The loss of lean tissue also results in a loss of strength and this may discourage an elderly person from engaging in even gentle physical activity. Thus, it is clearly important to minimize the loss of lean tissue by maintaining physical activity throughout life. This also maintains appetite and promotes an adequate nutritional intake. There may be little change in total body weight associated with losses of lean tissue because of an increase in the amount of body fat with age. The loss of lean tissue also represents a reduction in both total body water and potassium in the overall composition of the body.

Mobility

It is estimated that over 50 per cent of adults over the age of 65 years suffer from one form of disability and 33 per cent suffer at least one type of severe disability. Arthritis, hypertension, heart disease, hearing and visual impairments, orthopaedic impairments and diabetes are the most frequent problems that pose difficulties for this age group in carrying out daily activities. In addition to these, older adults suffer from progressive bone loss, leading to increased bone fragility and susceptibility to fractures, known as osteoporosis. There is an increased risk of sustaining fractures with age. After the age of 50 years, the lifetime risk of an osteoporotic fracture is 40 per cent for a woman and 14 per cent for a man. Hip fracture has the highest costs in terms of morbidity and mortality. It nearly always necessitates hospital admission, with an average length of stay of 30 days. Only about one-third of these patients regain their former mobility. Deaths within the first 6 months after a hip fracture are approximately 20 per cent. There are many factors that interact to increase susceptibility to osteoporosis that results in a fracture. Genetic factors play a role, and these interact with environmental and dietary factors. Prevention of fracture depends on attention to long-term diet, as well as maintenance of muscle strength and balance in old age to reduce the risk of falling. Supplementation of elderly people with calcium and vitamin D has been effective in reducing fracture risk, and is a well tolerated treatment. The use of drugs that slow bone resorption may also be preventative. It is important for the nutritional well-being of this age group to maintain mobility as long as possible.

The immune system

This becomes less efficient with age, with the result that there is a higher risk of infection. In particular, there are lower levels of T-lymphocytes, as well as an increased production of autoantibodies. A poor nutritional status, in particular, with relation to protein, zinc and vitamin levels, can contribute to poor immune function. This may expose the individual to more minor infections, but also increase the risk of more serious problems, such as pneumonia or wound infections.

The brain and nervous system

Cognitive function may decline with age and this is another factor that hinders independent living. Dementia is the most common cause of cognitive impairment, and is defined as a significant memory impairment and loss of intellectual functions. Increased oxidative stress and an imbalance in antioxidant status may both contribute to the decline in cognitive function. A study in the USA found that plasma levels of vitamin C, E and A, carotenoids and selenium were correlated with memory function among people aged over 60 years (Perkins et al., 1999). The same survey found that 7 per cent of elderly Americans suffered from poor memory. Antioxidants protect the integrity of blood vessels in the brain and, therefore, maintain circulation. This may also be effective in protection against stroke, which is the most common cause of vascular dementia. Other studies have shown that oxidative injury is present in the brains of patients with Alzheimer's disease and may play a role in its development. Various components of brain tissue appear to be affected, including lipids, proteins and DNA, and it is likely that several different antioxidants may be needed to protect the whole range of molecules. In addition, a number of B vitamins especially vitamin B_6, B_{12} and folate may play a role in the development of dementia through their involvement in the metabolism of homocysteine. Elevated levels of homocysteine have been implicated in development of cognitive impairment. Therefore, maintenance of an adequate diet before old age may be protective against some of the degenerative changes in the brain, and in turn facilitate better nutrition in old age.

Other factors

In addition, an elderly person is more vulnerable to many degenerative diseases, which often develop over a considerable number of years. These may include atherosclerosis, arthritis, lung diseases and cancers. All of these may directly affect dietary intake. Drug treatment for the disease may have an effect on appetite, digestion, absorption, excretion or metabolism of nutrients. Patients suffering from a number of chronic conditions may be taking several drugs, which can interact with one another and produce side-effects, such as nausea, diarrhoea, constipation or confusion.

Factors affecting nutritional status

In addition to ageing and its consequences, social and environmental factors may affect the nutritional status of an elderly person.

Inadequate intake

There are many contributory factors influencing a poor food intake. These are summarized in Table 13.4.

Physical/medical factors

- Reduced mobility, from rheumatism, arthritis or as a consequence of a stroke or lung disease, may be sufficiently severe to make the individual housebound or even bedfast.
- Dentition and the state of the mouth play an important part in the food intake.

TABLE 13.4 Factors contributing to poor food intake in the elderly

Physical/medical factors	Social factors	Psychological factors
Mobility	Money available	Depression
Selection of foods bought	Food storage/preparation facilities	Bereavement
Food preparation	Education/knowledge of nutrition	Mental illness
Dentition	Social isolation	Alcoholism
Appetite		
Disease		
Drugs		

- Appetite may be reduced by coexisting disease or by its treatment, for example, disease of the gastrointestinal tract, associated with nausea and vomiting or discomfort after eating, will severely limit appetite.
- Various drugs used in the treatment of a variety of illnesses may also have a depressing effect on the appetite.
- Mental illness and depression are also likely to affect food intake; there may be a complete disregard for eating with a loss of time sense so that mealtimes are ignored.

Social factors

- Availability of money: many of the retired live on a fixed income. They may spend in excess of 30 per cent of their income on food – considerably more than the UK average of 9.5 per cent.
- Lack of education about the importance of nutrition and the existence of out of date beliefs about food may prevent the elderly individual having a healthy diet, and may render them vulnerable to cranky notions that they see in the media.
- Social isolation may be the result of retirement, re-housing, death of friends and relatives, breakdown of the nuclear family or illness. Several studies have shown that food intake was less and nutritional status poorer among those living alone and experiencing isolation. In particular, the widowed and men were more acutely affected than the long-term single and women. Conversely, where an effort was made to share food and eat in company, the food intake was better.

Psychological factors

- Depression, often the result of bereavement, is probably one of the major causes of inadequate food intake in an otherwise healthy person and may persist for many years, resulting in malnutrition.
- Altered mental function, with memory loss and unusual behaviour, may also occur and result in erratic eating. There is an increase in the numbers of people cared for in the community rather than in institutions. It is important that the nutritional needs of these individuals are addressed. Severely demented patients are cared for in nursing homes and hospitals, where food and care are provided. It is still important, however, that nutritional intakes are monitored and checked for adequacy.
- Consumption of large amounts of alcohol may be a coping mechanism for depression or bereavement. The problems associated with excessive drinking may worsen other consequences of ageing.

Less efficient digestion and absorption

Relatively little is known about the effects of ageing on the functioning of the digestive tract. Reduced secretion of stomach acid and pancreatic enzymes may result in poorer digestion and absorption. There may also be minor malabsorption syndromes, associated with a decrease in the intestinal mucosal surface and broader, shorter villi. Absorption may also be reduced as a result of chronic use of laxatives. The extent of these changes in a normal elderly person is, however, unknown.

Altered needs

Many bodily functions become less efficient with ageing.

- There is decreased nutrient uptake by cells, so that an apparently adequate intake for a younger person may not produce the same levels in the cells in an elderly person.
- Energy needs decrease with ageing because of the reduction in basal metabolic rate consequent on reduction in lean tissue mass as well as reduced activity. The latter is a cultural phenomenon and attempts are being made to change perceptions about the importance of physical activity in older people. In many societies, people remain active to a very old age, yet in Britain activity levels are generally very low in this age group. A reasonable level of activity will ensure adequate energy intake to cover the expenditure and incidentally provide sufficient other nutrients in the diet to meet requirements. Conversely, a low activity level may result in such low intakes of energy that basic nutritional requirements cannot be met. Thus, there is an important nutritional argument for maintaining activity levels. In addition, activity will help to promote cardiovascular fitness and maintain muscle mass.
- Protein needs may be higher as protein synthesis, turnover and breakdown all decrease with advancing age. Homeostatic mechanisms regulating protein levels in the body may be less efficient in elderly people. In addition, ill health, trauma and disease states may upset the equilibrium. Insufficient energy intake may also compromise protein balance, as protein will be used to meet energy needs.
- The presence of disease and its treatment by drugs may affect nutritional needs and the effects may be exacerbated by drug interactions. Further problems may arise in a confused patient who fails to take drugs at prescribed times. Up to 60 per cent of drugs taken by the elderly are obtained without prescription. One of the commonest is aspirin, which interferes with the absorption of vitamin C and may cause bleeding along the gut. It may thus cause a vitamin C deficiency or anaemia. Laxatives are also frequently obtained without prescription and can deplete the body of potassium, causing depression and affecting cardiac function.

What is the nutritional state of older adults?

A major survey of diet and nutrition in people aged over 65 was carried out in Britain between 1994–95 as part of the National Diet and Nutrition Survey programme. The results were published in 1998 (Finch et al., 1998). The study covered free-living individuals as well as a sample living in institutions. Some of the main findings are summarized.

- The foods and drinks consumed by the largest proportion of the sample were: tea (95 per cent), potatoes (87 per cent), white bread (74 per cent) and biscuits (71 per cent). Whole grain breakfast cereals were eaten by 50 per cent of the sample, and the most commonly used type of milk was full fat. Butter was the most popular fat used. The most commonly consumed meats were ham and bacon, followed by beef, veal and meat dishes. Fish was eaten by 36 per cent of the sample. Cooked vegetables were consumed by up to 66 per cent of the group. Less than half the group ate fruit. Sugar was used by 55 per cent of the sample. Alcoholic beverages were consumed by fewer than 20 per cent of the sample. In general, these findings suggest a dietary pattern that is quite traditional and shows relatively low uptake of foods such as semi-skimmed or skimmed milk, low-fat or polyunsaturated spreads, or salads. The eating pattern of the older subjects and those living in institutions was even more traditional.
- More people are retaining their teeth into old age than was the case in the past. The state of dentition has an impact on the foods chosen, and limits intakes of fruit and uncooked vegetables. The quality of the diet was strongly related to the oral health of the subjects, with higher nutrient intakes in those subjects with some natural teeth. The difference in nutrient intake with dental state was not significant in the group in

institutions. However, these subjects had more dental plaque and caries, and consumed more sugar than the free-living subjects.

- Energy intakes were generally below the estimated average requirements (EAR) and were 15 per cent less than recorded in the previous survey, 25 years ago. However, more of the subjects were overweight (65 per cent of free-living sample) than previously and it is assumed that energy intakes were adequate for needs. More people in institutions (16 per cent) than in the community (4.5 per cent) were underweight. In general, energy intakes decreased with age in men but not in women.
- Proportions of macronutrients in the diet were in line with intakes across the adult population and did not comply with dietary guidelines. Intakes of NSP did not meet the dietary reference value (DRV), and there was a positive correlation between NSP intake and number of bowel movements.
- Average intakes for minerals and vitamins exceeded the reference nutrient intake (RNI). However, in both groups, there were numbers of individuals in whom the intakes fell below the LRNI. In general, subjects in institutions were less likely to have such low intakes. This could be linked to the use of milk and fortified foods in the menus. The findings are summarized in Table 13.5.
- Intakes of sodium and chloride were above the RNI in both groups of subjects. In the free-living group, systolic blood pressure levels were positively associated with urinary sodium/potassium ratio.
- In those subjects whose intake of non-milk extrinsic sugars (NMES) was within the normal population range of 8–15 per cent of total energy, there was no evidence that micronutrient intakes were compromised. Micronutrient intakes were however marginally lower at NMES intakes outside this range. In general, micronutrient intakes reflected energy intake.
- Biochemical assessments showed suboptimal indices for a number of nutrients. These are indicated in Table 13.6.
- Subjects from the community who were in manual social groups had lower average intakes of nutrients per unit of energy, but higher intakes of sodium.
- Lower intakes of energy were seen in both men and women who lived alone, compared to those who lived with others. In men living alone, this also resulted in lower intakes per unit energy of some nutrients. This was not the case in women.

Overall, these findings demonstrate that the diet of older adults in Britain is largely comparable to that of younger adults. However, dietary choice may be affected by factors such as social class, household composition and dentition, as well as state of health and age. Changes in dietary intake will lead to poorer indices of nutrients and

TABLE 13.5 Percentages of elderly subjects with nutrient intakes from food sources below the LRNI (data adapted from Finch et al., 1998)

Nutrient	Free-living subjects (average for men and women)	Subjects in institutions (average for men and women)
Vitamin A	4.5	1
Thiamin, niacin, vitamin B_{12}	<1	<1
Folate, vitamin B_6	4	5 (folate), <2 (B_6)
Riboflavin	7	3
Vitamin C	2	<1
Iron	3.5	5.5
Calcium	7	0.75
Phosphorus	22	30
Potassium	28	65
Zinc	6.5	8.5

TABLE 13.6 Prevalence of suboptimal indices for nutrients in elderly subjects (adapted from Finch et al., 1998)

	% in institution	% in free-living
Folate	40	15
Vitamin C	40	15
Riboflavin	40	40
Thiamin	10–15	10–15
Vitamin D	37	8
Zinc	7–15	2
Iron (low haemoglobin)		
Men	52	11
Women	39	9

may lead to poorer health. Institutional care can help to maintain nutrient intakes.

What are the nutritional requirements for the elderly?

There is still a lack of reliable data about the specific nutritional needs of elderly people and research is needed. In part, this is related to the heterogeneity of the group, which makes generalized recommendations difficult. In practice, most recommendations for nutrients are extrapolated from those for younger adults and, as such, may be inappropriate.

The principal guidelines for a healthy diet apply equally in those past retirement age. In many ways, it becomes even more important that nutrient-dense foods are eaten, since a smaller food intake increases the risk of nutrient needs not being met.

It should also be remembered that dietary reference values (DoH, 1991) and comparable figures published in other countries apply to healthy individuals. It may be that the presence of disease in certain older people may alter their nutritional needs. Therefore, it can be concluded that nutritional requirements are probably similar in the elderly to those in younger adults, but individual differences may occur, owing to particular circumstances. These may include health problems, decreased physical capacity, presence of drug–nutrient interactions, possible depression and economic constraints.

Advice about diet to people who have retired could include the following:

- enjoy food;
- follow basic healthy eating guidelines relating to fat, fibre, salt and sugar by using the Balance of Good Health (FSA, 2001);
- recognize that snacks can be an important part of the diet;
- make sure that fluid intakes are adequate;
- keep some food stocks in the house for emergencies;
- try to spend some time outdoors, especially in the spring and summer;
- if alone, try to arrange to share meals with friends/neighbours;
- ask for help with shopping when necessary;
- try to keep active;
- remember that food provides warmth.

In planning diets for an elderly person, particular attention should be paid to nutrients that have been identified as being 'at risk' in studies of this age group. These include: vitamin D, vitamin E, thiamin, pyridoxine, folate, vitamin C and vitamin B_{12}, as well as iron, zinc and calcium. Energy and protein intakes must be adequate to allow protein to be used for wound healing and tissue repair rather than for energy needs. In patients receiving diuretic therapy, potassium or magnesium levels may be at risk. A diet containing a variety of foods fitting in with the Balance of Good Health, a sufficient intake of fluids and a moderate activity level will ensure good nutritional status in an elderly person.

It should be recognized, however, that probably the most common nutritional disorder among the elderly in Western society is obesity. As at any other age, this is multifactorial in origin and is detrimental to health. If the overweight is very longstanding, the likelihood of successful, significant weight loss in an elderly person is small. Nonetheless, in cases of diabetes, hypertension and arthritis, weight loss is desirable and should be actively encouraged.

The most vulnerable elderly people are those who are ill and frail. It is necessary to identify those at risk as rapidly and efficiently as possible, before they enter a spiral of deficiency and inadequate intake, leading to further deficiency. Ten major risk factors have been identified:

- depression/loneliness;
- fewer than eight protein-containing meals/week;
- long periods without food;
- little milk drunk;
- high level of food wastage;
- disease/disability;
- low income;
- inability to shop;
- sudden weight change;
- fruit and vegetables rarely in the diet.

The presence of several of these factors points to increased nutritional vulnerability and the need for intervention.

Community services available for the elderly in the UK include the provision of luncheon clubs and day centres for those who are reasonably mobile, and 'meals on wheels' and home helps for those elderly who cannot get out, or are incapable of fully looking after themselves. They provide social contact as well as helping the nutritional status.

Approximately 5 per cent of the elderly in Britain are in institutions, including hospitals and residential or nursing homes. These are the most vulnerable subgroup, since it is largely because they are ill, infirm and incapable of caring for themselves that they live in these settings. The diet provided by the institution may be nutritionally incomplete, particularly with respect to vitamins C and D, although other nutrients have also been shown to be low. There may be problems for the individual with appetite, eating and swallowing. Many disease processes may make an adequate nutritional status difficult to achieve, or assess. However, every effort should be made to ensure that the elderly in institutions are properly fed. National Care Standards, including nutritional standards, were introduced in 2002 in the UK.

Finally, it should be remembered that, although some of the retired population do encounter nutritional problems, the great majority live a reasonably healthy life and succeed in caring adequately for themselves. A positive outlook and a continued interest in life are important prerequisities. When interest in food wanes, a decline in health will surely follow.

SUMMARY

1. The principles of the balanced diet apply to all adults; however, particular emphasis may be needed on some aspects rather than others in certain situations.
2. Men may have less access to information and be less prepared to make changes for a variety of reasons.
3. For women, nutritional needs differ at stages of the life cycle. Pressures from society, demands of pregnancy and their own health may provide conflicting messages about how to interpret the dietary guidelines.
4. Ethnic minority group members may have a traditional diet that is healthy but, by becoming Westernized, there is a reduction in nutritional quality of the diet.
5. A vegetarian diet can be a positive contributor to health but may lack some nutrients if not well planned.
6. Low income may be a major barrier to consuming a healthy diet.
7. A nutrient-dense diet is important with increasing age, as nutritional needs remain high but appetite decreases. Maintaining physical activity can help to promote appetite.

STUDY QUESTIONS

1. a The female body can experience several major biological changes during the life cycle. In what ways might these affect the dietary advice given to women?
   b Do you believe that dietary advice given to men should vary with their life stage?
2. a What are the main threats to health affecting members of the Asian community in the UK?
   b What changes to diet and/or lifestyle could be of benefit?
3. For what reasons does living on a low income pose a threat to eating healthily and/or having a healthy lifestyle?
4. Prepare a leaflet designed for those who care for the elderly, summarizing the main principles of eating healthily at this age.
5. a Discuss with a group of fellow students, or your tutor, some of the reasons why people generally appear to have difficulty achieving the dietary goals. What sources might you use to check how well goals are being achieved to help you in this discussion?
   b Identify ways in which meeting goals could be made easier.
   c Who might need to be involved in b above?

REFERENCES AND FURTHER READING

Appleby, P.N., Key, T.J., Thorogood, M. et al. 2002: Mortality in British vegetarians. *Public Health Nutrition* 5(1), 29–36.

British Nutrition Foundation 1995: *Vegetarianism, a briefing paper.* London: British Nutrition Foundation.

Buttriss, J., Hyman, K. 1995: *Focus on women: nutrition and health. Proceedings of a conference.* London: National Dairy Council.

Davies, L., Knutson, C.K. 1991: Warning signals for malnutrition in the elderly. *Journal of the American Dietetic Association* 91, 1413–17.

DEFRA 2001: *National Food Survey 2000 Annual report on food expenditure, consumption and nutrient intakes.* London: The Stationery Office.

DoH (UK Department of Health) 1991: *Dietary reference values for food energy and nutrients for the United Kingdom.* Report on Health and Social Subjects No. 41. Report of the Panel on Dietary Reference Values of the Committee on Medical Aspects of Food Policy. London: HMSO.

DoH (UK Department of Health) 1996: *Low income, food, nutrition and health: strategies for improvement.* A Report by the Low Income Project Team for the Nutrition Task Force. Wetherby: Department of Health.

DoH (UK Department of Health) 2001: *Health survey for England. The health of minority ethnic groups.* London: The Stationery Office.

Dowler, E., Calvert, C. 1995: *Nutrition and diet in lone-parent families in London.* London: Family Policies Study Centre.

Dowler, E.S., Turner, S., Dobson, B. 2001: *Poverty bites; food health and poor families.* London: Child Poverty Action Group.

Finch, S., Doyle, W., Lowe, C. 1998: *National Diet and Nutrition Survey: people aged 65 years and older.* Volume 1. Report of the diet and nutrition survey. London: The Stationery Office.

Food Standards Agency 2001: *The balance of good health.* London: FSA.

Food Standards Agency 2002a: *Food portion sizes*, 3rd edn. London: The Stationery Office.

Food Standards Agency 2002b: *McCance & Widdowson's The composition of foods*, 6th summary edn. Cambridge: Royal Society of Chemistry.

Gonzalez-Gross, M., Marcos, A., Pietrzik, K. 2001: Nutrition and cognitive impairment in the elderly. *British Journal of Nutrition* 86, 313–21.

Grundman, M., Delaney, P. 2002: Antioxidant strategies for Alzheimer's disease. *Proceedings of the Nutrition Society* 61, 191–202.

Hamlyn, B., Brooker, S. Oleinikova, K. et al. 2002: *Infant feeding 2000*. London: The Stationery Office.

Hill, S.E. 1990: *More than rice and peas. Guidelines to improve food provision for black and ethnic minorities in Britain*. London: Food Commission.

Key, T.J., Fraser, G.E., Thorogood, M. et al. 1998: Mortality in vegetarians and non-vegetarians: a collaborative analysis of 8300 deaths among 76000 men and women in 5 prospective studies. *Public Health Nutrition* 1, 33–41.

Leather, S. 1992: Less money, less choice: poverty and diet in the UK today. In *National Consumer Council, Your food: Whose choice?* London: HMSO, 72–94.

National Food Alliance 1994: *Food and low income: a practical guide for advisers and supporters working with families and young people on low incomes*. London: National Food Alliance.

Nutrition Society 1995: Nutrition for the elderly (Symposium). *Proceedings of the Nutrition Society* 54(3), 617–99.

Perkins, A., Hendrie, H.C., Callahan, C.M. et al. 1999: Association of antioxidants with memory in a multiethnic elderly sample using the Third National Health and Nutrition Examination Survey. *American Journal of Epidemiology* 150, 37–44.

Ritz, P. 2001: Factors affecting energy and macronutrient requirements in elderly people. *Public Health Nutrition* 4(2B), 563–8.

Schofield, C., Stewart, J., Wheeler, E. 1989: Dietary variety during and after pregnancy in Scotland and England. *Journal of Human Nutrition and Dietetics* 2, 7–18.

Sellen, D.W., Tedstone, A.E., Frize, J. 2002: Food insecurity among refugee families in East London: results of a pilot assessment. *Public Health Nutrition* 5(5), 637–44.

Sharma, S., Cruickshank, J.K. 2001: Cultural differences in assessing dietary intake and providing relevant dietary information to British African-Caribbean populations. *Journal of Human Nutrition and Dietetics* 14, 449–56.

Van Staveren, W.A., de Groot, L.C., Burema, L. et al. 1995: Energy balance and health in SENECA participants. *Proceedings of the Nutrition Society* 54(3), 617–29.

Williams, B. 1995: Westernised Asians and cardiovascular disease: nature or nurture? *Lancet* 345, 401–2.

14 DIET AND CORONARY HEART DISEASE

The aims of this chapter are to:

- ❑ define what is meant by coronary heart disease and describe its development;
- ❑ describe the lipid hypothesis for heart disease aetiology;
- ❑ study some of the ways in which evidence about heart disease causation has been collected;
- ❑ identify some of the suggested risk factors;
- ❑ describe the suggested role of dietary factors in the development and prevention of heart disease.

On completing the study of this chapter, you should be able to:

- ❑ explain the physiological processes involved in the development of heart disease;
- ❑ discuss the origins of the lipid hypothesis of heart disease;
- ❑ describe some of the other dietary factors that play a part in heart disease aetiology;
- ❑ explain the suggested interaction of antioxidant nutrients as protective factors;
- ❑ propose and explain dietary advice for the prevention of coronary heart disease.

Coronary heart disease, together with other diseases of the circulatory system, is one of the major causes of death in the Western world. Worldwide mortality due to coronary heart disease and stroke accounts for approximately 20 per cent of all deaths, and numbers are increasing as the world population becomes relatively older. Throughout Europe, cardiovascular disease accounts for about 40 per cent of overall mortality, the majority of these deaths are attributable to coronary heart disease, most of the remainder to stroke. Across Europe there is an East–West gradient, with higher mortality rates in central and Eastern Europe than in Western Europe. The differential between the highest and lowest mortality approaches a factor of 5. There are also higher rates of coronary heart disease, but not stroke, in Northern Europe than in the South, and the variation between North and South is approximately 2.5.

Death rates from coronary heart disease vary between the countries of the UK. The rates are highest in northern parts of England, Scotland and Northern Ireland, and lowest in the southeast and London. Heart disease rates among women in the UK are some of the highest in the world. In Scotland, the rate amongst women aged 35–74 is ten times greater than that in Japanese women.

People born in the Indian subcontinent living in the UK have heart disease rates 36 per cent higher than those in the population as a whole. Those in people originating from the Caribbean countries are lower than in the population as a whole, by 55 per cent in males and 24 per cent in females.

In the UK, the age-standardized death rate of people under 65 from circulatory diseases was 70 per 100 000 of the population in 1995. In France, which has the lowest rate in Europe, the death rate at the same time was 36 per 100 000. In 2001, there were 120 891 deaths in the UK from coronary heart disease alone. All of the circulatory diseases taken together account for 41 per cent of mortality in England. In addition, angina and other circulatory disorders, some resulting in stroke, are leading causes of ill health and disability.

CHANGES IN RATES OF CARDIOVASCULAR DISEASE

Most Western European countries, including the UK, have experienced a downward trend in heart disease rates since the 1980s and early 1990s. The most encouraging trends have been among the younger age groups. Rates have fallen by 40 per cent in the under 65s in the last decade. However, in the countries of Eastern Europe, such as Hungary, Poland and Romania, rates increased.

In the USA, Australia, New Zealand and Japan, rates have shown a dramatic reduction in the last 15–20 years, but the causes are unclear. The White Paper, Saving Lives – Our Healthier Nation (DoH, 1999) has set the target in the UK to reduce deaths from circulatory diseases by 40 per cent by 2010. This is estimated potentially to save 200 000 lives over this period.

Traditionally, coronary heart disease has been viewed as a disease of men because, in middle age, mortality is higher in men. However, after the menopause, women become increasingly susceptible to the disease and death rates of the two sexes are similar. Since women generally live longer than men, many more suffer from heart disease in old age. As a result of this perception, much of the early research has been focused on the disease in men, and both research and treatment in women has lagged behind. More recent studies have included women among the subjects.

There are many changes that occur in diet and environmental influences that make it very difficult to pinpoint those having the major effects. Positive factors may include health education that affects, for example, the intake of fats, fruit and vegetables and increases physical activity. On the other hand, negative factors may include the societal shift in dietary intake to more 'fast food', as well as political changes (such as in Eastern Europe during the 1990s), which cause stress, and increase alcohol intake and smoking rates.

Projections for the future indicate that prevalence of cardiovascular disease will continue to rise, despite some encouraging trends. This is attributable to the better treatment and survival after heart attack, albeit with increased morbidity. A further reason is the age profile of most populations, with an increase in the proportion of older people, who are at increased risk of these diseases.

This chapter will focus on coronary heart disease, as this is the major manifestation of cardiovascular disease in Western Europe. In addition, much more of the research in this area has been on the dietary determinants of coronary heart disease, rather than stroke.

WHAT IS CORONARY HEART DISEASE?

A heart attack (myocardial infarction) can result in sudden death. It occurs when the blood and hence oxygen supply to a part of the heart fails, because of a blockage in the vessels supplying the muscular walls of the heart. This makes the heart unable to continue working normally to supply blood to all the parts of the body and, most crucially, to the brain. If a large part of the muscle is deprived of oxygen, the heart attack may be fatal. Failure of a smaller part of the heart muscle may allow the rest of the heart to continue working and maintain the circulation.

These events are, however, the culmination of a process that may have been developing gradually over a long period of time, involving a series of changes to the walls of the coronary arteries. The process may be described in terms of atherogenesis and thrombogenesis (see Figure 14.1).

Injury to the coronary arteries

The blood vessel walls are continually exposed to wear and tear by the flow of blood. The wall is not completely smooth, especially where there are divisions of the vessels into smaller channels and associated branching. Blood flow becomes turbulent here, rather like the flow of a river where streams are joining or there is some obstruction to the flow.

Prolonged raised blood pressure will also increase stress on the walls. As a result, the wall of the vessel is continually repairing itself in response to the damage, using the blood platelets

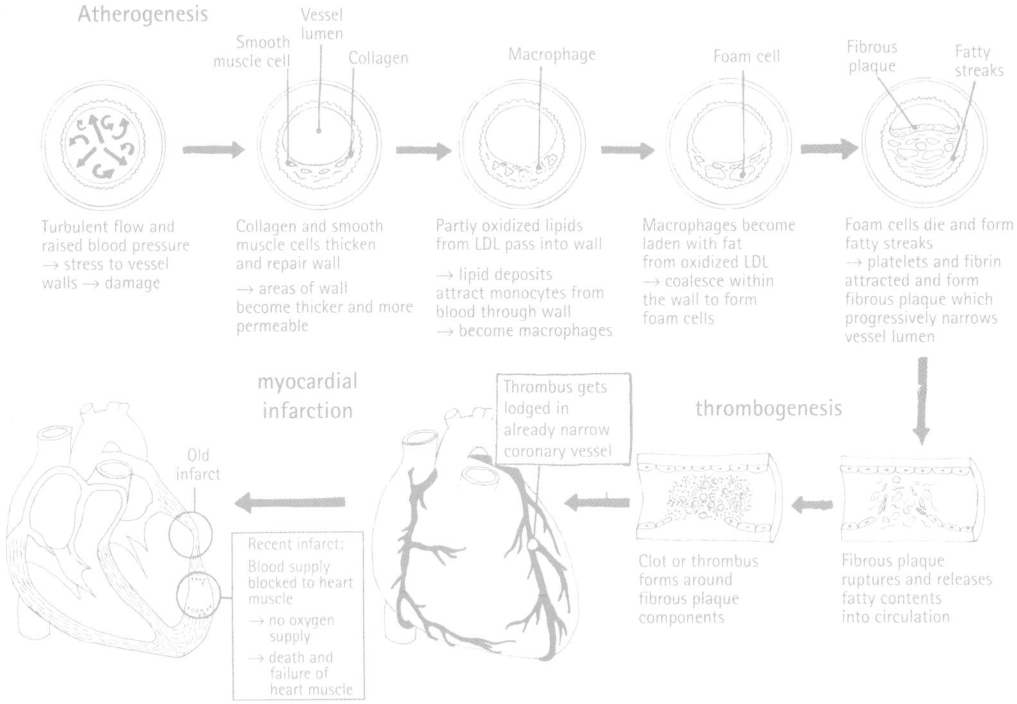

Figure 14.1 The development of coronary heart disease. LDL, low-density lipoprotein.

and forming minute blood clots. New collagen and smooth muscle cells may be laid down to strengthen the wall. Over a long period of time, these areas may become thicker and, since they are no longer perfect, become more permeable to substances and particles in the blood. Many factors contribute to the normal functioning of the endothelial surface of the blood vessel, including relaxing factors and growth factors, and these are considered to be important in maintaining functional integrity.

Fibrous plaque formation

The progression from the previous stage is not completely clear. It is normal for blood vessel walls to be permeable to substances required by the tissues, such as lipid-soluble material needed for metabolic processes. It is now believed that partly oxidized lipids present in low-density lipoprotein (LDL) entering the blood vessel wall are recognized as 'foreign' and are not allowed to pass through the endothelium of the blood vessel. Their presence attracts monocytes (a type of white blood cell), which adhere to and then enter the blood vessel wall. Various factors are now known to influence the adhesion of the monocytes, including nitric oxide (endothelial relaxing factor) and antioxidants (particularly vitamin E).

Having penetrated the blood vessel wall, the monocytes are converted to macrophages, which are scavenger cells whose purpose is to destroy the damaged lipids. However, the macrophage itself then cannot leave the wall and so these scavenger cells accumulate, laden with fat, and gradually coalesce to produce 'foam cells'. When these die, the fat they contain remains in the wall and becomes the origin of the fatty streaks that are believed to be a contributing factor in the atherogenesis of the heart disease process.

The fatty streaks also attract blood platelets and fibrin, which attempt to 'seal off' the damaged area. In the process, these clot-forming entities actually contribute to thickening, producing a fibrous plaque and ultimately hardening the blood vessel wall. Smooth muscle cells are laid down under the influence of growth factors, derived from platelets and other blood components. The plaque area grows, protruding progressively into the lumen of the vessel and further interfering with the blood flow.

Thrombosis and heart attack

Eventually the fibrous plaque becomes unstable and ruptures, releasing fatty contents into the circulation. These attract components of the clotting mechanism and a thrombus (or clot) is likely to form. If the blood vessel is already narrow at this point, the clot may block the flow of blood. The fibrous plaque components themselves may also become lodged in the vessel. Both of these processes will cause a myocardial infarction, if the blockage is in a coronary blood vessel. When the narrowing and thrombosis occur in a blood vessel supplying the brain, a stroke (or cerebrovascular accident) will be the result.

Various physiological and dietary factors are involved in the processes described above. An understanding of these is emerging from the many studies of coronary heart disease and its associated risk factors. The developments in molecular biology have added a new dimension to these studies, so that mechanisms that were originally only suggested as a possibility are now being described in detail at the molecular level. As more information becomes available, it clarifies some aspects but it also demonstrates that the picture is highly complex.

STUDYING CORONARY HEART DISEASE

The study of coronary heart disease is hampered by the absence of a close animal model for myocardial infarction, although aspects of the disease process can be mimicked in various animals. However, to obtain the most relevant data, studies are performed on human populations and, for ethical reasons, are limited in the scope of experimental work that can be done. Much of the research is, therefore, based on epidemiological data obtained from populations with high and low rates of heart disease, and attempts to associate these with diet and lifestyle characteristics. A number of approaches have been used. Dietary lipids have been the main focus of attention because of the lipid nature of the fibrous plaque contributing to the narrowing of the blood vessels.

Origins of the lipid hypothesis

Cross-community comparisons

The most widely known of the early studies is Keys' Seven Country Study, which compared fat intakes and serum cholesterol levels with subsequent 10-year coronary heart disease incidence in men aged 40–59 from seven countries (Keys, 1970). The strongest correlation was found between the percentage of energy derived from saturated fat in the diet and increased risk of heart disease. These results were compared more recently in a 25-year follow up of the subjects. In communities with a high incidence of heart disease, the intake of saturated fatty acids typically ranges between 15 and 25 per cent of the energy intake. At the extremes, saturated fat intakes in East Finland are 22 per cent and in Crete are 8 per cent of the energy. The corresponding rates of coronary heart disease are 1074 and 26 per 10 000 (age standardized rate), respectively. There was also a weaker, negative correlation between intake of polyunsaturated fats and heart disease.

Although these relationships could be seen across different population groups, with varying diets and cultures, they are more difficult to find in comparisons of individuals within one country. Nevertheless, it has been possible to produce an equation that predicts the change in serum cholesterol, given changes in the dietary intake of saturated and polyunsaturated fats. Two such equations have been produced by Keys and Hegsted. The Keys formula shows that saturated fatty acids (excluding stearic acid, C18) raise plasma cholesterol levels by twice as much as polyunsaturated fatty acids can lower it. This may not always be exactly so predictable for any one individual because of other behavioural or genetic factors. However, the ratio of polyunsaturated (P) fatty acids to saturated (S) fatty acids is a useful means of expressing the desirable proportion in the diet. Where the ratio is low ($P/S = 0.2$), the population generally has a high blood cholesterol level and a high risk of coronary heart disease. Increasing the P/S ratio to 0.5–0.8 has been considered a desirable goal, as heart disease rates are lower in populations where the normal diet approaches these proportions.

This basic premise is the first principle of the lipid hypothesis and is widely accepted. The corollary and the second principle, that both risk and mortality from heart disease can be reduced by lowering cholesterol, is still debated. Views have become polarized and the lack of consensus has been widely publicized in the media, with resulting confusion for both health professionals and the general population.

Prospective studies

These involve studying a cohort of individuals over a number of years and measuring those parameters that are believed to be related to heart disease. Over time, some individuals will develop the disease; it is assumed that they share particular characteristics, not seen in the unaffected members of the population. One of the best known of these studies is that in Framingham, Massachusetts, where a cohort of over 5000 individuals were first recruited in 1948. Data regarding their cardiovascular health and many possible causal factors have been systematically collected, using standardized methods of measurement. Data from the Framingham study have shown that raised serum cholesterol, high blood pressure and cigarette smoking are three major contributory risk factors in heart disease. The study also showed the comparative level of risk with increasing serum cholesterol levels. As newer risk factors are discovered, the data from Framingham can be reviewed to investigate other relationships. A newer data set is information from a sample of over 100 000 female nurses in the USA, from whom medical and dietary information has been collected, and who are being followed up prospectively. A review of ten within-population studies (Caggiula and Mustad, 1997), showed a positive significant relationship between intakes of saturated fat and coronary heart disease.

Intervention studies

The second principle of the lipid hypothesis suggests that, if a raised serum cholesterol level is associated with an increased risk of heart disease, then lowering it should reduce the risk. Many trials have attempted to demonstrate this by using advice, dietary manipulation, lifestyle changes or drug intervention either separately or in varying combinations.

In some studies, those with no pre-existing evidence of heart disease have been targeted (primary prevention). The main drawbacks of this approach are the size of the subject group needed to demonstrate any benefits and the difficulty of evaluation.

Some community projects have been successful, most notably the North Karelia project in Finland, where a programme of health education was targeted at the whole community, aimed at reducing the very high incidence of heart disease. Evaluation has found measurable improvements in the average values for key parameters, most notably a 13 per cent decrease in serum cholesterol. This was attributed to changes from butter to vegetable oil margarines, from whole fat to low-fat milk and from boiled to filtered coffee. In addition, blood pressure fell as a result of reduced salt intakes, and an increase in fruit and vegetable intake. Overall, coronary heart disease mortality declined by 55 per cent in men and 69 per cent in women. These results imply that some individuals have achieved substantial changes. However, such large projects can also have very disappointing results. For example, the World Health Organisation (WHO) Collaborative study, targeting factory workers in several European countries, achieved some reduction in heart disease mortality in Belgium and Italy, but not in the UK.

More specifically, focused trials recruiting those at high risk of heart disease have had mixed results. The Multiple Risk Factor Intervention Trial (MR FIT) found that both the study and control groups showed an improvement in mortality rates. This demonstrated the difficulty of human studies, where diet is not a constant variable. Figure 14.2 shows the relationship between plasma cholesterol and heart disease from this study.

A review by Truswell (1994) of 14 studies from the 1960s and 1970s, in which saturated fatty acids were exchanged with polyunsaturated fatty acids, found that the average cholesterol level was lowered by 10 per cent. This was

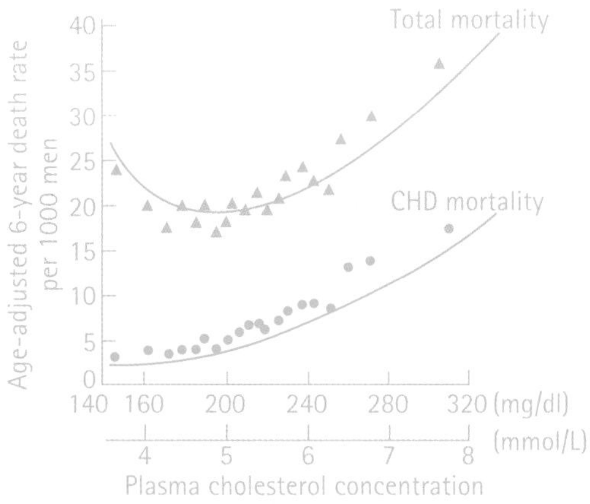

Figure 14.2 The increase in risk with increases in serum cholesterol levels. CHD, coronary heart disease. (From Martin et al., © 1986 The Lancet Ltd 1986. Reproduced with kind permission.)

associated with a 13 per cent reduction in coronary events and a 6 per cent reduction in mortality. Where cholesterol reduction was more than average, there was an even greater decrease in coronary events and mortality.

Trials using cholesterol-lowering drugs (e.g. Helsinki Heart Study, Lipid Research Clinic Trial) have also demonstrated that it is possible to reduce heart disease mortality. However, both of the trials mentioned also found an increase in non-cardiovascular mortality in the study group. Findings of this nature led to concern about the safety of cholesterol lowering in subjects who have not experienced heart disease. The Scandinavian Simvastatin Survival Study (1994) achieved a 25 per cent reduction in plasma cholesterol and 42 per cent fewer coronary deaths, and no excess mortality in the treated group.

Secondary prevention targets those who already possess signs or symptoms of heart disease, or who have suffered a heart attack. In recent years, interventions have introduced other dietary manipulations as the lipid hypothesis has become more sophisticated. Some of these studies have achieved excellent results. The DART study (Burr et al., 1989) showed that advice to eat fatty fish resulted in a reduction of 29 per cent in mortality within 2 years; this was not seen in a group advised about fat intakes or about cereal fibre intake. The Lyon Diet Heart Study (De Lorgeril et al., 1994) increased the levels of alpha-linolenic acid as part of the dietary intervention, and achieved a 70 per cent reduction in mortality and 73 per cent fewer non-fatal coronary events. Addition of long-chain *n*-3 fatty acids to the diet, resulted in a 20 per cent reduction in coronary heart disease mortality (GISSI Prevenzione Investigators, 1999).

It is clear that the lipid hypothesis does not fully explain all the causes of coronary heart disease. In particular:

- the saturated/polyunsaturated fat relationship is an oversimplification of the link between diet and heart disease;
- some of the saturated fatty acids have more potent effects than others;
- the role of different polyunsaturated fatty acids in the atherosclerosis process is determined by the position of the first double bond in the chain and hence the fatty acid family;
- further evidence suggests that monounsaturated fatty acids are important in determining development of coronary heart disease;
- the *trans* fatty acids that are found in the diet may also have a role.

We shall return to these issues later in the chapter.

RISK FACTORS

Coronary heart disease is a multifactorial condition, determined by the interaction of different combinations of factors, known as risk factors. Many of these have now been identified. A risk factor does not necessarily cause the disease nor does its presence mean that an individual will definitely develop heart disease. They can, however, help to explain cross-cultural and inter-individual differences. Although the factors are modulated by individual susceptibility, the presence of several factors in any one individual does suggest that there is a greater chance of developing disease. In addition, there are synergistic effects between the risk factors. For example, the calculated risk from smoking is much greater in an individual who also has raised blood cholesterol levels than in one whose levels are in the normal range. Adding the extra risk factor of raised blood pressure further elevates the risk by an amount greater than that seen for hypertension alone. This is illustrated in Figure 14.3.

It should also be remembered that the development of heart disease is a process and that risk factors may be involved at different stages. Therefore, some may contribute to the laying down of fatty deposits in the blood vessels, and others influence the formation of a thrombosis or determine the response of the heart muscle to a lack of oxygen supply.

The main risk factors associated with heart disease are shown in Figure 14.4. Some of the factors are believed to increase risk and others to reduce risk. Therefore, any high risk factors can be ameliorated by enhancing those that reduce the risk.

Genetic predisposition

This may be associated with increased risk. Often those who develop heart disease have a strong family history of the disease. It has even been suggested that any advice to reduce heart disease risk should only be targeted at those with a family history, as this will account for most of the new cases. Equally, it should be remembered that there may be a genetic predisposition to not develop heart disease.

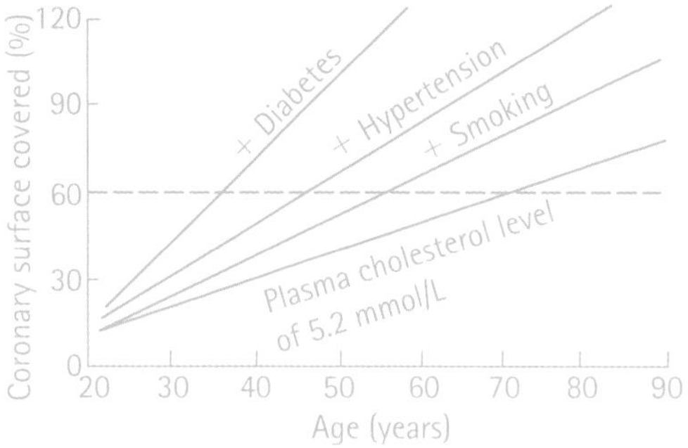

Figure 14.3 Additive effects of risk factors on damage to coronary arteries. (From Grundy, 1988. Copyright 1988, American Medical Association. All rights reserved.)

Age

It was stated earlier in this chapter that the risk of heart disease increases with age in both men and women. Morbidity statistics show the peak age in men to be 55–64 and in women 75–84. This implies that the disease develops over a period of time, which is in line with the proposed mechanisms described earlier. In women, there is a relative protection against the disease during the reproductive years and an increase in incidence after the menopause. This also accounts for the gender differences in risk in middle age, with a higher risk seen in men than women before the ages of 50–55.

Social class

Contrary to the common perception, it is not the 'stressed businessman' who is most likely to develop heart disease. The highest incidence of the disease is in the lowest social class and shows an inverse class gradient. Standardized mortality ratios for England and Wales show

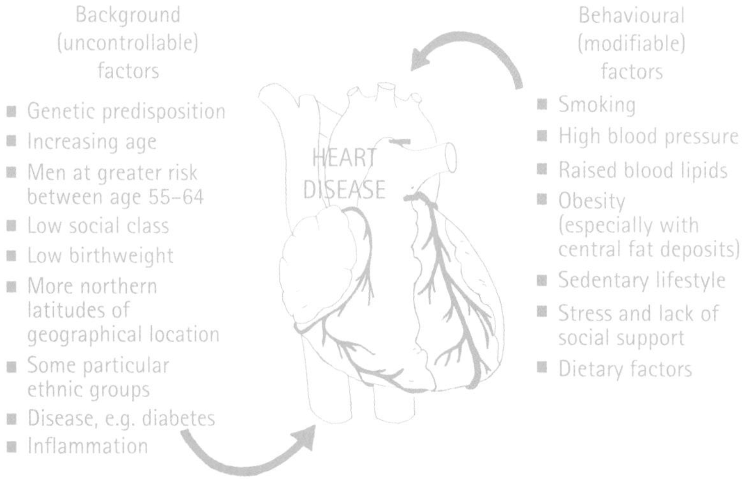

Figure 14.4 Main risk factors in the development of coronary heart disease.

Figure 14.5 Social class and gender differences in heart disease mortality. SMR, standardized mortality ratio; it compares the true mortality of population with the experience that would have been expected if it had a standard mortality rate. An SMR in excess of 100 indicates mortality rates higher than expected in a standard population. (From DoH, 1994. Crown Copyright is reproduced with the permission of the Controller of Her Majesty's Stationery Office.)

this quite clearly for both genders. Furthermore, improvements in heart disease rates have been largest in the professional classes, so that the gap between these and the unskilled groups is widening (Figure 14.5). There is also a difference in height between social classes in the UK, those in the higher social classes being taller. This results in an inverse relationship between heart disease and height.

Birthweight

Individuals who were born small for gestational age have been shown in a number of studies to have a higher risk of coronary heart disease. In addition, there is an increased risk of many of the risk factors, such as hypertension, raised cholesterol levels and higher levels of the blood clotting factors. Those individuals who were thin at birth, with less well-developed skeletal muscle are also at risk of glucose intolerance, which may result in Type 2 diabetes in adult life. This in its turn may also result in a higher risk of coronary heart disease, as it is associated with some of the other factors mentioned above. The risk seems to be greatest in those people who become overweight as adults having been small infants. Maintenance of a normal body weight helps to minimize the risk.

Geographical location

Crude heart disease prevalence trends indicate that the disease occurs more commonly in northern latitudes and is less common nearer the equator. It has been suggested that low levels of ultraviolet light during winter months may in some way be responsible perhaps via a mechanism involving vitamin D levels. This would also link with the increased incidence of heart attacks in winter. Immigrants tend to experience the heart disease risk of their host country after a relatively short period of time. However, as has already been mentioned, it has been found that some of the immigrant groups in the UK have much higher heart disease rates than the indigenous population. Thus, although environmental factors play an important part, other mechanisms are also involved.

Disease

Of the many diseases affecting humans, diabetes is one of the most prevalent and people with Type 2 diabetes have an increased risk of heart disease, often associated with obesity and raised lipid levels. The insulin resistance syndrome that occurs in these cases is associated with central obesity and a number of metabolic abnormalities, affecting carbohydrate and fat metabolism, and resulting in raised lipid levels and poor oxidative capacity in skeletal muscle and liver. The current guidelines on dietary management of diabetes stress reduced fat intakes to minimize the risk. Previously, recommended diets controlled carbohydrate intakes strictly and allowed much higher fat intakes, which exacerbated the problem of heart disease.

There is some reported evidence that a chronic inflammatory state associated with the presence of infective organisms (e.g. *Helicobacter pylori*, found in the stomach, *Chlamydia pneumoniae*, which can cause respiratory infection, or even oral bacteria that cause gum disease) may elevate cytokine levels, which affect the endothelial function of the blood vessel, and may facilitate immune responses and trigger clotting mechanisms. Patients with periodontal disease have been shown to have higher levels of plasma clotting factors. Conversely, bacteria responsible for periodontitis have been found in atherosclerotic plaques. C-reactive protein (CRP), a marker of inflammation has now been shown to correlate with incidence of heart disease.

Smoking

Similar proportions of men and women (28 per cent) are smokers in England. Smoking is much more prevalent in manual social classes and in lower income groups. Persuading at-risk subjects to stop smoking can result in a significant reduction of their heart disease risk. It is thought that the free radicals that enter the body from cigarette smoke contribute to the disease process by causing peroxidation of lipids. The altered lipids are then taken up by macrophages in the blood vessel walls and contribute to the fatty streaks. A further potential effect of smoking is the reduction in oxygen-carrying capacity of the red blood cells owing to higher levels of carbon monoxide, which can exacerbate ischaemia in tissues fed by narrowed blood vessels. Dietary intake studies also show that smokers tend to have poorer diets and consume lower levels of antioxidants from fruit, which compounds the risks from free radicals. There appears to be a clear linear relationship between the numbers of cigarettes smoked per day and heart disease risk.

High blood pressure

The Health Survey for England (Erens and Primatesta, 1999) showed that 40.8 per cent of men and 32.9 per cent of women were hypertensive, with a higher prevalence of high blood pressure in more economically deprived groups. A higher proportion of those subjects with high blood pressure were also found to be physically inactive, have high total cholesterol and lower levels of high-density lipoprotein (HDL) cholesterol.

Raised blood pressure is one of the main contributors to heart disease, possibly because it potentiates the damage to blood vessel walls and increases the transfer of substances across the blood vessel wall. Both of these may play a part in the development of the fibrous plaque. Reduction of blood pressure by drug treatment, weight loss or dietary modification is likely to be of benefit. Better control of hypertension may account for some of the reduction in heart disease seen in Western countries in recent years.

Raised blood lipids

Above normal levels of cholesterol, especially in the low-density lipoprotein fraction, are strongly linked with increased risk of heart disease, as evidenced by many studies. Those individuals with familial hyperlipidaemias have a well-recognized high risk of developing heart disease, often at a very young age. Recent interest has focused on the possible role of lipoprotein(a), closely related to LDL, but carrying an additional apoprotein molecule. Raised levels of this molecule appear to be more strongly linked to myocardial infarction than even LDL. These may explain the high incidence of heart disease in South Asians in the UK. Chylomicrons and very low density lipoprotein (VLDL), both of which are rich in triglycerides, are elevated in some individuals, resulting in prolonged lipaemia (presence of fats in the blood) after meals. These raised levels seem to be caused by a defective rate of clearance from the circulation by the enzyme lipoprotein lipase (LPL). Both chylomicrons and VLDL are likely to be atherogenic and constitute risk factors. More attention is now being focused on dietary factors that contribute to raised levels of the VLDL fraction. Measures to reduce blood lipid levels in individuals as well as population groups could result in reduced incidence of heart disease.

Weight

Early studies, such as the Seven Countries Study by Keys, failed to find a causative effect of overweight on heart disease risk because many of the other risk factors are also aggravated by a higher body fat content. Using more sophisticated analyses, it is now clear that excess body fat is a direct contributor to coronary heart disease, as well as acting indirectly through many of the risk factors, such as diabetes, hypertension and raised blood lipids. In particular, when body fat distribution is taken into account, and people are divided into 'apples' (those with predominantly abdominal fat deposits) and 'pears' (peripheral fat deposits, mostly around the buttocks and hips), a strong relationship with heart disease is seen for 'apples'. In general, the relative risk of cardiovascular disease for individuals with a body mass index (BMI) >30 is about 2–3 times that of people with a BMI <25. The use of waist circumference as a guide to the need for weight loss is a useful quick measure to indicate increased risk. Weight loss by dietary restriction and with physical activity can improve all the modifiable risk factors and thus reduce the risk of coronary heart disease.

Physical activity

A proportion of people have been shown to have minimal levels of physical activity. The Health Survey for England (Erens and Primatesta, 1999) found that 20–25 per cent of men and women reported no physical activity in the 4 weeks prior to the survey. However, 37 per cent of men and 25 per cent of women reported activity at the recommended level. This includes activity of moderate intensity for at least 30 minutes on at least 5 days of the week. The remaining subjects had activity levels between these limits.

Many long-term studies have found lower mortality in those who have a more active lifestyle, compared with more sedentary controls and, therefore, exercise has been promoted as desirable in the reduction of heart disease risk. Changes to activity levels are followed by changes in risk of death, with an improvement of risk seen in previously sedentary subjects who begin an activity programme. Even moderate levels of activity appear to confer benefit, although the evidence is stronger for men than women. The mechanisms involved are unclear but, at a basic level, activity helps in the maintenance of energy balance and prevents development of overweight. Exercise has been shown to increase the beneficial high-density lipoprotein. Abdominal fat deposits appear to be particularly sensitive to mobilization by exercise and, in individuals with central obesity, even moderate exercise can produce improvements in the metabolic profile. Other possible beneficial effects include changes in clotting factors (linked to endurance-type exercise) or in the density of capillaries in the tissues, which provides protection against ischaemic damage, if blood vessels become narrowed. Inactivity may be as important a risk factor as hypertension, smoking or hypercholesterolaemia.

Psychosocial factors

These are less well defined than other factors. Data from the Whitehall studies show higher rates of heart disease in lower employment grades, with the gradients being steeper for women than men (see Ashwell, 1996; DoH, 1994). It is suggested that stress and lack of social support may be linked to coronary heart disease.

Dietary factors

There are several constituents of the diet for which there is evidence of a link with heart disease. Most notably this applies to the fats that have been linked with lipid levels in the blood. In addition, other components, such as total energy intake, dietary fibre (non-starch polysaccharides), sugar, salt, alcohol and antioxidant nutrients, have all been studied in

Figure 14.6 A summary of dietary risk factors for coronary heart disease. HDL, high-density lipoprotein; LDL, low-density lipoprotein; MI, myocardial infarction; PUFA, polyunsaturated fatty acid.

relation to stages in the development of heart disease. The dietary risk factors are summarized in Figure 14.6.

Fats

Dietary cholesterol

Meat, egg yolks and dairy products contain fairly large amounts of cholesterol and many people concerned about their blood lipids have in the past attempted to reduce their intake of these foods. However, changing the amount of cholesterol in the diet has only limited effects on blood cholesterol concentrations in most people. This is because several compensation mechanisms exist. Only about half of the cholesterol ingested is absorbed from the gut; a typical dietary intake of 400 mg/day will, therefore, only result in the absorption of 200 mg of cholesterol. The essential nature of cholesterol in the body means that the body synthesizes the remainder of its needs, about 1 g of cholesterol per day. If dietary intake increases, the amount synthesized is reduced to compensate; this is achieved by regulating one of the enzymes – hydroxymethyl-glutaryl coenzyme A (HMG-coA) reductase – in the cholesterol synthesis pathway in the liver through a negative feedback mechanism. In addition, HDL activity can also increase to scavenge excess cholesterol from the tissues for removal in bile.

However, control is not exact and an increase in cholesterol intake in the diet can raise blood cholesterol levels. It has also been shown that there are individual, genetically determined differences in response to dietary cholesterol, with hyporesponders and hyperresponders. This makes it difficult to generalize about the effect of dietary cholesterol.

Saturated fatty acids

Originally, it was postulated that all saturated fatty acids in the diet were equally harmful, causing an elevation of blood cholesterol/LDL levels. It is now recognized that myristic acid (C14) is the main fatty acid responsible for raising the serum cholesterol level. This contributes to the formation of fibrous plaques and is described as atherogenic. Both lauric acid (C12) and myristic acid also suppress the clearing mechanism at LDL receptors, which removes LDL cholesterol from the circulation, thus contributing to raised circulating levels. Palmitic acid (C16) has probably less effect on cholesterol levels in the blood than originally suggested by Keys. However, palmitic acid is the main saturated fatty acid in most diets and, therefore, has an important effect because of its prevalence. In addition, the different fatty acids appear to have varying effects on the formation of thrombi in the blood. Myristic acid and stearic acid (C18) are con sidered to be the most thrombogenic, together with *trans* fatty acids. A reduction in thrombogenic effects is associated with monounsaturated fatty acids, seed oils and fish oils.

Monounsaturated fatty acids

Monounsaturated fatty acids (MUFAs), particularly oleic acid (18:1), were originally believed to be neutral in their effect on blood cholesterol levels and were not included in the original equations of Keys and Hegsted. Studies of heart disease prevalence among peoples in Mediterranean countries showed a lower rate than expected. The diet in these countries (particularly Greece and southern Italy) contains more MUFAs, especially oleic acid from olive oil, than is found in northern European diets. This led to the suggestion that this type of fatty acid may be protective against heart disease. It should, however, be remembered that there are many other features of a Mediterranean diet and lifestyle, such as large intakes of fruit, vegetables and wine, which may better explain the lower prevalence of heart disease. However, a number of studies have now confirmed that substitution of some of the saturated fats in the diet by MUFAs results in a reduction of LDL cholesterol, equal to about half of that achieved by *n*-6 polyunsaturated fatty acid (PUFA) substitution. In addition, however, there is an elevation of HDL cholesterol, an effect not obtained with *n*-6 PUFAs.

The proposed mechanism is an increase in LDL clearance by the liver as a result of increased receptor activity. In addition, as MUFAs contain only one double bond, they are more resistant to the harmful effects of free radicals, which attack PUFAs and can lead to the early stages of fibrous plaque formation. Observed effects on thrombogenesis have also been reported, with reduced levels of clotting factor activation. Overall, MUFAs are considered to be a beneficial component of the diet, with no harmful effects on the known risk factors for coronary heart disease. New equations predicting the change in total serum cholesterol consequent on modifications to the dietary intake of MUFAs, in addition to saturated fatty acids (SFAs) and PUFAs, have now been developed based on metabolic ward studies (e.g. Mensink and Katan, 1992). It should, however, be remembered that, in terms of weight control, the intake of MUFAs, as of other fats in the diet may need to be regulated.

Polyunsaturated fatty acids

Polyunsaturated fatty acids in the diet originate from two main sources: *n*-6 acids from plant foods and *n*-3 acids mainly from marine foods, and it is now recognized that the two families have different effects on coronary heart disease risk factors.

n-6 PUFAs. Fatty acids from this family have a LDL cholesterol-lowering effect, independent of any change in saturated fat intake. The effect is achieved, it is believed, by increasing the removal of LDL from the circulation by enhancing the activity of the LDL receptor sites, which thus opposes the effect of the saturated fatty acids on these receptors. Although *n*-6 PUFAs are also reported to reduce HDL levels in the blood, this is to a smaller extent than the effect on LDL and, consequently, the HDL/LDL ratio increases.

The *n*-6 PUFAs in membrane lipids are, however, vulnerable to free radical attack, resulting in peroxidation. Once established, this produces a chain reaction with further peroxide formation and potential for further damage. At present, there is little evidence that high intake of *n*-6 PUFAs in any way contributes to enhanced peroxidation in the body, but the vulnerability of the double bonds in these molecules suggests that this could be a possibility. Accordingly, it is advisable to be cautious about excessively high intakes of PUFAs and intakes should be below 10 per cent of total energy. European recommendations (EURODIET, 2001) are that intakes of *n*-6 PUFAs should not exceed 5 per cent (range 4–8 per cent) of total energy.

n-3 PUFAs. The *n*-3 fatty acids reduce VLDL levels and hence may eventually cause a reduction in LDL. The effect is linked to a more rapid clearance of VLDL rich in *n*-3 PUFAs than those containing SFAs, resulting in less post-prandial lipaemia on a *n*-3 PUFA-rich diet. However, the main interest in these fatty acids is associated with their action on blood clotting, which arose from studies on Greenland Eskimos who, despite a diet high in fat, have very low rates of heart disease. In addition, these subjects have prolonged bleeding times. Their diet contains a large amount of marine foods providing high levels of long-chain *n*-3 PUFAs. The *n*-3 series of prostaglandins and eicosanoids has less aggregating potency than those made from the *n*-6 family. In addition, the vasoconstricting effects on blood vessel walls are less. The overall effect is that the *n*-3 series is less likely to produce inflammation, thrombosis or increases in blood pressure. All of these responses are likely to reduce the risk of heart attack. Ingestion of significant amounts of *n*-3 PUFAs is believed to displace the *n*-6 series from enzyme sites, so that *n*-3 series eicosanoids are produced. Research has attempted to ascertain the ratio of *n*-6:*n*-3 PUFAs in the diet that could ensure optimal outcomes in respect of coronary heart disease. Current advice for populations based on EURODIET (2001) is that *n*-3 PUFAs should constitute 1 per cent of total energy, providing a *n*-6:*n*-3 ratio of 5:1.

Data from the DART study (Burr et al., 1989) also suggested that the higher intake of *n*-3 acids stabilizes the rhythm of the heart and allows it to continue beating normally during a heart attack, ensuring a higher chance of survival. The Lyon Heart Study (De Lorgeril et al., 1998) demonstrated a significant protective effect of additional alpha-linolenic acid together with a Mediterranean diet. Supplementation with long-chain *n*-3 PUFAs in the GISSI trial (GISSI Prevenzione Investigators, 1999) caused a reduction in total mortality. It is on the basis of studies such as these that an increase in *n*-3 PUFA intake is recommended, either by increasing fish consumption, or inclusion of more sources of alpha-linolenic acid in the diet.

Trans *fatty acids*

The naturally occurring unsaturated fatty acids have a *cis* orientation; *trans* fatty acids are produced by chemical alteration of the molecule. This occurs in the stomachs of ruminants and result in a dietary intake of naturally formed *trans* fatty acids in foods such as milk, dairy products, beef and lamb. In addition, the diet contains artificial *trans* fatty acids produced during food processing or manufacture of fat spreads by hydrogenation (approximately 65 per cent of the total intake). These fats are used in the manufacture of biscuits, pies, cakes and potato crisps. Most *trans* fatty acids have so far been monounsaturated, predominantly *trans*-oleic acid. The manufacture of high PUFA margarines, using emulsifier technology and the deodorizing of vegetable oils has resulted in increased levels of *trans* PUFAs, including both *n*-6 and *n*-3, and there could be an increased intake of *trans*-alpha-linolenic acid in the future.

Studies suggest that large amounts of *trans* fatty acids (greater than currently consumed in the UK) raise LDL cholesterol and depress HDL, albeit to a smaller extent than seen with lauric and palmitic acids. Other evidence points to an elevation of lipoprotein(a) by up to 30 per cent. Current intakes in the UK are in the range of 4–6 g per person, but the top 2.5 per cent of consumers may take in more than 12 g/day. Intakes are higher in the USA, with an average of 8.1 g/person per day.

Overall, *trans* fatty acids have an adverse effect on both LDL and HDL, and this appears to be greater than that following an equal amount of saturated fatty acids. Nevertheless, since saturated fat represents a greater proportion of fat intake, reducing these is of greater importance. Consideration should perhaps be given to including information about *trans* fatty acids in nutritional labelling. It is recommended that *trans* fatty acids should comprise no more than 1 per cent of total energy intake.

Conjugated linoleic acid (CLA) is a *trans* fatty acid formed during the conversion of linoleic acid to oleic acid by rumen bacteria. It is found in milk and dairy produce, and in beef and lamb. Animal studies have shown an anticancer and antiatherogenic activity by this acid, and current research is investigating potential health benefits.

Total fat

When total fat intake was studied by Keys (1970) in the Seven Countries Study, it was found that there was an association with serum cholesterol levels and heart disease mortality. However, this effect was dependent on the saturated fat intake. More recent data have suggested that the total fat intake may be closely linked with the activity of Factor VII, one of the clotting factors, and may thus have a role to play in the thrombosis phase of the aetiology of heart disease. The current view is that total fat intake needs to be controlled in individuals who are not within the ideal body weight range. In these cases, a reduction in fat, together with increased physical activity is a useful contribution to reducing the risk of coronary heart disease. In people who are at or near their ideal body weight, the balance of fats should be the main focus, rather than aiming to change total fat intakes.

Total energy

A low energy intake has been associated with a high incidence of heart disease. Low levels of food intake not only contain small amounts of energy, but also low nutrient levels, including many of the other protective factors that are necessary to sustain normal physiological functioning in the body. It is thought possible that this level of intake is a consequence of a low energy output and a sign of a sedentary lifestyle. In addition, low levels of physical activity are associated with increased body weight, which in itself is considered to be a risk factor. The incorporation of physical activity into everyday life is probably the best way to escape from this cycle.

Salt

There are possible links between salt intake and hypertension. Since hypertension is a recognized risk factor in coronary heart disease, it can be argued that reducing salt intake in those who are susceptible might reduce their risk of heart disease. However, it is now clear that a broader dietary approach can be more effective in reducing blood pressure. Data from the Dietary Approaches to Stop Hypertension (DASH) trial showed a dietary change that included low-fat dairy products, nuts, fruit and vegetables resulted in greater reductions in blood pressure than salt restriction alone (Appel et al., 1997). The DASH diet included increased intakes of potassium, calcium and magnesium, as well as lower sodium intakes, and it is now recognized that all of these factors are effective in changing blood pressure. These findings add further support to the importance of potassium intakes in the control of blood pressure.

Calcium

For many years it has been noted that the incidence of coronary heart disease is lower in those geographical areas that have hard water. Several mechanisms have been put forward, with supporting evidence. Dietary calcium combines with fats, especially saturated fatty acids producing soaps, which remain unabsorbed and are excreted from the body. In a study of British and French farmers, calcium intake was inversely related to blood levels of triglycerides. In addition, there was an inverse relationship with platelet clotting activity. Finally, as discussed above, calcium intakes are inversely related to blood pressure, as has been demonstrated in a number of large cohort studies. In general, calcium intakes, especially from dairy produce, appear to be associated with a lower risk of coronary heart disease and low-fat cheese may be considered a constituent of healthy diets.

Alcohol

Heavy drinking in excess of 55 units for men and 35 units for women per week is associated with raised triglyceride and VLDL levels, and thus increases heart disease risk. In addition, binge drinking has been associated with sudden death due to myocardial infarction or stroke. However, a moderate alcohol intake (within 'safe' limits) has been shown to have a protective effect against heart disease. The mechanisms appear to involve both the atherogenesis and thrombogenesis aspects of coronary heart disease. A number of studies have found an increase in HDL levels on alcohol consumption, which falls within 24 hours when alcohol intake stops. The elevation of HDL is approximately similar to that achieved by physical activity. In addition, moderate alcohol intake has been shown to reduce platelet aggregation. In large amounts, alcohol can cause platelet aggregation. In this case, alcoholic beverages that contain antioxidants, such as red wine, may be protective.

The relationship between alcohol consumption and heart disease is usually found to follow a J-shaped curve, with increased risk in non-drinkers and heavy drinkers. The lowest risk occurs in the middle range of alcohol intakes, taking 2–4 drinks per day on 3–4 days per week. Ideally, consumption should be with meals, as is seen in Mediterranean countries. There has been debate about the type of alcoholic drink that may be most beneficial, and many studies suggest that red wine has the greatest protective effects. However, in general, it appears that the consistent effects are attributable to the alcohol per se, rather than additional constituents particular to a specific beverage. However, antioxidants in red wine, most notably resveratrol, may contribute an additional protective benefit.

Some concern has been expressed by health educationists about the desirability of promoting alcohol consumption as a means of preventing heart disease because of the implications for health of alcohol in amounts greater than 'moderate'.

Fibre (non-starch polysaccharides)

Sources of soluble fibre, especially from oats, have been shown to reduce serum cholesterol levels, although the effects are not large. Insoluble fibre does not appear to have a similar effect on cholesterol. Nevertheless, a significant inverse relationship between fibre intake and myocardial infarction and coronary mortality has been demonstrated in two prospective studies, in Finland and the USA, in large cohorts of men. The relationship was strongest for cereal fibre and persisted when confounding variables were taken into account. It has been suggested that the effects occur due to the satiating effect of fibre-rich foods that results in a lowered fat intake and possibly a reduced total energy intake.

However, soluble fibre may increase sterol excretion from the body, thereby lowering cholesterol levels. High fibre intake has been associated with a decrease in the level of insulin and increased insulin sensitivity, thus improving metabolic function. Additionally, a high-fibre diet also affects the clotting factors and may be associated with a lower blood pressure. Overall, it is likely that the effects of fibre on heart disease are not mediated through a single mechanism and no adverse harmful effects have been reported from increased sources of fibre in the diet.

Antioxidants

The inability of the lipid hypothesis to explain the link between diet and heart disease fully, and the completion of studies that show inconsistent or contrary results have led over the years to a search for other influencing factors. Several studies demonstrated that levels of antioxidants in both diet and serum exhibit good correlations with heart disease incidence – often higher levels of correlation than are seen in the same studies for fat indices. In particular, the MONICA study (Gey et al., 1991) has shown inverse relationships between heart disease mortality and intakes of beta-carotene, vitamin C and vitamin E. The strongest correlations ($p < 0.001$) were seen with alpha-tocopherol, vitamin C and beta-carotene in food supplies and the rate of coronary heart disease. Correlations also existed with the dietary sources of these nutrients, most notably vegetables, vegetable oils, sunflower seed oil, seeds, nuts and fruit. In the USA, two large prospective studies (of male health professionals and female nurses) found a lower incidence of coronary heart disease in the subjects who consumed vitamin E supplements.

However, these results were not replicated in a series of intervention studies in various countries, in which supplements of the major antioxidants, mainly vitamin E and beta-carotene, were assigned to subjects. In general, these studies showed either no beneficial effect of supplementation with these antioxidants or an adverse effect of supplementation, with a higher rate of coronary heart disease or cancer than the control groups. It is suggested that antioxidant nutrients can act as pro-oxidants in certain conditions, which may include the administration of large amounts of a single antioxidant.

Thus, it is likely that antioxidants work together to produce the effects seen in whole diet studies, and that advice should be targeted towards fruit and vegetable consumption. It is possible that fruit and vegetables contain other substances that have not yet been taken into account and that have even more effect on heart disease development. There is interest in other factors found in fruit and vegetables, such as polyphenols or flavonoids. The recommendation of the WHO is to eat five servings of fruit and vegetables per day.

There are good grounds for believing that the antioxidant nutrients do play a preventive role in the formation of fibrous plaques. It is appropriate at this point to summarize all of the functions of antioxidants in protection against free radicals.

Mechanisms of action of antioxidants

Free radicals are produced by most of the oxidative reactions in the body. The most important of these radicals are:

- the hydroxyl radical. OH
- superoxide radical. O_2
- singlet oxygen. $^1O_2$
- nitric oxide. NO.

Also included are the peroxyl radical, hydrogen peroxide and hydroperoxyl. All share the common property of having an exceedingly short lifespan and, therefore, are very unstable. They can attack vital cell components, inactivate enzymes and damage genetic material. It is, therefore, reasonable to assume they play a part in degenerative diseases.

The body has a complex antioxidant defence system to counteract these radicals. This is made up of endogenous and exogenous components.

- Endogenous antioxidants are mainly enzymes that catalyse radical quenching reactions (many of these are dependent on dietary minerals for activation) or bind pro-oxidants, which might catalyse free-radical reactions.
- Exogenous antioxidants are mainly vitamins that quench free radicals.

Endogenous antioxidants

The antioxidant enzymes include:

- superoxide dismutase (SOD), which neutralizes the superoxide radical and which requires zinc and copper, or manganese for activation;
- catalase, which is specific for hydrogen peroxide and requires iron for its activity; and
- glutathione peroxidase, which removes peroxides and is a selenium-requiring enzyme.

Many minerals are clearly involved in activating these enzymes. However, copper and iron can also act as pro-oxidants when freely present. This explains why there are binding proteins present to prevent this happening, most notably caeruloplasmin and albumin to bind copper, and transferrin and ferritin to bind iron.

Exogenous antioxidants

The most important of these are vitamins C and E, and the carotenoids. Plant flavonoids are possible members of this group.

Vitamins C and E quench free radicals by providing H atoms to pair up with unpaired electrons on free radicals. This inactivates the vitamins, which then need to be regenerated. Glutathione is believed to regenerate vitamin C and vitamin C can regenerate vitamin E (Figure 14.7). In its turn, vitamin E may promote the antioxidant activity of beta-carotene against lipid peroxidation. It is suggested that vitamin C is the primary antioxidant in the plasma and is consumed first in destroying free radicals. Vitamin E is the major antioxidant in the lipid parts of membranes. Lipid peroxidation does not begin until after the vitamin C has been used. It is important that regeneration can take place, however, so that a continued supply of the vitamins is available. These interactions highlight

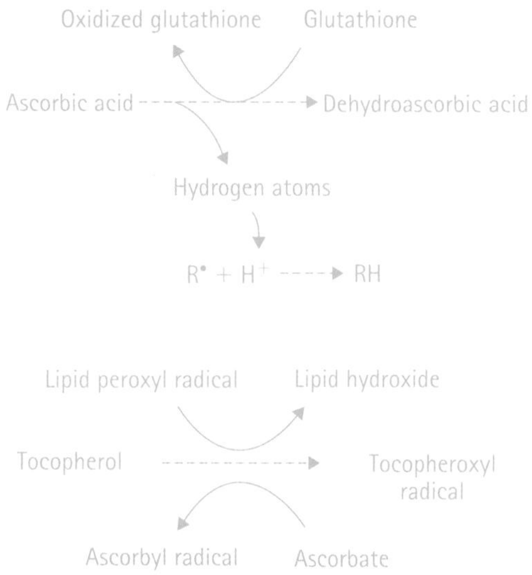

Figure 14.7 Interactions between glutathione, vitamin C and vitamin E during antioxidant activity. R• free radical.

the importance of maintaining a balance between the different exogenous antioxidants supplied to the body.

In conclusion, the theories about antioxidants allow some of the other factors discussed earlier to be linked together. It has been suggested that the desire for weight loss, which preoccupies so many women and which encourages them to eat low-calorie fruits and vegetables, helps to protect them from heart disease by adding more antioxidants to their diet. Smokers, who have a greatly increased risk of heart disease, are recorded as having very low intakes of fruit and vegetables and consequently poor vitamin C status. When linked to the increased burden of free radicals, this may explain their greater risk. Finally, alcoholic beverages, most notably wines, contain phenolic substances that also act as antioxidants. This may explain why there are lower rates of coronary heart disease among populations in wine-drinking countries.

Homocysteine

It has been known since the late 1960s that raised levels of homocysteine in the blood are associated with severe arteriosclerosis. Initially, this was considered to be a problem in individuals with inborn errors in the metabolism of homocysteine. However, in recent years, it has been found that raised homocysteine levels are an independent risk factor for vascular disease, and the effect is graded. The evidence for this comes from a range of different studies, including retrospective case-control, cross-sectional and prospective studies. The metabolism of homocysteine is linked to that of methionine and cysteine, and utilizes a number of B vitamins as cofactors. These include folate, pyridoxine, riboflavin and vitamin B_{12}. Deficiencies in the metabolism of homocysteine, with resultant elevated plasma levels, are associated with mutations in one of the enzymes (methylene tetrahydrofolate reductase; MTHFR) involved in the metabolic pathway. Lower activity levels of the enzyme have been identified in approximately 30 per cent of the population, with a smaller percentage being homozygous for the mutation. The reference range of homocysteine in the plasma is still debated, but the following are generally accepted:

5–15 μmol/L	normal range
15–30 μmol/L	moderate elevation
30–100 μmol/L	intermediate elevation
>100 μmol/L	severe elevation

It has been proposed that homocysteine may be directly toxic to endothelial cells, through a mechanism involving nitric oxide that normally causes endothelial relaxation. This would facilitate monocyte adhesion and promote the process of fatty streak formation. A further possible mechanism is through an increased coagulation tendency, by an inhibition of the normal fibrinolytic mechanisms that disperse blood clots. However, neither of these mechanisms has yet been conclusively proven and much remains to be discovered about the relationship of homocysteine to the processes of vascular disease.

Dietary interventions can lower homocysteine levels. Most importantly, folate status is inversely associated with homocysteine levels, with as little as 200 μg/day of folate causing a reduction in plasma homocysteine levels. Evidence is less conclusive for supplementation with riboflavin, pyridoxine or vitamin B_{12}, although a combination of these may be beneficial. It should also be remembered that folate is provided by fruit and vegetables in the diet, so that an increase in these foods in line with other aspects of dietary intervention will also help to increase folate status. Fortification of grain products with folic acid, at a rate of 1.4 μg/g of product has been introduced in the USA since 1999. Early indications are that, in the first year after this was introduced, there was a 3.4 per cent reduction in mortality from stroke and heart attack. Mean homocysteine levels have fallen, and mean plasma concentrations of folate have increased.

More controlled studies in this field are still required.

FUTURE DIRECTIONS

There is still a huge amount to learn about coronary heart disease. Developments in molecular biology and the human genome project may in the future allow research to identify the interaction between risk factors and particular genes. Animal models with specific genetic modifications are already being used to study mechanisms to understand existing knowledge. Improved targeting of dietary intervention and drug therapy may be a consequence.

SUMMARY

1. The role of diet in the aetiology of coronary heart disease is complex.
2. Early hypotheses about links with fat have been discovered to explain only part of the relationship.
3. New findings about the roles of other fats, such as monounsaturated fatty acids, *n*-3 fats and *trans* fatty acids have modified the original lipid hypothesis.
4. The importance of other dietary factors, in particular the antioxidants, provides opportunities to link some of the earlier findings together.
5. Dietary guidelines promoting lower fat, and increased fruit and vegetables intakes address many of the postulated mechanisms relating to coronary heart disease. Weight control and promotion of physical activity remain important preventive factors.

STUDY QUESTIONS

1. Distinguish between atherogenesis and thrombogenesis, and describe the mechanisms that are currently offered as explanations of these processes.
2. Which dietary factors are thought to be involved in:
   a. atherogenesis
   b. thrombogenesis?
3. What are the main tenets of the lipid hypothesis and what changes to it have been suggested in recent years?
4. a. Explain what you understand by the antioxidant nutrients.
   b. Produce a diagram to show how they might play a part in protecting against heart disease.
5. Discuss with a colleague how you believe the theories about the dietary links with heart disease are reflected in current dietary guidelines. Can you explain all of the guidelines on a scientific basis?
6. Produce a poster or leaflet to summarize the main aspects of dietary advice for the prevention of coronary heart disease. Make the information as practical as possible.

REFERENCES AND FURTHER READING

Appel, L.J., Moore, T.G., Obarzanek, R. et al. 1997: A clinical trial of effects of dietary patterns on blood pressure. *New England Journal of Medicine* 336, 1117–24.

Ashwell, M. (ed.) 1996: *Diet and heart disease: a round table of factors*, 2nd edn. London: Chapman & Hall.

Bellizzi, M.C. 1995: Wine and vegetable oils: the French paradox revisited. *British Nutrition Foundation Nutrition Bulletin* 20, 256–65.

Brown, A.A., Hu, F.B. 2001: Dietary modulation of endothelial function: implications for cardiovascular disease. *American Journal of Clinical Nutrition* 73, 673–86.

Burr, M.L. 1993: Fish and ischaemic heart disease. *World Review of Nutrition and Dietetics* 72, 49–60.

Burr, M.L., Fehily, A.M., Gilbert, J.F. et al. 1989: Effects of changes in fat, fish and fibre intakes on death and myocardial infarction: Diet and Reinfarction Trial (DART). *Lancet* ii, 757–61.

Caggiula, A.W., Mustad, V.A. 1997: Effects of dietary fat and fatty acids on coronary artery disease risk and total and lipoprotein cholesterol concentrations: epidemiologic studies. *American Journal of Clinical Nutrition* 65(Suppl.), 159–610S.

De Lorgeril, M., Renaud, S., Mamelle, N. et al. 1994: Mediterranean alpha-linolenic acid-rich diet in secondary prevention of coronary heart disease. *Lancet* 343, 1454–9.

DoH (UK Department of Health) 1992: *The health of the nation: a strategy for health in England.* London: HMSO.

De Lorgeril, M., Salen, P., Martin, J.L. et al. 1998: Mediterranean dietary pattern in a randomised trial. Prolonged survival and possible reduced cancer rate. *Archives of Internal Medicine* 158, 1181–7.

DoH (UK Department of Health) 1994: *Nutritional aspects of cardiovascular disease.* Report on Health and Social Subjects No. 46. Report of the Cardiovascular Review Group of the Committee on Medical Aspects of Food Policy. London: HMSO.

DoH (UK Department of Health) 1999: *Saving lives – our healthier nation.* London: The Stationery Office.

Erens, B., Primatesta, P. (eds) 1999: *Health survey for England: cardiovascular disease '98.* Volume 1: Findings. London: The Stationery Office.

EURODIET 2001: Report and proceedings. *Public Health Nutrition* 4, 2(A).

Gey, K.F., Puska, P., Jordan, P. et al. 1991: Inverse correlation between plasma vitamin E and mortality from ischaemic heart disease in cross-cultural epidemiology. *American Journal of Clinical Nutrition* 53, 3265–345.

GISSI Prevenzione Investigators, 1999: Dietary supplementation with n-3 polyunsaturated fatty acids and vitamin E after myocardial infarction, results of the GISSI Prevenzione trial. *Lancet* 354, 447–53.

Grundy, S.M. 1988: Cholesterol and heart disease: a new era. *Journal of the American Medical Association* 256, 2849–58.

Halliwell, B. 1994: Free radicals, antioxidants and human disease: curiosity, cause or consequence? *Lancet* 344, 721–4.

Hardman, A.E. 1999: Physical activity and cardiovascular risk. Review in depth. *Journal of Cardiovascular Risk* 2, 285–329.

Hegsted, D.M., Ansman, L.M., Johnson, J.A. et al. 1993: Dietary fat and serum lipids: an evaluation of the experimental data. *American Journal of Clinical Nutrition* 57, 875–83.

Hu, H., Stampfer, M.J., Manson, J.E. et al. 1997: Dietary fat intake and the risk of coronary heart disease in women. *New England Journal of Medicine* 337, 1491–9.

Hulshof, K.F.A.M., van Erp-Baart, M.A., Anttolainen, M. et al. 1999: Intake of fatty acids in Western Europe with emphasis on trans fatty acids. The TRANSFAIR study. *European Journal of Clinical Nutrition* 53, 143–57.

Jacob, R.A. 1995: The integrated antioxidant system. *Nutrition Research* 15(5), 755–66.

Keys, A. (ed.) 1970: Coronary heart disease in seven countries. *Circulation* 41(Suppl.), 11–211.

Kinane, D.F., Lowe, G.D.O. 2000: How periodontal disease may contribute to cardiovascular disease. *Periodontology* 23, 121–6.

Kromhout, D. 2001: Epidemiology of cardiovascular disease in Europe. *Public Health Nutrition* 4(2B), 441–57.

Law, M.R., Wald, N.J., Thompson, S.G. 1994: By how much and how quickly does reduction in serum cholesterol concentration lower risk of ischaemic heart disease? *British Medical Journal* 308, 367–72.

Martin, M.J., Halley, S.B., Browner, W.S. et al. 1986: Serum cholesterol, blood pressure and mortality: implications from a cohort of 361 622 men. *Lancet* ii, 933–36.

McKinley, M.C. 2000: Nutritional aspects and possible pathological mechanisms of hyperhomocysteinaemia: an independent risk factor for vascular disease. *Proceedings of the Nutrition Society* 59, 221–37.

Mensink, R.P., Katan, M.B. 1992: Effect of dietary fatty acids on serum lipids and lipoproteins – a meta-analysis of 27 trials. *Atherosclerosis and Thrombosis* 12, 911–19.

Renaud, S., Lanzmann-Petithory, D. 2001: Coronary heart disease: dietary links and pathogenesis. *Public Health Nutrition* 4(2B), 459–74.

Rimm, E.B., Klatsky, A., Grobbee, D. et al. 1996: Review of moderate alcohol consumption and reduced risk of coronary heart disease: is the effect due to beer, wine or spirits? *British Medical Journal* 312, 731–6.

Scandinavian Simvastatin Study Group 1994: Randomised trial of cholesterol lowering in 4444 patients with coronary heart disease: the Scandinavian Simvastatin Survival Study (4S). *Lancet* 344, 1383–9.

Schaefer, E.J. 2002: Lipoproteins, nutrition and heart disease. *American Journal of Clinical Nutrition* 75, 191–212.

Shaper, A.G., Wannamethee, G. 1991: Physical activity and ischaemic heart disease in middle-aged British men. *British Heart Journal* 66, 384–94.

Slavin, J., Martin, M.C., Jacobs, D.R. et al. 1999: Plausible mechanisms for the protectiveness of whole grains. *American Journal of Clinical Nutrition* 70, 459S–63S.

Troisi, R., Willett, W.C., Weiss, S.T. 1992: Trans fatty acid intake in relation to serum lipid concentrations in adult men. *American Journal of Clinical Nutrition* 56, 1019–24.

Truswell, A.S. 1994: Review of dietary intervention studies: effects on coronary events and on total mortality. *Australia and New Zealand Journal of Medicine* 24, 98–106.

Various authors 2000: Symposium on reducing cardiovascular disease risk: today's achievements, tomorrow's opportunities. *Proceedings of the Nutrition Society* 59, 415–40.

15 DIET AND CANCER

The aims of this chapter are to:

- describe what is meant by cancer;
- discuss the ways in which the relationship between diet and cancer is studied;
- identify the main relationships that have been indicated;
- describe the guidelines on healthy eating for the reduction of cancer risk.

On completing the study of this chapter, you should be able to:

- discuss the links between certain specific cancers and dietary patterns and explain the suggested mechanisms, where appropriate;
- discuss some of the problems inherent in studies on diet and cancer;
- advise the practical changes needed in a Western diet to reduce the risk of cancer.

Cancer affects one in three people in the UK at some time in their life, and is responsible for approximately one-quarter of all deaths, numbering some 160 000 cases per year. Lung cancer accounts for almost one-quarter of all cancer deaths and it is the leading type of cancer in men, followed by cancer of the prostate. In women, breast cancer causes most deaths, followed by lung cancer. In both men and women, cancer of the colon and rectum is the third major type of cancer.

More people now die from cancer than was the case 100 years ago. However, this is a reflection of a longer life expectancy and larger numbers of elderly people in the population. Because risk increases with age, the majority of cancer deaths occur in people aged over 65 years. Different cancers show different trends, however. Deaths from lung cancer are clearly linked to smoking and these have followed trends in smoking throughout the century. Melanoma, a cancer of the skin, has increased in recent years, probably as a result of increased exposure to the sun as more people take holidays abroad. On the other hand, stomach cancer rates have declined dramatically since the 1950s. Several explanations may be offered for this, including dietary changes. However, a major factor recently discovered is the role of *Helicobacter pylori* in the development of the disease. Antibodies to this bacterium are much more common among people brought up in overcrowded housing conditions, who then have a higher risk of stomach cancer. Improvements in housing provision may have had the added benefit of reducing exposure to this bacterium and, consequently, contributed to reduced rates of stomach cancer. This example illustrates the often multifactorial nature of the aetiology of cancer, and the consequent difficulties of study.

Other factors that need to be taken into account in studying statistics on cancer are the improvements in detection and diagnosis, and advances in treatment, both of which may increase figures for the apparent incidence of the disease. Thus, we are not working with a static baseline from which to explore trends. It is also important to note that changes in the environment and lifestyle factors may impact on cancer statistics, and these must be continuously studied to give more clues about the aetiology of cancer at various sites.

According to the statistics, there have been no marked changes in cancer incidence rates that could be attributed to toxic hazards, such as pesticides and pollution at average levels of exposure. However, when groups of individuals are exposed to abnormal levels, for example of radiation, as happened after the nuclear accident in Chernobyl in 1986, then higher rates of particular cancers are found. Unusual occurrences of cancer in a community are always suspicious, since they may be coincidental or linked to a particular environmental event. Finding an answer can help to further our understanding of the development of the disease.

Around the world there are also differences in the occurrence of particular cancers. In Africa, Asia and Latin America, there tends to be a higher rate of cancers of the upper respiratory and digestive systems (aerodigestive system) (mouth, pharynx, larynx and oesophagus), the stomach, liver and cervix. Conversely, cancers of the breast, endometrium, prostate, colon and rectum are more common in Europe, North America and Australia. Cancers of this latter group are now increasing in the urbanized areas of the developing countries. Lung cancer is the commonest cancer worldwide. Migration from one type of community to another is often associated with a change in the pattern of cancers seen in the migrants.

WHAT IS CANCER?

Cancer is now accepted as a genetic disorder of somatic cells, in which an accumulation of genetic changes causes a normal cell to give rise to one which is abnormal in form or function. Generally, several changes have to occur for cancer to develop, varying between different types of cancer. The fundamental change occurs within the genetic material and may be inherited or, in the great majority of cases, occurs sporadically.

The resulting abnormal cells fail to respond to some or all of the regulatory signals that control division, growth, differentiation and programmed cell death (apoptosis). In addition, the affected genes may malfunction in their role, for example, as tumour suppressors, 'proof readers' of encoded material or repair genes. There are many types of cancers. They have different characteristics, probably originate in varying ways, occur in different parts of the body, have different courses of development; and require various treatments.

The developing tumour causes damage to its host by interfering with the normal functioning of the tissue or organ where it grows. It also draws on the host for nutrients to support its growth. Some cancers produce factors, which cause increased catabolism of the body's own tissues, resulting in a state of rapid weight loss and deterioration.

Although the process of development of cancer (or carcinogenesis) is not fully understood, it is clear that there are several stages that take place over a period of time (Table 15.1). The boundaries between the stages may not be as clear as implied here, but they provide a useful framework. The exact duration of each stage is unknown, but opportunities may arise for the process to be stopped, and possibly reversed, before it reaches the later stages.

STUDYING THE RELATIONSHIP BETWEEN DIET AND CANCER

In 1997, the World Cancer Research Fund (WCRF) and the American Institute for Cancer Research (IARC) published a report in which studies relating to diet and cancer from the previous 15 years were reviewed and their scientific evidence assessed in a consistent manner. Such a systematic review is an important tool for exploring existing research findings. This evidence was used as the basis for recommendations. Various approaches to the study of cancer exist and new evidence is continually emerging. The WCRF are currently developing a systematic methodology for the identification, assessment and recording of information from the scientific literature to form the basis of a new review. Worldwide, the occurrence of cancer is greater in the industrialized than in the developing countries, with up to 30-fold differences

TABLE 15.1 Summary of stages in cancer development

Stage of development	Associated change
Initiation	Exposure to harmful agent (e.g. chemical carcinogen, virus, free radical, radiation) or error in transcription: may permanently alter the DNA material The cell may remain in this state for a long period It is also possible for the DNA damage to be repaired, or the damaged cell to be destroyed by the body's normal regulatory systems Molecular biology research suggests that there are genes that can both promote and suppress these changes. This may explain the increased risk of certain cancers in families
Promotion	Substances that increase the rate of cell division may cause the damaged DNA to replicate before it has been repaired or destroyed This may not happen for 10–30 years after the first step Promoters are believed to include oestrogens, dietary fat, alcohol There may also be inhibitory agents, including antioxidants, dietary fibre, calcium, other constituents in plant foods, additives
Progression	The cells undergo further development and begin to grow in an uncontrolled manner, producing a tumour

in rates of particular cancers. This suggests that there may be important environmental factors involved in the aetiology. Many of these have been investigated in observational studies comparing different communities, groups within communities and migrant groups moving from one community to another. However, such studies do not provide evidence of causality or information about biological mechanisms, and must be supported by experimental findings. Developments in identification and measurement of biological markers and rapid gains in information about human genetics will provide opportunities to link observational data with molecular mechanisms.

Much of the current evidence is based on many epidemiological studies, whose results allow researchers to calculate the relative risk, or odds ratio of disease, resulting from exposure to a particular factor. It is on the basis of such data that risk factors for the development of various cancers can be proposed.

Ecological or correlational studies

These aim to show an association between the incidence of cancer in a population with a high or low occurrence of a particular environmental factor. This type of evidence can only point to the need for further, more detailed studies as the existence of a correlation does not imply causality. Changes over time in either the diet or the incidence of the cancer may provide further clues.

Case-control studies

These attempt to identify individuals with cancer and closely match each one with a control individual without disease. Comparison of environmental factors, including diet, can then be made, with the objective of identifying differences that may have contributed to the development of the cancer. In addition to the difficulties of obtaining accurate measurements of dietary intake, there are a number of other drawbacks to this approach.

- Studies that rely on information about dietary intake several years ago are imprecise. This is particularly true for a person who has recently been given a diagnosis of cancer, which tends to be a devastating event. In addition, the development of symptoms associated with the disease may have already resulted in dietary changes.

- Cancer is believed to develop over a long period of time; differences in diet a short time before the diagnosis may not reflect differences when the cancer was initiated or promoted.

Prospective cohort studies

These offer the most promising approach. They involve the recruitment of a large cross-section of the population and follow up the sample over a number of years, thus monitoring development of disease. Data about diet and lifestyle factors, together with biochemical measurements are taken initially and at intervals. The use of biomarkers, for example, biological function tests, blood or urine levels of substances, carries less risk of measurement error. Thus, if and when disease does occur, data will be available that cover the period when the disease was developing. A study of this type – the European Prospective Investigation into Cancer and Nutrition (EPIC) – is currently taking place in ten countries in Europe. Recruitment started in 1992, with a target of 500 000 subjects and first results were reported in 2001. The study will continue to collect data for a further 10 years. The major disadvantage of this type of study is the need for very large numbers of subjects. Research on 'fetal programming' and evidence from studies on growth that point to relationships with later disease, may indicate that even a prospective study over 10 or 15 years may be of insufficient duration to identify factors that may trigger the cancer process.

Meta-analysis

Data from separate studies can be reanalysed by 'meta-analysis'. By cooperating with the investigators, it is possible to record all the outcomes of a number of studies in a similar way and thus increase the power of the analysis. In this way, it may become possible to quantify the relationship between exposure to a hazard and the risk of a particular disease obtained by epidemiological study, even when that risk is only moderate. It is important that only those studies that have similar methodologies are used, and that all relevant studies are included, irrespective of their results, for the analysis to be unbiased and worthwhile. More such analyses will no doubt be carried out in the future.

ENVIRONMENTAL CAUSES OF CANCER

Various attempts have been made over the last 20 years to evaluate the environmental contribution to the development of cancer; some estimates suggest that this may be up to 80 per cent. Of these, the most important factors are:

- diet, which may account for an average of one-third of cancer deaths (although the suggested range for different cancers is between 10 and 70 per cent);
- smoking, which is causal in 30 per cent of cancer deaths (range between 25 and 40 per cent);
- physical activity, which contributes to maintenance of a normal body weight, prevention of excessive adiposity and is an important protective factor.

In comparison, other factors believed to be important causes of cancer, such as food additives, pollutants, industrial products and geophysical factors, taken together probably account for 6 per cent of all known cancer deaths (range 0–13 per cent). It should be noted that some food additives, like antioxidants and preservatives, may actually be protective against cancer.

In looking at the above data, it is not surprising that there is a growing interest and urgency in modifying diets and lifestyles in an attempt to reduce cancer risk. The World Cancer Research Fund estimated that attention to diet, smoking and physical activity could reduce cancer incidence by 30–40 per cent, preventing 3–4 million cases of cancer worldwide annually.

Role of diet

Food or nutrients may contribute to the development of cancer in a number of ways, broadly classified as follows.

- Foods may be a source of pre-formed (or precursors of) carcinogens.
- Nutrients may affect the formation, transport, deactivation or excretion of carcinogens.

- Nutrients may affect the body's resistance to carcinogens and, therefore, be important protective factors.

Diets are extremely complex and their measurement is subject to error. This is particularly a problem in a population whose diets are relatively similar. If the error is not consistent and is greater than the variation in intakes, it can result in misclassification of individuals and a miscalculation of risk. Random errors can also reduce the power of studies to detect relationships between intake and disease, but these errors can be minimized by repeated measurements or the use of large cohorts. Other difficulties arise because of the co-variation in particular nutrients. For example, fat intakes and energy intakes may change simultaneously, meat intakes may reflect the protein content of the diet, fruit and vegetables in the diet affect the overall intake of non-starch polysaccharide (NSP). Finally, there is good evidence from many studies that subjects tend to underreport their dietary intake, and this does not happen in a systematic manner with some nutrients more likely to be underreported, in particular protein, sugars and fat missed from a diet record. Again, this can be taken into account in large prospective studies, if they are well designed. Despite these difficulties, epidemiological evidence from the last 15 years has identified a number of consistent trends in the relationship between diet and some cancers. Detailed mechanisms underlying these associations remain to be elucidated.

Possible promoting factors

Total energy intake

Restricting the food intake of mice without modifying the proportion of the individual nutrients has long been known to halve the incidence of spontaneous tumours of the mammary gland and lung and to reduce susceptibility to known carcinogens. This effect of restricted energy intake appears to be independent of any reduction in fat content of the diet. In mice, increased activity was as effective at reducing tumour development as restricted energy intake. Increased exercise may promote activity of the immune system, thereby increasing resistance.

In humans, rapid growth in childhood, and especially growth in height may also, in ways as yet unknown, contribute to a higher risk of cancer. Data from the National Health and Nutrition Examination Survey (NHANES) 1 study found a positive correlation with height and a number of cancers, including colorectal cancer. Follow-up of children under 16 years, first studied by Boyd Orr in 1937–39, has also shown a significant positive association, with a 20 per cent increased risk of all cancers not associated with smoking, for every 1 MJ greater daily energy intake (Frankel et al., 1998). Potential confounding variables, such as social class and household size, were taken into consideration in the analysis.

High energy intakes also contribute to risk by leading to greater adiposity and therefore overweight, if not accompanied by increased energy expenditure. Therefore, restriction of energy intake and avoidance of overweight are probably important at key stages of life. In women, being overweight at puberty and after the menopause appears to be linked to increased breast cancer risks, but pre-menopausal overweight may be protective. These findings are linked to pre-sensitization of breast tissue to oestrogens in the young adolescent, and unopposed production of oestrogens by adipose tissue after the menopause. Both may promote the development of oestrogen-dependent tumours. Levels of ovarian hormones appear to be influenced by nutritional status; thus, a high caloric intake may increase production and thereby risk of breast cancer. A correlation between breast cancer risks, sex hormone levels and energy intakes has been found in countries across the world. Sex hormones produced or modified by adipose tissue may also play a part in cancer of the endometrium in women and possibly the prostate in men.

A review of data on energy intake and cancers also indicates a positive relationship with large bowel cancer. This may reflect greater exposure to carcinogens with the greater food intake but more evidence is needed in this area.

Fat intakes

Fat has been described as a promoter of carcinogenesis, although the effect of dietary fat is often difficult to distinguish from that of energy intake, as fat obviously contributes to the total energy content of the diet. Associations with fat intake have been reported for cancers of the breast, colon and prostate, as well as weak relationships for cancer of the ovary, kidneys and pancreas.

In the case of breast cancer, there is still considerable controversy. Estimated fat consumption in different countries of the world shows a strong positive correlation with age-adjusted death rates from breast cancer. In the USA, the Nurses Health Study (Willett et al., 1992) found no association between total fat intake or intake of fibre and the incidence of breast cancer in both pre- and post-menopausal women. It is possible that the prevailing higher fat intakes lead to earlier menarche in girls, thereby prolonging the exposure of breast tissue to circulating oestrogens and increasing risk. This has not, however, been fully investigated. Although in animals there is evidence of a promoting effect of *n*-6 fatty acids and an inhibitory effect of *n*-3 fatty acids on mammary tumour growth, this effect has not been demonstrated in humans. It has been suggested that *n*-6 fatty acid intakes may already be above the threshold of this promoting effect, after which no further increase is seen. This may explain the absence of evidence in women. Nevertheless, it is probably prudent to limit fat intakes, even if this simply reduces total energy intake, and thereby provides some protection.

Dietary changes in Japan in the last 40 years have included a dramatic increase in fat intake, paralleled by a reduction in complex carbohydrates. Associated with these dietary changes has been an increase in colon cancer, suggesting a link. Evidence for the involvement of fat intake is stronger in the case of colon cancer, particularly in relation to fat of animal origin, cholesterol and red meat consumption. Further evidence from the US Nurses Health Study has shown a 2.5-fold increase in risk of colon cancer in women consuming beef, pork and lamb daily, compared with those eating these meats less than monthly. Association with chicken and fish was negative, and there was no association with cholesterol intakes. It has been proposed that dietary fat causes a greater secretion of bile acids; these may be fermented by anaerobic bacteria in the colon to produce mutagenic compounds, leading to abnormal cell proliferation in the colon. However, other dietary factors may modify this process, most notably NSPs and protective factors in fruit and vegetables. The lowered pH of the bowel as a result of soluble NSP fermentation may be protective.

Prostate cancer has also been weakly associated with a high fat intake, but more evidence is needed to support this. Overall, it remains problematic to separate the effects of higher fat intakes from those of a high energy intake and overweight.

Alcohol

There is an association between consumption of alcohol and cancers of the aerodigestive tract (mouth, throat and oesophagus), as well as the liver. The EPIC study has confirmed that the risk of these cancers is nine times greater in those drinking 60 g ethanol or more (7–8 units) a day compared with those drinking 30 g or less. The effects of alcohol as a causative agent are potentiated by smoking, with those smoking more than 20 cigarettes a day having a 50-fold greater risk than non-smoking, moderate alcohol drinkers. The risks of oral and pharyngeal cancers can be offset to some extent with a high intake of fruit and vegetables.

Oesophageal cancer has been increasing since the early 1970s in the UK, which parallels the increase in alcohol consumption, with a latency of 15–20 years. It is not clear if the relationship is simply with the amount of alcohol consumed; some evidence suggests that spirits are more harmful than beer and wine. Oesophageal cancer also occurs in parts of the world where alcohol consumption is low. In these cases, it is thought to be related to micronutrient deficiencies in the diet.

Alcohol consumption, above a moderate level, has also been shown in the EPIC study to be associated with a rise in breast cancer, although there was no evidence of a dose–response relationship with wine consumption.

Salt

Salt has been suggested as a causative factor in stomach cancer because it was noted that mortality from this cancer was closely related to the incidence of stroke in communities. This was found to be true between countries, between different regions of the same country and different subgroups of the population. Salt has high osmotic activity and has been reported to cause gastritis in animals, resulting in early damage to the mucosa. Other factors are also important, most notably the presence of *Helicobacter pylori*, which is now known to be a major cause of chronic atrophic gastritis and which must be taken into account in future studies on the exact role of salt as a factor in causation of stomach cancer.

In addition to sodium chloride, other forms of preservation using nitrates and nitrites as well as pickling have been associated with stomach cancers. Nitrates occur in the diet as preservatives in foods, such as ham, bacon and sausages, in beer, and are naturally present in vegetables as well as in the drinking water, particularly in agricultural areas owing to contamination from fertilizers. Dietary nitrates may not cause cancer per se, but it has been proposed that the conversion to nitrites and subsequently to carcinogenic nitrosamines is more likely in the presence of low gastric acidity. Both *H. pylori* infection and a high salt intake are thought to cause low gastric acidity and this may complete the link with nitrites.

The decline in both stroke mortality and gastric cancer over the last 20–30 years may be explained by decreases in salt intake with advances in food preservation. Refrigeration and deep freezing have reduced the use of salt as a preservative for meat, fish and vegetables. In addition, there has been much greater all year round availability of fruit and vegetables. The vitamin C content of these inhibits the formation of nitrosamines in the stomach, and may be an important protective factor. Conversely, nitrosamine formation is promoted by thiocyanates from cigarette smoke and smokers have been shown to have higher rates of gastric cancer. The decline in smoking may also have had an effect on the incidence of this disease.

Meat and fish

Nitrogenous residues from meat digestion, as well as other proteins, may be metabolized in the large bowel to produce ammonia and the amount produced increases with meat consumption. Ammonia has been shown to induce cell proliferation in human colonic cells and to produce adenocarcinomas in rats. Other products from meat ingestion that may contribute to the promotion of colon cancer are N-nitrosocompounds, which increase with red meat (but not white meat or fish) intake, and heterocyclic amines. The latter are formed during the cooking of meat, and are dependent on temperature, duration and amount and type of fat in the meat. High-temperature cooking, for example, grilling, barbecuing and frying, also produces polycyclic hydrocarbons and has been associated with higher cancer risk. Molecular biology has identified 'fast' and 'slow' acetylators among human subjects. The conversion of heterocyclic amines to carcinogenic products in 'fast acetylators' appears to increase their risk of developing adenomatous polyps, which are considered to be pre-cancerous. Subjects who are slow acetylators appear to be much less at risk.

Processed meats, including ham, sausages, bacon, have also been linked to moderately increased risk of colon cancer, which has been shown in the EPIC study to be 50 per cent greater in those subjects consuming 60 g/day of processed meat than in those consuming none. Early results from the EPIC study have not, however, shown a significant increase in colon cancer with red meat intake, but some protective effect was indicated from white meat and fish intakes, and further results are awaited. A number of other cancers have been linked in some studies with meat consumption. These include cancer of the breast, lung, prostate and pancreas, but in all cases the evidence for an association is weak. There is some evidence that stomach cancer may be linked with consumption of processed meat (see 'Salt' section above). The great variety of ways in which people preserve and cook meat across the world, makes this a particularly challenging area for study.

Other promoters of cancer

A number of other dietary factors have been linked with the promotion of cancers (Table 15.2), although the data so far are equivocal and no firm connections have been proved. In most

TABLE 15.2 Some proposed links between dietary components and cancers

Dietary component	Suggested link with cancer site	Mechanism/interpretation
Moulds: aflatoxin	Liver	Grows on peanuts: important cause of cancer in some countries in Africa
Caffeine	Bladder, pancreas	Relationship very weak, at normal levels of consumption May be protective in colon cancer
Iron	Colon and rectum	Relates to tissue levels of iron, not dietary intakes; may represent a breakdown of iron regulatory mechanisms
High levels of maternal nutrition/adiposity	Testicular cancer	Endocrine environment of developing fetus affected, predisposes both to undescended testes and cancer
Calcium	Colon and rectum	Weak relationship; possible action through binding of intestinal fats and thus reduces bile acid secretion
Vitamin D	Colon and rectum	May control cell growth and differentiation; weak association
Folate	Colon and rectum	Inverse relationship between plasma levels and colorectal polyps; aggravated by high alcohol intake

cases, it is difficult to separate the effect of the proposed factor from that of associated dietary components.

Possible protective factors

Non-starch polysaccharides (dietary fibre)

Early observations, such as those of Burkitt et al. (1972), found a low incidence of diseases of the bowel in communities that had a large consumption of plant foods. This was developed into a theory about the protective effects of dietary fibre in a number of diseases. Knowledge about this fraction, now called 'non-starch polysaccharides' in the UK, is currently much more extensive. It is believed that NSPs may protect against colon cancer by three possible mechanisms.

- High levels of NSP in the diet lead to increased bulk, mainly due to an increase in colonic bacteria, and, therefore, faster transit time through the colon. As a result, potentially harmful carcinogenic substances are present in a more dilute form and are in contact with the colonic mucosa for a shorter time.
- Fermentation of soluble NSP (as well as resistant starch) in the colon yields a number of short-chain fatty acids, which influence epithelial cell function. Most notable is butyric acid, which has been shown to be an antiproliferative and differentiating agent, able to induce apoptosis (programmed cell death) in the large bowel epithelium.
- As a result of the formation of the short-chain fatty acids, NSP in the diet reduces the pH of the bowel. This allows primary bile acids to bind to calcium, preventing them from being converted to mutagenic secondary bile acids. The lower pH also increases the number of aerobic bacteria, which do not produce carcinogenic products from bile acids. More of the bile acids are excreted, bound to components such as lignin. Studies in which subjects were supplemented with wheat bran showed a reduced mutagenicity in stool samples.

Problems with interpreting studies on intakes of 'fibre' and the incidence of cancer arise because of confusion over the definition of the fractions of fibre in the diet and the lack of detailed food composition data on this. Controversy over which fractions of fibre intake are more important in prevention of colon cancer continues, with some studies supporting a role for fruit and vegetables, and others for cereal fibre. Further difficulties arise from the effects of a change of NSP content in the diet on its other constituents, which may also be involved in cancer development.

It is also possible that a high intake of vegetables and fruit, and perhaps cereals, indicates an increased intake of other substances, such as antioxidants or flavonoids, which may be protective, rather than just the NSP they contain. The EPIC study has reported a 40 per cent lower incidence of colon cancer in subjects eating a high-fibre diet (32.5 g), compared with those eating only 12 g of fibre.

In the case of breast cancer, women consuming 'high-fibre' diets have been found to excrete more inactivated conjugated oestrogen in the faeces, with resultant lower plasma levels. However, evidence that high-fibre diets are protective against breast cancer is weak. Recent evidence suggests that soya products may offer some protection against breast and prostate cancer because of the presence of phyto-oestrogens. These are believed to increase the synthesis of oestrogen-binding proteins, and thereby reduce the levels of these hormones in both men and women. Related compounds called lignans may be found in whole cereals, seeds and fruit, and may in part account for some of the findings attributed to 'dietary fibre' in protection against breast cancer.

Fruit and vegetables

One of the most consistent findings in all of the literature on diet and cancer is that incidence is lower where fruit and vegetable intakes are high. Conversely, there is no recorded increased risk of any cancer associated with fruit and vegetable consumption. The initial understanding of the mechanisms involved was that the antioxidant nutrients present in fruit and vegetables were responsible for the protective effect. The suggested mechanism links the antioxidant nutrients to the prevention of oxidative damage to the DNA by free radicals, and hence the initiation of damage. These nutrients also protect lipids in cellular membranes and may contribute to the stabilization of cells (see Chapter 14). Fruit and vegetables are also a source of NSPs and many other nutrients, which may play a role through different mechanisms. In addition, fruit and vegetables contain a wide variety of other chemically active substances that may play an important role in the overall effect, and research in this area is still relatively new (see Chapter 17). A problem associated with studies of fruit and vegetables is the inconsistency of definition of terms used. For example, potatoes or pulses may or may not be included in the vegetables group. Tomatoes may be included as either fruit or vegetables and in some studies, fruit and vegetables are subdivided into smaller groups by colour. In reviews of evidence, therefore, the whole group of fruit and/or vegetables may be considered in general.

There is moderately strong evidence that colorectal and stomach cancers are fewer in incidence in communities where there is a high level of intake of fruit and vegetables (above 500 g/day). These findings have been confirmed by early data from the EPIC study. There is also some evidence for a protective effect against breast, lung and oesophageal cancers. Finally, although there are too few data at present to draw any firm conclusions, there is also a probable protective effect against prostate, cervical, pancreatic and bladder cancers.

Antioxidant nutrients

Fruit and vegetables provide the three most studied antioxidants, namely vitamin A (and carotenoids), C and E. Proposed mechanisms of action for a protective effect have been explored, but no firm conclusions have been possible.

Retinoids (vitamin A family) regulate epithelial cell differentiation and could, therefore, influence tumour growth in tissues. Carotenoids are powerful quenchers of singlet oxygen and, therefore, act as antioxidants to minimize damage. It has also been postulated that the role of carotenoids may be mediated through potentiation of immune system activity.

Initial epidemiological studies had suggested that vitamin A (as retinol) was protective against lung cancer. More recent data have shown a consistent inverse relationship between the incidence of lung cancer and intakes of various carotenoids (precursors of vitamin A) as well as high plasma levels of beta-carotene. Nevertheless, results of supplementation trials have not been encouraging. Supplementation of 30 000 Finnish male smokers with either beta-carotene and/or vitamin E or placebo resulted in an increased mortality from lung cancer and coronary disease in the carotene group (Alpha-tocopherol, Beta-carotene Cancer Prevention Study Group, 1994). Similar results have occurred in at least two other trials. Studies on lung cancer are often difficult to interpret because of the strong confounding effect of smoking. However, excessive amounts of any single antioxidant are undesirable, since an imbalance can promote some pro-oxidant activity. Supplementation with beta-carotene has also been associated with an increased risk of colon cancer in two studies.

The Nurses Health Study in the USA found a 20 per cent rise in breast cancer rates between the highest and lowest intakes of vitamin A and carotenoids. Among women with the lowest dietary intake of vitamin A, the use of a supplement reduced the risk of breast cancer. Results for stomach and prostate cancers, however, do not show a consistent trend.

Vitamin C may also be an important protective factor against cancers of the oesophagus, stomach and pancreas. This role may be linked to its antioxidant properties, especially in association with vitamin E. It also has a protective role for the mixed function oxidase systems in the liver, which are important for destroying foreign and harmful substances. The most researched function of vitamin C is its role in inhibiting nitrosamine formation in the stomach, thereby reducing the risks of stomach cancer. Levels of vitamin C in the stomach are reduced by *H. pylori* infection, which results in a loss of gastric acid secretion and consequent increase in stomach pH. This situation favours bacterial colonization and increased formation of nitrites and nitroso-compounds.

Results of studies into the relationship between vitamin E and cancers at various sites are inconclusive, with better results obtained in smokers than non-smokers. Results are complicated by the interaction of vitamin E with selenium status and plasma cholesterol levels. A supplementation study with various combinations of nutrients in a poorly nourished population in Linxian, China, achieved a significant reduction in mortality from stomach cancer in those subjects receiving vitamin E, beta-carotene and selenium (Blot et al., 1993). It is likely that initial intakes were low, thus contributing to the positive finding.

Most of the findings described above relate to fruit and vegetable intakes as part of the whole diet. It is perhaps unsurprising, therefore, that attempts to replicate the results with single constituents of these foods have been unsuccessful. What is more concerning is that unexpected adverse effects have occurred. This emphasizes once again the need for a balance of nutrients in the diet, to provide appropriate amounts for their metabolic role at cellular level.

Other chemically active constituents

A number of phenolic compounds are found in fruit and vegetables. These include flavonoids, such as quercetin and catechins, which act as antioxidants and may have roles in gene blocking or suppression. However, no convincing evidence exists at present of a protective role in cancer. Phyto-oestrogens are also a class of phenolic compounds, the most important examples are isoflavones, found in soya, and lignans, which occur in linseed, lentils, asparagus, broccoli and leeks. These compounds can act as oestrogen agonists (promote or mimic the action) and antagonists (oppose the action), depending on the receptors to which they bind. It is this potential to prevent a normal oestrogen response that may offer protection against hormone-dependent tumours, such as breast and prostate. However, the evidence base to support this proposal is weak at present.

Members of the brassica vegetable family (cabbage, broccoli, cauliflower, Brussels sprouts) are particularly rich in glucosinolates, which have been shown to have blocking and suppressing properties in the development of cancers. However, large amounts may also be potentially toxic, so a cautious approach and more research are needed. Garlic, onions and leeks, all of which belong to the Allium family, also have potential blocking and suppressing properties, which have been demonstrated in rats to suppress the formation of gastric cancer. Epidemiological studies suggest a possible protective role in humans.

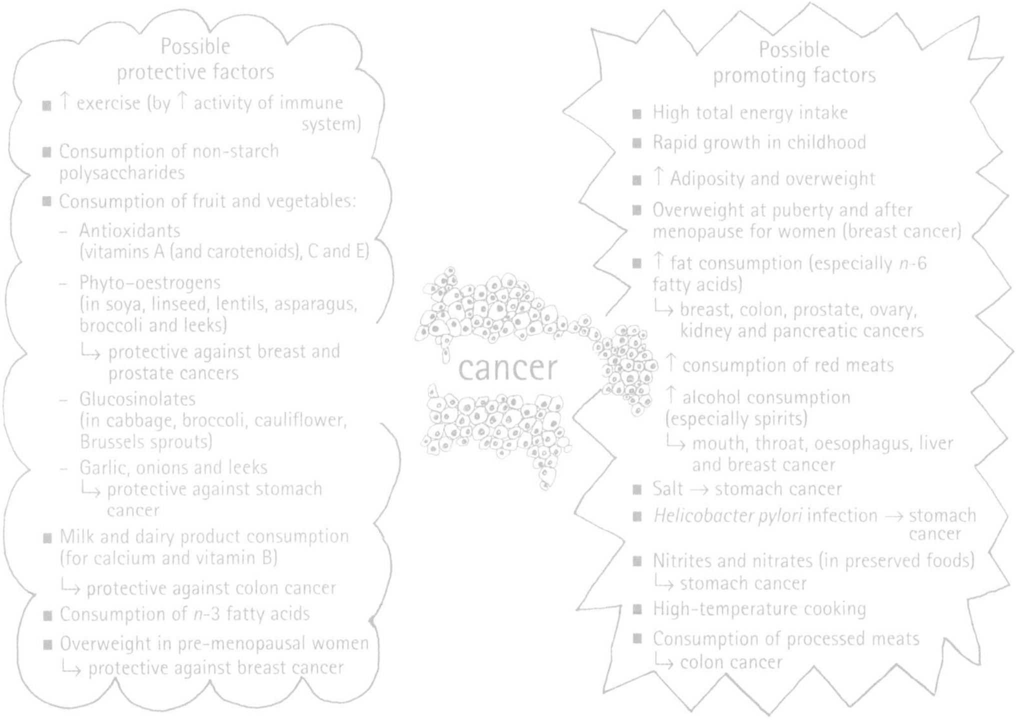

Figure 15.1 Possible promoting and protective factors in the diet in relation to cancer development.

Further research is needed, however, to demonstrate if the positive effects of fruit and vegetables in the prevention of cancer may be attributed to any of these constituents.

Calcium

In recent years, a number of studies have indicated an inverse relationship between the intake of calcium, particularly in the form of dairy products, and colon cancer. It is suggested that calcium binds fatty acids and bile acids in the colon, preventing them from causing damage to the mucosa. It is possible that calcium itself has an antiproliferative action on the colonic cells, thus preventing tumour formation. In addition, a role for vitamin D in prevention of colon cancer has also been proposed, linked to its function in control of cell proliferation. Milk may produce benefits in other ways. Whey proteins are rich in cysteine, which is a precursor of the antioxidant glutathione. In addition, milk contains lactoferrin, which can bind iron in the digestive tract, making it less available to act as a pro-oxidant.

Supplementation studies have again produced equivocal results, once more indicating that attention to foods rather than individual nutrients may be the key to prevention. Figure 15.1 summarizes possible promoting and preventive effects of nutrients.

PREVENTION OF CANCER

In the UK, healthy eating policy is embodied in the 'Eight Guidelines for a Healthy Diet', the Department of Health Dietary Reference Values (DoH, 1991) and the Balance of Good Health. All of these give advice about a diet that aims to reduce the intake of foods containing fats and sugars and to increase the intakes of starchy carbohydrates, fruit and vegetables. Ensuring a moderate intake of sources of protein, from meat, fish, dairy products and their alternatives for vegetarians, will also provide other minerals and vitamins. Maintaining a normal body weight through adequate, but not excessive energy intakes and exercise is also important.

TABLE 15.3 Summary of diet and health recommendations (WCRF, 1997)

Factor	Public health goal	Advice to individuals
Food supply and eating	Populations to consume nutritionally adequate and varied diets based primarily on foods of plant origin	Choose predominantly plant-based diets rich in a variety of vegetables and fruits, pulses and minimally processed starchy staple foods
Maintaining body weight	Population average BMI throughout adult life to be within the range 21–23, in order that individual BMI be maintained between 18.5 and 25	Avoid being underweight or overweight, and limit weight gain during adulthood to less than 5 kg
Maintaining physical activity	Populations to maintain throughout life, an active lifestyle, equivalent to a PAL of at least 1.75, with opportunities for vigorous physical activity	If occupational activity is low or moderate, take an hour's brisk walk or similar exercise daily and also exercise vigorously for a total of at least 1 hour each week
Vegetables and fruit	Promote year-round consumption of a variety of vegetables and fruit, providing 7% or more of total energy	Eat 400–800 g or five or more portions a day of a variety of vegetables and fruit, all year round
Other plant foods	A variety of starch or protein-rich foods of plant origin, preferably minimally processed, to provide 45–60% total energy. Refined sugar to provide less than 10% total energy	Eat 600–800 g or more than seven portions of a variety of cereals, pulses, roots, tubers and plantains. Prefer minimally processed foods. Limit consumption of refined sugar
Alcoholic drinks	Consumption of alcohol is not recommended and excessive consumption is to be discouraged. For those who drink alcohol, restrict it to less than 5% total energy for men and 2.5% for women	Alcohol consumption is not recommended. If consumed, limit drinks to less than two drinks per day for men and one per day for women
Meat	If eaten at all, red meat to provide less than 10% total energy	If eaten at all, limit intake of red meat to less than 80 g daily. Choose fish, poultry or meat from non-domesticated animals in place of red meat
Total fats and oils	Total fats and oils to provide 15% to no more than 30% total energy	Limit consumption of fatty foods, particularly those of animal origin. Choose modest amounts of appropriate vegetable oils
Salt and salting	Salt from all sources should amount to less than 6 g/day for adults	Limit consumption of salted foods and use of cooking and table salt. Use herbs and spices to season foods

BMI, body mass index; PAL, physical activity level.

In 1998, the Department of Health Report on Nutritional Aspects of the Development of Cancer published a number of specific recommendations in this area. In essence, they do not differ from the broader guidelines on healthy eating.

They are:

- to maintain a healthy body weight within the body mass index (BMI) range 20–25 and not to increase it during adult life;
- to increase intakes of a wide variety of fruit and vegetables;
- to increase intakes of non-starch polysaccharides (dietary fibre) from a variety of food sources;
- for adults, individuals' consumption of red and processed meat should not rise; higher consumers should consider a reduction and, as a consequence of this the population average will fall.

These recommendations should be followed in the context of the Committee on Medical Aspects of Food Policy (COMA)'s wider recommendations for a balanced diet rich in cereals, fruits and vegetables. In addition, it was recommended that:

- beta-carotene supplements as a means of avoiding cancer should not be used;
- caution should be exercised in the use of high doses of purified supplements of other micronutrients, as they cannot be assumed to be without risk.

The World Cancer Research Fund has identified the 'five-star' foods for cancer prevention:

- foods rich in beta-carotene – spinach, carrots, broccoli and tomatoes;
- foods rich in vitamin C – citrus fruits, berries, melons, green vegetables, tomatoes, cauliflowers and green peppers;
- foods rich in selenium – bran, wheat germ, tuna fish, onion, garlic and mushrooms;
- foods rich in vitamin E – wholegrain cereals, wheat germ, soya beans and leafy greens;
- foods rich in complex carbohydrates – bread, cereals, beans and peas.

These foods should be eaten in place of fattier items and can help to reduce overweight. They may also contain other important substances that may help the body's resistance to cancer.

The World Cancer Research Fund Report, published in 1997, took a global perspective on the prevention of cancer and made recommendations that were also consistent with the prevention of other diseases. They contain policy goals and advice for individuals. It was, however, intended by the report that the relative importance of the different recommendations would vary in different parts of the world, for their populations. They are summarized in Table 15.3.

In addition to the recommendations detailed above, the WCRF also identified safe storage, preservation and preparation of foods as well as the presence of additives and residues as important areas for public health policy. Recommendations were also made against the use of dietary supplements and tobacco use. Overall, the recommendations shown in Table 15.3 go further than those of the UK in recommending a move to a more plant-based diet. Many of these changes would be difficult to implement for the majority of people in the UK. However, selecting a diet from the Balance of Good Health in the proportions recommended will provide a good balance of the nutrients needed. What is also needed is the motivation and the desire to be healthy! Although much research is still required to further elucidate the role of dietary factors in certain cancers, we already have sufficient information to make recommendations that can significantly reduce the risk.

SUMMARY

1. Diet may play a major role in the development of cancer.
2. Particular aspects of the diet that may be involved as promoters and protective factors have been identified.
3. Dietary guidelines for the prevention of cancer have been proposed. These include a high intake of fruit and vegetables and avoidance of excess intakes of fat and energy. Protein intake, especially from meat sources, should also be moderated. Lifestyle changes, including regular physical activity are needed to support the dietary adjustments.

STUDY QUESTIONS

1 Why is it difficult to study the relationship between nutrition and cancer?

2 a In what ways have dietary fats been linked with the development of cancers?

b Why is it difficult to distinguish the effects of fats from those of total energy intake in cancer causation?

3 List the reasons why an increase in non-starch polysaccharides (dietary fibre) intake might protect against some cancers.

4 How does the advice on diet for cancer prevention compare with general healthy eating guidelines?

5 a In what ways might the antioxidant nutrients be useful in the prevention of cancers?

b Does the scientific evidence currently support this theory?

REFERENCES AND FURTHER READING

Alpha-tocopherol, Beta-carotene Cancer Prevention Study Group 1994: The effect of vitamin E and beta-carotene on the incidence of lung cancer and other cancers in male smokers. *New England Journal of Medicine* 330(15), 1029–35.

Bingham, S.A. 1999: High meat diets and cancer risk. *Proceedings of the Nutrition Society* 58, 243–8.

Blot, W.J., Li, J.-Y., Taylor, P.R. et al. 1993: Nutrition intervention trials in Linxian, China: supplementation with specific vitamin/mineral combinations, cancer incidence and disease specific mortality in general population. *Journal of the National Cancer Institute* 85, 1483–92.

Burkitt, D.P., Walker, A.R.P., Painter, N.S. 1972: Effect of dietary fibre on stools and transit times and its role in the causation of disease. *Lancet* ii, 1408–12.

Burr, M.L. 1994: Antioxidants and cancer. *Journal of Human Nutrition and Dietetics* 7, 409–16.

DoH (UK Department of Health) 1991: *Dietary reference values for food energy and nutrients for the United Kingdom.* Report on Health and Social Subjects No. 41. Report of the Panel on Dietary Reference Values of the Committee on Medical Aspects of Food Policy. London: HMSO.

DoH (UK Department of Health) 1998: *Nutritional aspects of the development of cancer.* Report on Health and Social Subjects 48. London: The Stationery Office.

Frankel, S., Gunnell, D.J., Peters, T.J. et al. 1998: Childhood energy intake and adult mortality from cancer: the Boyd Orr cohort study. *British Medical Journal* 316, 499–504.

Key, T. 1994: Micronutrients and cancer aetiology: the epidemiological evidence. *Proceedings of the Nutrition Society* 53, 605–14.

National Dairy Council (NDC) 1995: *Nutrition and cancer.* Fact File 12. London: NDC.

Riboli, E. 1991: Nutrition and cancer: background and rationale of the European prospective investigation into cancer and nutrition (EPIC). *Annals of Oncology* 3, 783–91.

Riboli, E., Norat, T. 2001: Cancer prevention and diet: opportunities in Europe. *Public Health Nutrition* 4(2B), 475–84.

Willett, W.C., Hunter, D.J., Stampfer, M.J. et al. 1992: Dietary fat and fibre in relation to role in breast cancer. *Journal of the American Medical Association* 268, 2037–44.

Williams, C.M. 1996: Nutrition and breast cancer: facts and controversies. In Buttriss, J., Hyman, K. (eds) *Focus on women: nutrition and health.* London: National Dairy Council.

World Cancer Research Fund 1997: *Food, nutrition and the prevention of cancer: a global perspective.* Washington, DC: World Cancer Research Fund and American Institute for Cancer Research.

16 CHALLENGES TO NUTRITIONAL STATUS

The aim of this chapter is to:

- identify situations that provide an additional challenge to the maintenance of the nutritional status. This may be as a result of obstacles to food intake, difficulties in digestion and absorption, or altered metabolic states that affect what the body can obtain from the food ingested.

On completing the study of this chapter, you should be able to:

- identify a number of conditions or situations that impose an additional challenge to nutritional status;
- use the framework of nutrient 'intake–processing–utilization' to explain how each of the situations creates a threat to nutrition;
- provide some practical solutions to help people in these situations.

In considering challenges to nutrition, it is useful to consider the stages through which food has to travel to achieve its purpose of providing our bodies with the necessary nutrients. A useful framework is that of 'intake-processing-utilization', which summarizes this pathway from food in the marketplace or kitchen to metabolism at the cell level. Obstacles or problems at any of the stages of this pathway will affect the ultimate achievement of satisfying nutritional requirements. This framework will be used in the following discussions.

ADVERSE REACTIONS TO FOOD

Since the 1980s there has been a considerable growth of public interest in adverse reactions to food, all of which are often (mistakenly) grouped together as 'food allergy'. The extent of these problems is difficult to ascertain precisely, as levels of self-reporting are invariably greater than can be confirmed by rigorous testing.

It is useful to start with some definitions of terms that are consistent with current practice in the UK. It should be noted, however, that there are variations in these classifications within Europe and the USA.

Adverse reactions to food may be of three types:

- food poisoning – includes reactions resulting from contaminants within the food;
- food aversion – includes psychological reactions, which may not be reproduced on covert introduction of the food;
- food intolerance – includes reproducible adverse reactions to food.

The first of these occurs as a result of triggers from outside the individual and is believed to be the most commonly occurring of the adverse reactions. The remaining two types relate to responses that are initiated within the individual in response to the food eaten and are considered to be less common.

Food poisoning

This occurs as a result of the consumption of contaminated food or water that results in disease of an infectious or toxic nature. In the UK and Europe, the causative agents are most likely to be microorganisms. However, in other parts of the world, food poisoning may occur as a result of chemical contamination, parasites or toxins naturally present in the food or acquired within the food. Bacterial food poisoning occurring in the UK includes that caused by *Campylobacter*, *Salmonella* spp. and *Escherichia coli*. Some bacteria produce toxins, which cause the symptoms; these include *Staphylococcus aureus*, *Bacillus cereus* and *Clostridium botulinum*. Foods that may be contaminated include eggs, poultry, cold meats, rice and spices. Among the viral causes of food poisoning, the most widespread are highly infectious, small round structured viruses (SRSVs), which may contaminate shellfish, but more probably are introduced into food from infected food handlers. Consumers in semi-closed communities, such as hospitals, hotels and schools are particularly vulnerable.

Contamination of food can occur, for example, from use of dirty water, sewerage overspill, and agricultural chemicals. Some plant foods may contain toxins, for example, uncooked red kidney beans or some fungi, or may be contaminated with moulds, for example, aflatoxins, which affect groundnuts (peanuts).

Most commonly, food poisoning causes rapid vomiting and diarrhoea, although a few of the agents can cause serious damage to the liver, kidneys, nervous system and may even be fatal. The young, sick and elderly are the most vulnerable to serious consequences from bacterial food poisoning.

Food aversion

Many people may be able to list foods that they avoid, generally because of a sensory preference or dislike. This may be taken to an extreme avoidance of almost all foods in the case of anorexia nervosa. In some cases, an individual believes that the food causes them unpleasant symptoms, perhaps as a result of an experience in the past where the food was temporally associated with sickness or gastrointestinal upset. In this case, the food is avoided because of an aversion to it and an associated psychological belief that the food is harmful. When tested blind, however, it is generally not possible to reproduce any alleged symptoms, and the conclusion must be drawn that this is a psychosomatic adverse reaction rather than one that has a true physiological basis.

Aversion may also be applied to foods that are believed to affect other aspects of health, for example, tiredness, sleep problems, palpitations, bloatedness and flatulence. The individual excludes particular foods to correct these symptoms, although double-blind testing generally fails to find any scientific basis for this practice. To date, in most of these cases, there is no evidence to support a link between the food and the symptoms.

Food intolerance

This is the only group of adverse reactions to food for which reproducible responses can be produced on challenge. Precise figures for prevalence are difficult to obtain because:

- questionnaires are unreliable because of bias from respondents;
- diagnosis is time consuming (e.g. use of elimination diets followed by challenge);
- there are no simple reliable tests and these also may not be particularly sensitive;
- there is an almost limitless number of foodstuffs and additives that can provoke a response;
- reactions vary between individuals and, especially in children, may change over time;
- responses may occur immediately or after a considerable period after ingestion; these are poorly understood and difficult to diagnose.

Although many studies have attempted to quantify the extent of food intolerance, a lack of consensus over definitions and methodologies has made it difficult to arrive at reliable results on prevalence.

In 1994, a study in the UK found that, in a sample of over 18 000 people, 20 per cent complained of food intolerance, commonly citing eight different foods (Young et al., 1994). When tested with a controlled challenge, food intolerance was confirmed in only 1.4–1.8 per cent of the total. This is in line with the generally accepted figure of 1–2 per cent of the adult population exhibiting food intolerance, with a higher prevalence in children of perhaps 5–8 per cent.

Food intolerance may be further subdivided into:

- allergic reactions – immunoglobulin E (IgE)-mediated and non-IgE-mediated;
- pharmacological reactions;
- enzyme reactions.

The clinical presentation of food intolerance may be immediate or delayed onset, and is likely to affect the following tissues and systems (see Figure 16.1 for a summary).

- *Gastrointestinal system.* Symptoms include mouth tingling or swelling, abdominal pain, bloating of the abdomen, vomiting and diarrhoea or constipation. In chronic intolerance, there can be bleeding or loss of plasma protein into the gut lumen, with damage to the gut mucosa.
- *Skin.* Dermatitis, urticaria, angio-oedema and eczema are common consequences.
- *Respiratory system.* Rhinitis, laryngeal oedema and asthma (including wheezing, breathlessness) may occur.
- *Central nervous system.* Symptoms include migraine and possibly some behavioural abnormalities (including hyperactivity and depression), although the evidence for these is controversial.

Food allergy is a form of specific food intolerance that causes reproducible symptoms and includes an abnormal reaction by the immune system. Our diet contains a variety of substances that can stimulate immune responses. They are usually proteins or simple chemicals bound to proteins and are termed allergens. Usually these allergens are prevented from being absorbed by secretory immunoglobulin A (IgA) lining the gut. However, IgA is absent in the first months of life, so that allergens can be absorbed. Breast milk contains IgA, and may offer some protection. Avoidance of contact with potential allergens is important at this age, especially where there is a family history of allergy, although complete protection is unlikely. However, in general our immune system has evolved responses that allow it to be tolerant to the antigen burden represented by ingested food. This is known as oral tolerance. In some cases, these allergens induce an immune response, usually producing antibodies, which can be detected in the serum, but which are not pathogenic – known as immunological acceptance.

In a minority of individuals, however, this response is abnormal and results in pathological changes when the allergen is ingested, resulting in a food allergy. The immune system responds inappropriately against the allergen to stimulate IgE antibodies sensitized to the particular allergen. These are mainly attached to mast cells and on stimulation cause immediate degranulation of the mast cells and the release of a range of chemical mediators. These include histamine and prostaglandins, which have potent effects.

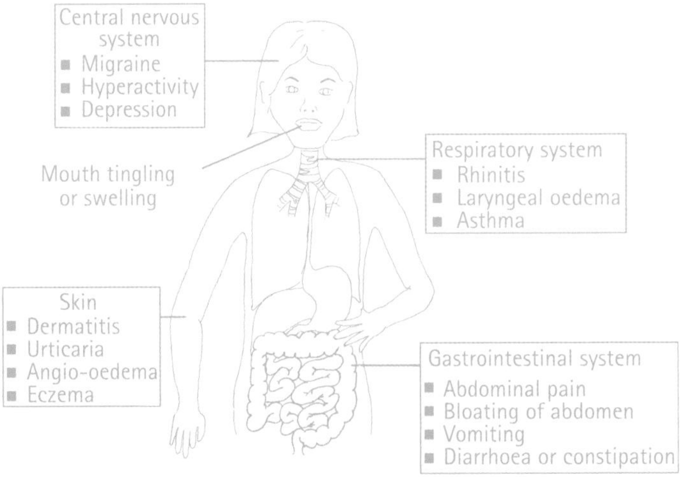

Figure 16.1 Symptoms of food intolerance.

The consequent reaction depends on the size of the dose, the speed of absorption and the distribution of the allergen in the body.

The response to the release of histamine and prostaglandins generally includes some or all of the following:

- dilation of small blood vessels (redness);
- increased permeability of blood vessels (swelling/oedema);
- contraction of smooth muscle in the airways (breathing difficulties) or intestines (causing abdominal pain); and
- stimulation of nerve endings in the skin (itching and pain).

Reactions may be seen in the following:

- the mouth, immediately following ingestion;
- the gastrointestinal tract, when the allergen reaches this area;
- one of many other sites, including the skin and respiratory system, including the nose and airways;
- several other sites, causing a widespread and possibly life-threatening reaction (see Figure 16.2).

The severity of the reaction varies between individuals and may range from mild to life threatening (anaphylactic shock), resulting from a severe fall of blood pressure and possibly

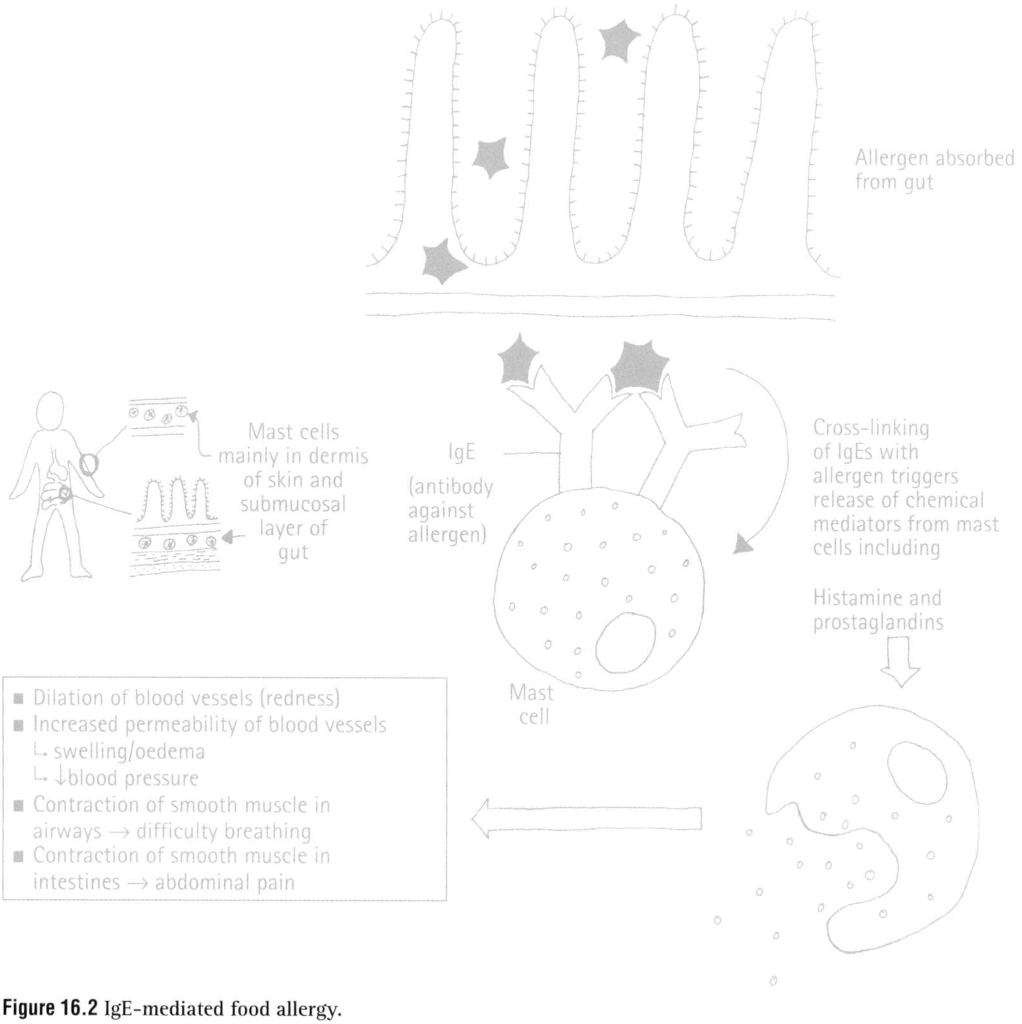

Figure 16.2 IgE-mediated food allergy.

difficulties in breathing. Immediate help in the form of an adrenaline injection is required for anyone suffering from such a major allergic reaction. Fortunately, most are not so extreme and recovery follows, resulting from the body's own homeostatic mechanisms, which cause endogenous adrenaline release.

Why do individuals develop food allergy?

Genetic predisposition is an important determinant of susceptibility to allergic disease, also called atopy. The susceptibility is more likely to be inherited from the mother than the father but, with two atopic parents, the likelihood is greatly increased. However, although the susceptibility is inherited, the actual allergens to which a child is sensitive are not necessarily the same as its parents. Babies that are born small for gestational age are more at risk of developing allergies in their first year. This suggests that growth faltering in the womb may play a role in poorer immunocompetence.

Studies suggest that the risk of atopy in a child can be reduced by avoidance of potential allergens in the mother's diet from very early pregnancy. In addition, breastfeeding for more than 4 months can reduce the development of atopic disease. Delaying the introduction of solids until after 4 months is also recommended, as well as the use of low allergen foods, such as baby rice, potatoes, fruit and vegetables.

There has been a general increase in the incidence of food and other allergies over the last 30 years. An explanation that is gaining acceptance is that modern children are exposed to fewer infectious diseases and live in a generally clean environment. This does not challenge the immune system, which is less well developed as a result, and reacts inappropriately when presented with harmless antigens, resulting in an allergic reaction.

A further explanation offered for the rising incidence of allergy is the change in balance between *n*-6 and *n*-3 fatty acids in our diets. The *n*-6 fatty acids are more predominant and fewer *n*-3 acids are consumed. The former are associated with more pro-inflammatory eicosanoids, including prostaglandins, which have an important role in allergic responses.

Foods associated with allergic reactions

Almost any food can produce an allergic reaction but some are much more likely to cause problems than others.

In children, the most common causes of food allergy are cows' milk, eggs, peanuts, fish, wheat, tree nuts, soya beans, soya products, vegetables or fruits. Milk allergy has been reported in 2–3 per cent of infants in Western countries, although in the majority (about 80 per cent), the allergy disappears by the age of 3 years. This is not surprising, as milk forms the basis of the infant's diet and cows' milk protein is often the first foreign protein to be introduced. Children with persistent milk allergy may develop hypersensitivities to other foods, especially egg, soya, peanuts, citrus, fish, tomato and cereals, as these are introduced into their diet. It is estimated that the prevalence of true food allergy in young children is about 1.4 per cent (range 0.5–3.8 per cent in the literature). Although children may grow out of some allergies, those to peanuts, tree nuts, fish and shellfish may persist into adult life.

Apart from the foods listed above for children, adults may experience cross-reactions between similar proteins in different foods. For example, tree and grass pollens can provoke reactions to fruits and vegetables. Clusters of hypersensitivities to members of the same botanical family can occur. Reports exist of allergy to apple and pear, kiwi fruit and avocado, potato and carrot, celery, cucumber, carrot and watermelon. These rarely cause anaphylactic reactions, although some have been reported.

Of great concern is the growing prevalence of peanut and tree nut allergy, both of which are associated with severe life-threatening reactions more commonly than the more traditional foods associated with allergies. In some individuals, sensitivity to peanuts is so great that as little as 100 μg of peanut protein can provoke symptoms. At present, the exact prevalence is unknown, but a prevalence of 0.5 per cent among UK children in 1996 was reported. The UK Department of Health (1997) has recommended that pregnant women with any history of atopy in the family should avoid eating peanuts during pregnancy.

The increased prevalence is reportedly linked to the increased exposure of young children to peanut proteins in peanut butter, cereals, confectionery and baked goods. Cold pressed peanut oil used in cooking may contain peanut protein. Many children appear to have become sensitized at a very young age, possibly from peanut oils in infant foods. There have been reported deaths from peanut allergy, resulting from rapid anaphylaxis affecting the larynx. Avoidance of peanuts is vital, as well as other pulses (or legumes) and other nuts. The use of adrenaline syringes in emergency is essential.

Non-IgE-mediated reactions

Adverse responses to food may not always involve IgE, and mast cells and other parts of the immune system may be involved, such as T-lymphocytes and scavenger cells. The reaction is generally delayed and may take several hours or even days to develop. In addition, the reactions to trigger foods may involve one system or several and may, therefore, imitate the reactions to IgE-mediated allergy described above. It is very difficult to identify and confirm the relationship between particular foods and an adverse reaction that occurs some time later and that also may be initiated by a number of different foods and possibly also environmental conditions.

The best defined example in this group is gluten sensitivity, whereby the immune system of genetically susceptible individuals reacts inappropriately to dietary gluten, causing a variety of problems. In coeliac disease, the target organ is the gastrointestinal tract, predominantly the region of the small intestine, in which a variety of changes are seen, resulting in malabsorption of nutrients. The skin may be affected, with an itchy blistering rash on the knees, thighs and elbows. There have also been reports of neurological manifestations of gluten sensitivity, although the evidence of this is not scientifically strong, and these disorders may be a result of nutritional deficiency consequent on malabsorption. Diagnosis of coeliac disease has classically been by small-bowel biopsy, but serological tests for antibodies found in the circulation are now also used. Exclusion of gluten from the diet resolves the changes affecting both the gut and the skin. A gluten-free diet should be maintained for life and lists of permitted foods are provided by the UK Coeliac Society. It is estimated that the prevalence of gluten sensitivity is 1 in 300 in Europe, with a 10 per cent risk of the condition in first-degree relatives of those already diagnosed. Although often identified in young children, the condition may be 'silent' and not diagnosed until adulthood. In this case, there may already be a number of existing nutritional deficiencies, such as folate or iron deficiency leading to anaemia, or inadequate calcium absorption resulting in poor bone development.

Other conditions for which a non-IgE-mediated allergic response has been investigated, but not confirmed include:

- urticaria and dermatitis;
- infantile colic;
- irritable bowel syndrome;
- asthma;
- migraine;
- hyperactivity and attention deficit hyperactivity disorder (ADHD);
- rheumatoid arthritis.

In all of the above, where there is an apparently strong history of food intolerance in the individual, it is important to test thoroughly with appropriate scientific techniques, if specific foods are causing the symptoms of illness. It is likely that, in some of these conditions, food is one of a number of triggers for the symptoms, which makes the diagnosis very difficult. Once identified, if a food has to be eliminated, this should be done with qualified professional advice to ensure the maintenance of adequate nutritional intake.

Pharmacological reactions

Some foods contain pharmacologically active agents or may cause the production of such agents in the body. Usually these are harmless unless ingested in relatively large amounts. Even when released in the body, the amounts needed are much larger than those involved in the IgE-mediated allergic reaction discussed earlier. For example, foods such as cheese (Roquefort, Parmesan, mature Cheddar), wine (and other fermented products), bananas, yeast extract, avocados, chocolate, oranges and some fish products (e.g. pickled fish) contain biogenic amines, such as histamine, tyramine, phenylethylamine and octopamine. Other foods may directly cause the release of histamine from mast cells; this has been shown to occur with chocolate, tomatoes and strawberries. Caffeine is another agent that can produce this type of intolerance, resulting in tachycardia (increased heart rate), irritability, sleep disturbances and intestinal colic. The dose at which this occurs may be as little as two cups of coffee or three cups of tea. Prunes contain hydroxyphenylisatin, which is a stimulant of intestinal motor activity and can produce rapid transit through the gut. Sodium nitrite present in preserved meats can cause intolerance symptoms, including flushing, headaches, urticaria and abdominal symptoms.

Food additives

Many people believe themselves to be sensitive to food additives. Mentioned most often in this context are:

- colouring agents, such as tartrazine;
- preservatives, such as benzoic acid and benzoates;
- antioxidants, such as butylated hydroxytoluene (BHT) and butylated hydroxyanisole (BHA).

The diagnosis of these reactions is very difficult, as no immunological effect is involved. Moreover, additives are rarely consumed singly, so individual reactions are difficult to identify. However, concern has been expressed that, for their size, children who eat a large amount of processed foods containing additives may be consuming an unacceptably high level of additive 'cocktail', which could have adverse effects. Often, where apparent sensitivity exists to food additives in children, it accompanies other allergic conditions, such as eczema, and may exacerbate their symptoms.

Sulphite used in preservation of wine, other acidic drinks or fruit and vegetables may liberate sulphur dioxide, which may aggravate asthmatic reactions. Some people believe they are sensitive to monosodium glutamate, which is used as a flavour enhancer in many foods and is present in large amounts in some Chinese dishes. Responses described include tachycardia, flushing and wheezing, but blind trials have failed to show a consistent link with a specific array of symptoms.

Food safety requires that some additives are used in food preservation but it is important that their safety for humans is reviewed regularly, and their use controlled. Without additives, foods would be hazardous, owing to bacterial contaminants and deterioration, and food-transmitted infections actually already cause more reactions in people than any effects of food additives.

Enzyme defects

The most common of these is the inability to digest lactose in milk, generally due to the disappearance of lactase after infancy. Congenital lactase deficiency, when active lactase is absent from birth, is rare. Other disaccharidase enzyme activities in the gut may be compromised, for example, by some drug therapies and in chronic or binge alcohol consumption. In all of these cases, symptoms of intolerance occur when sugars are consumed. These result from the bacterial fermentation of lactose (or more rarely other sugars) in the colon and the resulting osmotic effects, causing bloating and diarrhoea.

Other enzyme defects that occur may be inborn and have systemic effects when metabolic pathways cannot be completed. Examples include alcohol dehydrogenase deficiency, which affects metabolism of alcohol, or fructose intolerance where fructose metabolism is incomplete and results in hypoglycaemia. In addition, there are a number of inherited disorders of amino-acid metabolism that require lifelong dietary modification to prevent serious consequences.

Diagnosis

To obtain a reliable diagnosis, strict criteria must be adhered to. An adverse reaction to a food can only be confirmed if the symptoms disappear when the food is removed from the diet and reappear when it is re-introduced. Great care must be taken if there is any risk of anaphylaxis, and patients who believe they are at risk may refuse to undergo testing. Because of the risk of a severe reaction on re-introduction, this should be carried out under supervision. A careful history of diet and symptoms needs to be taken to identify possible triggers. The testing procedure should be

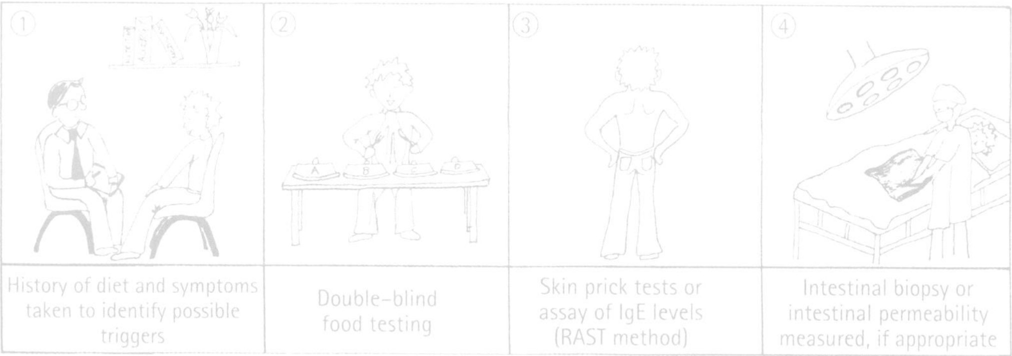

Figure 16.3 Diagnosis of food intolerance.

performed by a double-blind technique, so that neither the clinician nor the subject knows when the suspect food is introduced, within a range of food testing. If several foods are involved and if the reaction is delayed, the procedure may take many weeks to complete. Where there is a suspected allergy, skin prick tests or assay of IgE levels – radioallergosorbent test (RAST) method – may be used as laboratory tests. Even with these, failure to obtain a positive result may not necessarily indicate the absence of hypersensitivity. Intestinal biopsy or intestinal permeability may also be measured in the clinical setting, if this is considered appropriate (see Figure 16.3).

A large number of other tests are available directly to the public. Most of these have not been scientifically validated and, therefore, are not considered to be of value in the diagnosis of food allergy. They are potentially dangerous as they are likely to result in misdiagnosis of food allergy and potential harm from restricted diets. Even without testing, individuals may be tempted to use self-diagnosis and elimination of foods from the diet. This can readily result in omission of key foods and nutrients, which can produce deficiencies and is particularly hazardous in children. Dietary manipulation should only be undertaken under the supervision of a dietitian.

NUTRITION AND THE IMMUNE SYSTEM

There are close links between the nutritional status of the individual and the effectiveness of the immune system in providing an appropriate response in the event of challenge. It has been recognized for many centuries that infectious disease was more common in undernourished populations and that famines were associated with epidemics. The understanding of the two-way relationship between nutrition and immunity is now much greater as new challenges have emerged that demonstrate their interdependence (see Figure 16.4). The inappropriate response to food components that leads to adverse reactions has been discussed above. The appearance of human immunodeficiency virus (HIV) infections and the acquired immunodeficiency syndrome (AIDS) has provided a further example of how immune status and nutrition are related. Other nutritional challenges have an impact on immune function, for example, in chronic disease, in the very young and the elderly.

A brief outline of the role of nutrition in immunity is given here.

Effect of infection on nutritional status

The presence of infection has a potential impact on nutritional state. This can be as a consequence of:

- loss of appetite and poor dietary intake;
- failure to digest or absorb nutrients, either through loss by vomiting or diarrhoea, or loss of digesting/absorbing ability through lack of enzymes, damage to the mucosa of the gut or intestinal hurry caused by infestation with parasites;

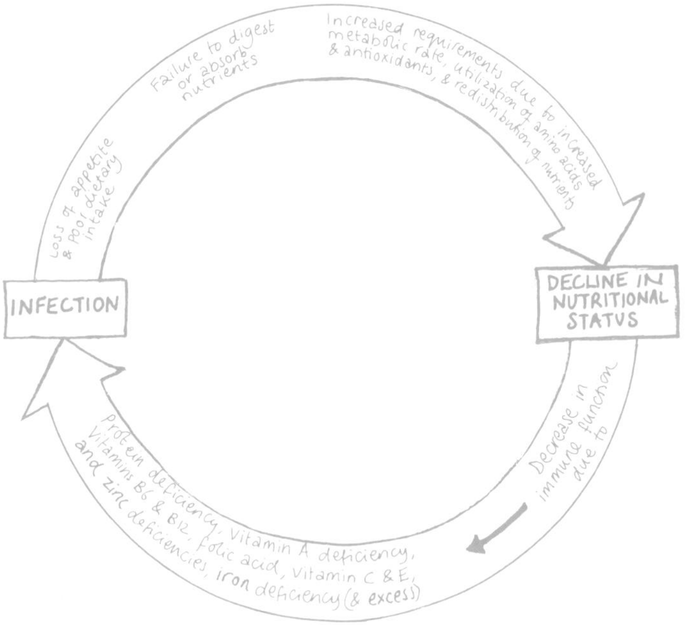

Figure 16.4 The relationship between infection and nutrition.

- increased requirements owing to raised metabolic rate consequent on fever, increased utilization of certain nutrients, such as amino acids and antioxidants, or a redistribution of nutrients between different body compartments as part of the immune response.

Therefore, nutritional state may decline during an infection and compromise the body's ability to combat it and recover. This is one of the reasons for a higher mortality from infections in poorly nourished individuals, compared to those with better nutritional status.

Effect of nutritional status on immunity

The most studied aspect of this relationship is that between protein energy malnutrition and immune function. Almost all aspects of the immune system depend on adequate protein status. This includes the organs of the immune system, such as the thymus, spleen and lymph nodes, which produce phagocytic white blood cells. In addition, the biologically active proteins, such as immunoglobulins, acute-phase proteins and cytokines are dependent on adequate protein status. Cytokines are a large and diverse group of proteins secreted by cells for the purpose of altering its own function or that of adjacent cells; cytokines may have multiple activities, and include tumour necrosis factor and interleukins. It is, therefore, not surprising that protein deficiency makes the individual vulnerable to almost all infections. Specific amino acids have also been identified as particularly important in sustaining an immune response during acute infections, and following trauma or surgery. These are the sulphur-containing amino acids (methionine and cysteine), arginine and glutamine. Some enteral feeds have been developed containing these amino acids for use in hospital patients.

The role of dietary fat in immune function has received considerable interest. In experimental studies, a reduction of total dietary fat intake, from 40 to <30 per cent of energy, resulted in improved immune activity in a variety of subjects. This has led to the suggestion that high-fat diets may have a suppressing effect on human immune function. Polyunsaturated fatty acids (PUFAs) of the *n*-6 series, when consumed in amounts typical of the Western diet, have no clear effects on immune function. However, *n*-3 PUFAs, such as those found in fish oils and linseed oil, have been reported to have a suppressing effect on immune responses. For this reason, there is interest in their role as potential anti-inflammatory agents for use in conditions where the immune system is responding inappropriately to triggers and causing chronic disease states. These include rheumatoid arthritis, Crohn's disease, ulcerative colitis and psoriasis. Results of trials to date are inconclusive and further work is still needed.

Among the micronutrients, both vitamins and minerals are important in immune function.

Vitamin A deficiency is closely linked with susceptibility to infection, especially of the respiratory system in malnourished children. The role of vitamin A appears to be widespread, in maintaining the integrity of epithelial surfaces as well as in the production and function of both cellular and humoral aspects of the immune system. Other vitamins that have been proposed and studied with regard to an immune function role are vitamins B_6 and B_{12}, folic acid, and vitamins C and E.

The most important mineral in relation to immune function is zinc and subjects who are deficient have immune impairment. Supplementation with zinc of malnourished children decreases the risk of diarrhoea and increases the number of T lymphocytes. In small for gestational age infants, a supplement of zinc (5 mg/day), given for 6 months increased immune function. However, it should also be noted that excess intakes of zinc (300 mg/day) can impair immune function.

Iron deficiency has also been associated with impaired immune function. However, excess iron may inhibit immune function, although the mechanisms are unclear. Selenium is concentrated in tissues involved in the immune system, such as lymph nodes, spleen and liver, and various components of the immune system have been shown to be impaired in selenium deficiency. The bactericidal activity of phagocytes is impaired. There have been reports also of benefits of selenium supplementation in HIV-infected subjects.

Overall, it is clear that adequate nutritional status is needed for correct immune function. Supplementation with multi-nutrient mixtures can improve immune function in those individuals whose previous intakes were poor. However, there is little evidence to support enhancement of immune function by the use of supplements in those who are adequately nourished. Indeed, there is a possibility that for some nutrients an excess intake may result in suppression of immune action. More research is needed in this area.

NUTRITION IN HIV INFECTION AND AIDS

Nutritional status is an important consideration in patients with HIV infection, and improvements or maintenance of nutritional adequacy may have important implications for survival. A major advance in the management of patients with HIV infection has been the development of highly active antiretroviral drugs, which have been able to significantly improve the prognosis. Many patients with HIV, however, have no access to these drugs and, for this group, attention to nutrition can make a difference. Malnutrition can affect the length of survival by:

- reducing immune responsiveness;
- causing organ damage;
- reducing the effectiveness of therapies;
- contributing to progressive debility.

Body weight

One of the most readily available markers of nutritional status is body weight. Weight loss is reported as a major clinical sign in HIV infection, and has for some time been considered inevitable and irreversible. There is now a better understanding of the variations in weight as more of the components of the weight change have been studied. Survival appears to be increased in patients with a higher body mass index (BMI; in the range 25–30), although deliberate overeating and development of obesity is not encouraged. The composition of this body weight is probably also important, with a higher lean body mass being more advantageous than increased fat stores. An exercise programme may help to boost the amount of lean tissue.

Weight loss can occur at all stages of the HIV infection and is not constant, but rather occurs intermittently, suggesting that it is not simply caused by the underlying HIV infection. The initial loss is of fat but, in later stages, may be predominantly of lean body mass. There can be periods of weight stability and significant weight gain is also possible.

Several factors are thought to be responsible for weight loss in HIV infection:

- increased resting energy expenditure, owing to the 'hypermetabolism of the disease';
- concurrent infections;
- reduced food intake – this may arise for a number of reasons, including difficulties of obtaining and/or eating food, and loss of appetite;
- malabsorption.

Increased metabolism

Although the metabolism may be increased, by approximately 10 per cent in patients with HIV infection, and perhaps up to 30 per cent during periods of opportunistic infections, it is now thought not to be the main cause of weight loss. Careful studies have demonstrated that the increase in resting energy expenditure is more than outweighed by the reduction in physical activity. In addition, and especially during periods of infection, there is a marked reduction in food intake that contributes to the negative energy balance and weight loss. To maintain body weight, the periods of reduced food intake need to be compensated by increases following recovery from infection. It is proposed that these periods would be an ideal time for aggressive nutritional support to help re-establish body weight. This can be by enteral or even parenteral feeding, if necessary and appropriate. It is also important that other nutrients are provided at this time and that the aim is not simply to gain weight.

Patients with HIV infections appear to lose protein during weight-loss episodes. Usually, when food intake is low, the physiological response after the first 3 days is for protein to be spared and for fat stores to be predominantly used for energy. In HIV infection, however, the response is similar to that seen in trauma or physiological stress, with the breakdown of body protein and negative nitrogen balance. Reversing this loss should aim at optimizing the anabolic processes, perhaps by the use of hormones, as well as the use of appetite stimulation. Resistance exercise can help increase lean body mass in these cases.

Patients with HIV infection have also been found to have abnormal lipid metabolism, with raised plasma triglycerides, which becomes more elevated as HIV progresses to symptomatic AIDS. Conversely, cholesterol and phospholipid levels are lower in HIV-infected subjects. Treatment with antiretroviral drugs has also been found to lead to a metabolic syndrome, termed lipodystrophy, with abnormal lipid levels, reduced glucose tolerance and insulin sensitivity. In addition, there is a redistribution of body fat, with a loss of subcutaneous fat, including the legs, arms and face, and increased abdominal adiposity and deposition of fat across the back (buffalo hump) and on the breasts. The development of this condition in patients treated successfully for HIV infection is a paradox, and raised future health problems, which are similar to those seen in obese individuals, who are at risk of coronary heart disease, diabetes and pancreatitis. The causes of this metabolic syndrome are unexplained but may be due to a delay in clearance of lipids from the circulation, with resulting consequences of raised circulating lipids. Low-fat diets, exercise and drugs to reduce plasma lipids may be a way forward.

Concurrent infection

Opportunistic infections and cancer are causes of major, rapid weight loss in patients with AIDS. Treatment of the infection can reverse the weight loss. The management of these has become better as knowledge has increased.

Reduced food intake

This may arise for a number of reasons, including:

- a loss of desire to eat due to anxiety or depression;
- a deliberate desire to lose weight;
- an inability to obtain food or afford to buy food;
- problems with eating, owing to painful mouth or throat infections, or side-effects of drug therapy;
- the consequences of eating, with nausea, gastric pains, and diarrhoea.

Malabsorption

Abnormal function of the gastrointestinal tract is a fairly common aspect of AIDS, although it may only affect nutritional status in later stages of the disease. Common features include fat malabsorption together with episodes of diarrhoea, which may be linked to malabsorption of bile salts. Where malabsorption is an important feature, there is chronic progressive weight loss. Pathogens may be present in the gut, depending on the degree of immunosuppression of the patient. They may interfere with all aspects of gut functioning, including chewing and swallowing, cause gastric pain and consequent reluctance to eat, reduce absorption, cause nausea and vomiting, general malaise and anorexia.

As with any condition where the body is faced with a reduced food intake and increased needs, maintaining good nutrition whenever possible is important. Food provides not only nutritional support, but also psychological support and social activity, and this should be recognized in any nutrition therapy.

Studies have shown that low plasma vitamin A levels are associated with accelerated progression of HIV and increased risk of mortality. Vitamin A supplementation has significantly reduced mortality and morbidity in HIV-infected children. Other studies have shown that low serum vitamin B_{12}, vitamin E, selenium and zinc levels are associated with increased risk of progression to AIDS. Multivitamin supplementation of pregnant women, improves the survival chances of their babies with fewer low birthweight and preterm deliveries.

Although as a general principle an optimal diet may well prolong a person's survival, it is possible for someone in this vulnerable state to fall prey to nutritional misinformation, and perhaps end up consuming a very unbalanced diet. Many supposedly beneficial diets have been proposed, including supplementation with very large doses of vitamin C, use of 'live' yogurt, macrobiotic diets or herbal supplements. At present, there is no evidence that any one feature of these diets will be especially beneficial in HIV infection. However, a patient's desire to help themselves through the diet is important to respect and may encourage them to take an interest in other aspects of their food intake. It is important that adequate levels of all nutrients are provided and not compromised. The development of antiretroviral drugs has brought a new approach to the management of patients with HIV infection, with better survival, but with new complications resulting from metabolic disturbances that increase risks of other diseases.

DRUG–NUTRIENT INTERACTIONS

Drugs used in medical treatment may affect nutritional status by influencing food intake or metabolism; similarly, their action and effectiveness may be altered by a person's pre-existing nutritional state.

These interactions between drugs and nutrients have been a focus of interest only in the last two decades. They can occur within the gastrointestinal tract, in the blood or at the cellular site of action of the drug. The consequence of any interaction will vary with the drug, its formulation, the timing of food intake, and the nutritional status and disease state of the individual concerned.

Effects of diet on drugs

Most drugs are taken into the body by mouth and, therefore, are processed by the gastrointestinal tract. Many drugs have to be solubilized by the digestive secretions before they can be absorbed. In a fasted subject, drugs will pass quickly through the stomach, reaching the small intestine within minutes. Drugs taken with food or after meals are likely to be more slowly absorbed than those taken following a period of fasting. The presence of food and fluid also facilitates the solubilization of solid drugs. The increased flow of blood in the splanchnic circulation associated with eating may enhance the bioavailability of some drugs, for example, some of the beta blockers.

Nevertheless, there are some drugs that are better absorbed in the fasting state, such as penicillin and tetracycline. In particular, tetracycline is less well absorbed when taken with foods containing calcium, magnesium, iron or zinc, and should, therefore, not be taken within 2 hours of food containing dairy produce or protein. The presence of protein in the meal reduces the absorption of L-dopa, but a low-fat diet enhances the effectiveness of the lipid-lowering agent lovastatin. Unpleasant flushing can occur when chlorpropamide is taken with alcohol or nifedipine (a calcium-channel blocking agent) with a high-fat meal. A high-fibre diet can bind some drugs; this may be of benefit, protecting against harmful effects, or a disadvantage, if absorption is too slow.

Dietary factors affecting drug metabolism

Adequate protein intake is required for normal drug metabolism and a low protein status may be linked with prolonged drug action. Fat-free diets may also reduce the activity of drug-metabolizing enzymes. Vitamin C is required for hepatic cytochrome P450, a key component of the microsomal oxidizing system, which metabolizes drugs. Many of the other enzymes involved in the phase I (oxidation, hydroxylation, reduction or hydrolysis) reactions, which alter the functional groups on the drug molecules, require vitamins, especially the B complex, and minerals to act as cofactors. Dietary factors are also needed to supply the groups needed to conjugate drugs in phase II reactions. These include glucuronate, glutathione, acetate and sulphate, all of which facilitate the solubilization and excretion of drugs.

This presents a potential problem for individuals with a chronic disease. If the disease affects their food intake, yet is treated by drugs, the effectiveness of the drugs and their potential side-effects may be significantly influenced by the nutritional status. In other words, those who require the drug therapy may well be in the most nutritionally vulnerable state and least able to metabolize the drugs.

Dietary factors affecting drug excretion

A low-protein diet may alter urinary pH, decrease renal blood flow and reduce the excretion of certain drugs. Some drugs are preferentially excreted in acidic conditions and reabsorbed when the pH of the urine becomes more alkaline. Lower clearance via the kidney may increase levels in the blood, resulting in side-effects. This has been reported in patients with gout, who are taking allopurinol and a low-protein diet. When several drugs are taken, there may be competition between drugs for renal excretion, with higher levels remaining in the blood.

Effects of drugs on nutrition

Food intake

One of the most important influences of many drugs is their effect on appetite. In some cases, this may be the declared aim of using the drug, when weight loss is required. However, other drugs may induce nausea or cause oral ulceration, which makes food intake painful. A notable example of this group of drugs are those used in cancer chemotherapy. Effects further along the gastrointestinal tract, such as abdominal pain, bloating or diarrhoea, may also reduce the desire to eat.

Some drugs can increase appetite as an unwanted side-effect. Major examples are the benzodiazepine tranquillizers and lithium used in manic depressive illness. Cyproheptadine is an antihistamine drug that has been used to encourage individuals with a wasting condition to increase their food intake.

Gastrointestinal function

Drugs may affect absorption from the digestive tract. Examples of such effects include:

- an alteration in pH (by antacids) and thus a change in the solubility of minerals for absorption;
- inhibition of folate deconjugating enzymes by sulphasalazine, which is used in inflammatory bowel disease, thus preventing liberation of folate from foods or competition with carrier molecules for folate transport;
- induction of catabolism of 25-OH vitamin D by anticonvulsants, reducing circulating levels and interfering with calcium absorption;
- binding of fat-soluble vitamins to mineral oil laxatives;
- destruction by long-acting antibiotics, such as neomycin, of gut flora that synthesize some vitamins;
- reduced vitamin B_{12} absorption owing to interaction with peptic ulcer drugs (H2 antagonists);
- damage to mucosal surfaces of the gut and small intestinal enzymes by excessive intakes of alcohol.

Metabolic effects of drugs on nutrients

Some drugs may be specific antagonists of the metabolic role of vitamins and may result in alterations in mineral status by specific effects on excretion. Specific vitamin antagonists include those that are intended to inhibit the vitamin or those that affect the vitamin as a side-effect. The most important of the specific antagonists are those for folic acid, which are used in cancer chemotherapy, against *Pneumocystis carnii* infection in AIDS, and as antimalarial and anti-inflammatory agents. Coumarin derivatives, used as anticlotting agents, are vitamin K antagonists.

Nitrous oxide used as an anaesthetic and the antituberculosis drug isoniazid, however, have unwanted side-effects, interfering with B_{12} and B_6, respectively.

Drugs may also lead to excessively high levels of sodium, potassium, calcium and magnesium by interfering with normal regulatory mechanisms. This may be a particular problem with drugs used in cardiac patients receiving diuretic therapies or when several drugs are used together. Diuretics can also result in mineral depletion. In both these cases, the mineral intake of the diet may need to be monitored.

The group in the population most at risk from these many interactions are the elderly. It has been reported that nursing home residents consume on average eight different medications per day. This may also be seen in elderly people living elsewhere, who may take a range of both prescribed and non-prescribed drugs. Interactions between the pharmacological effects of these substances are inevitable. If, at the same time, the physiological processes to cope with the metabolism of the drugs are beginning to be less efficient and maybe the nutritional intake is not as good as it could be, there is potential for undesirable side-effects. These may take the form of excessively large or inadequate therapeutic effects, both of which have medical implications.

NUTRITION AND THE ATHLETE

High levels of energy expenditure impose unusual physiological demands on the body. There is an increased need for energy and associated nutrients for increased metabolism as well as adequate fluids to maintain body temperature in the face of large amounts of heat production in exercising muscles. Exercise generates large amounts of free radicals because of the increase in oxidative processes. Thus, there is an increased need for antioxidant factors in the body and these should be plentiful in the diet.

To enable the body to make the most of its nutrient supplies, regular training facilitates the development of a more profuse blood supply in the muscle and shifts metabolism to more energy sparing pathways. In addition, physical activity confers a number of health advantages. A large follow-up study of 1800 British male civil servants showed that those who took vigorous exercise in their leisure time had less than a quarter of the fatal heart attacks seen in the inactive group.

In addition, exercise promotes a sense of well-being, believed to be related to altered levels of neurotransmitters in the brain. There is generally less body fat and more lean body mass than in comparable non-exercisers and a healthier blood lipid profile, with higher levels of high-density lipoproteins (HDLs). Those who exercise can consume more fat in their diet without increasing their adipose tissue levels. People who exercise regularly may also adopt other aspects of a healthier lifestyle, particularly not smoking.

The dietary needs of the athlete are, in essence, very similar to those of the average individual. Differences may arise, however, because of increased energy needs, the timing of meals to ensure an adequate intake around a busy schedule, and the importance of maintaining a high intake of carbohydrate during training and after competition. Fluid balance is also important.

Athletes can be very vulnerable to suggestions about their diet and may follow a succession of dietary fads and ideas, often spending a huge amount of money on pills and potions. When dietary advice is proposed, they may be reluctant to change what they believe to be a 'winning' diet, even if this is not nutritionally sound. If an athlete can be persuaded to adopt a sound healthy diet, it could remove a whole area of worry from the training programme and allow the focus to be concentrated on the physical training regime. In addition, careful attention to nutrition can make the difference between winning and coming second. It is the responsibility of the nutritionist to work with the athlete, to identify specific nutritional goals that are achievable and to provide strategies that match individual circumstances.

Energy needs in sport

The key consideration in any sports performance is the need for energy that is additional to that required for maintaining normal metabolism and everyday physical activity. Not all individuals undertaking sport have high energy requirements: in some sports, energy expenditure may be little more than is found in a moderately active person. Total amount of energy used is also dependent on body size, so a lightweight athlete will use less energy than one with a large body size. Exercising intensively on an energy-restricted diet can cause increased protein breakdown and may cause physiological stress. This, in turn, can result in a suppression of immune function. It is also very important to remember at this point that energy needed for growth must also be met. In teenage athletes, high levels of activity and inadequate intakes will compromise growth. Thus, adequate levels of energy must be provided.

Provision of energy for sport (Figure 16.5)

At the cellular level, the muscles use adenosine triphosphate (ATP) in their contraction. A constant supply of this must, therefore, be maintained. In the first moments of exercise, the body will use its store of ATP, contained in the muscles, but after 3 seconds this has been exhausted. The next source is generation of ATP from creatine phosphate, also stored in the muscle, which can provide about 15 seconds' worth of ATP. This may be enough for a short burst of activity, such as a single jump, throw or lift. After this, ATP must come from other metabolic substrates, namely carbohydrates, proteins and fats. All of these can be transported to the muscle cell and broken down for energy; however, they are not used in equal amounts. Proteins do not usually contribute much to total energy expenditure in

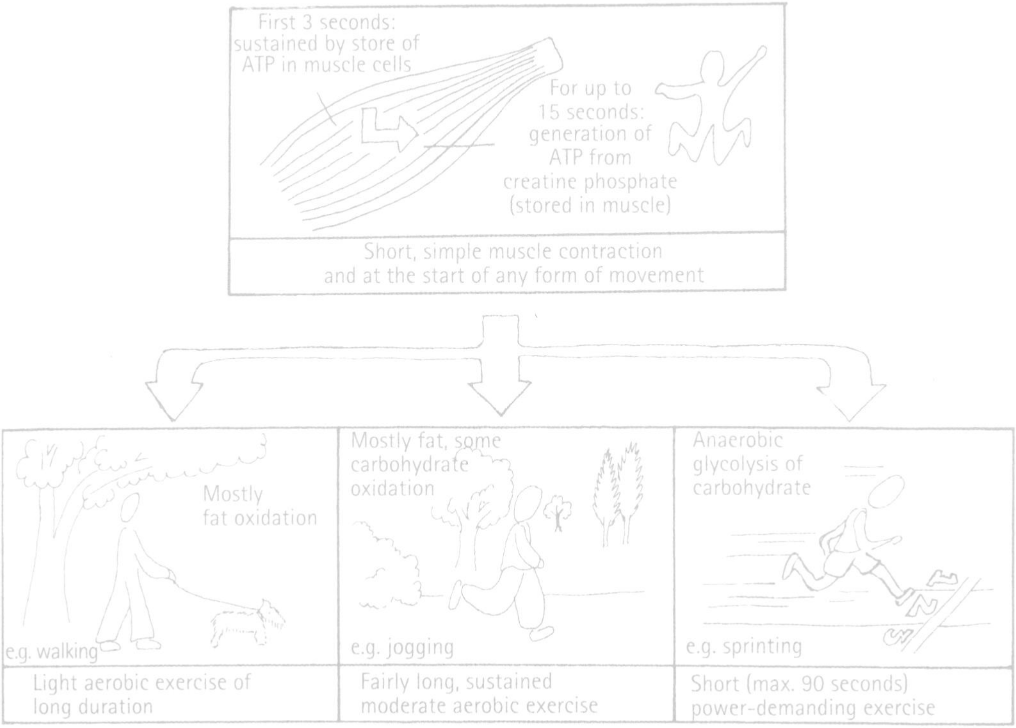

Figure 16.5 The provision of energy in sport.

exercise except in very prolonged, endurance events or in very intense exercise, when they may supply about 10 per cent of the total energy. The major supply comes from fats and carbohydrates. The choice of fuel is made on the basis of several aspects of the exercise, of which the most important is the intensity.

At rest, almost all the body's energy is supplied from fat oxidation. This is the most efficient source of energy, providing 80–200 units of ATP per molecule. Its main drawback, however, is that it is a slow producer of energy and uses more oxygen than carbohydrate metabolism does. Energy obtained from fat has been likened to a steam engine – it can use up fuel for long periods of time and maintain a steady pace. Even at low rates of exercise, the body has to use a small amount of carbohydrate to complete the oxidation of fats. Thus, stores of carbohydrate in the form of glycogen are important.

As exercise intensity increases, ATP must be produced more quickly to maintain energy supplies. This can be achieved by using increasingly more carbohydrate, which can produce 38 units of ATP per molecule of glucose as long as the oxygen supply is adequate, that is, under aerobic conditions. If the intensity of exercise becomes so great that the production of energy outstrips the supply of oxygen, glucose can still be broken down, albeit very inefficiently (no other substrate can be broken down in this way), but will only produce 2 units of ATP per molecule of glucose, by anaerobic metabolism. Such a burst of energy can be harnessed for a short and intense exercise, such as a 100-m race or a power lift. However, it is an incomplete metabolic process and lactic acid is produced. This has several consequences, particularly in the production of fatigue. A build-up of lactic acid reduces the pH in the muscle to the point where contraction can no longer occur. This terminates the exercise, so anaerobic exercise is of necessity of short duration (a maximum of about 90 seconds). The body's tolerance to lactic acid also increases with training, increasing the length of time the exercise can continue. Once the need for a rapid energy supply stops, oxygen can once again meet the needs of the metabolic pathways and the 'incomplete' oxidations can be brought to a conclusion, with the further oxidation of lactic acid into pyruvic acid, and thence via the Krebs cycle. This has been termed 'repaying the oxygen debt'.

To maintain muscle contraction at a rapid rate, the following two conditions must be met.

- The oxygen supply must be as great as possible. This is improved by training, which allows a greater utilization per minute of oxygen, as lung capacity increases.
- There must be adequate supplies of glycogen. This is also improved by training, since the ability to use fat as fuel increases in a trained athlete and, therefore, extends the period of availability of carbohydrate.

In summary, whatever the intensity of the exercise, both fat and carbohydrate are generally used. At low levels, the balance is mostly in favour of fats, with little carbohydrate used. At high intensity, the exercise is fuelled mostly by carbohydrates, unless it is at maximal intensity and proceeds anaerobically, when carbohydrate is the sole fuel. Most exercise will predominantly occur at a level between these extremes, with perhaps only short bursts of intense action. However, the longer the duration of exercise, the greater the proportion of fat:carbohydrate used. Eventually, the supply of carbohydrate is exhausted and exercise has to stop. In addition to supplying the muscles, carbohydrate is also needed to maintain blood glucose levels, to meet the energy requirements of the vital organs, most notably the brain. These levels are maintained by the liver, which uses stored liver glycogen, but also manufactures new glucose from glycerol (from fat metabolism) and amino acid residues, in a process known as gluconeogenesis. Falling blood glucose levels contribute to fatigue. Low blood glucose levels also cause physiological stress, which results in release of hormones, such as cortisol, which in turn have a negative effect on immunity.

From the above it can be seen that maintaining a high level of stored glycogen in the muscle is important to extend duration of exercise. Many studies on exercising subjects, first carried out in the 1930s, have shown that exercise time to exhaustion can be lengthened in subjects consuming a diet containing a high proportion of carbohydrate. This increases exercise times compared with times achieved by subjects on normal

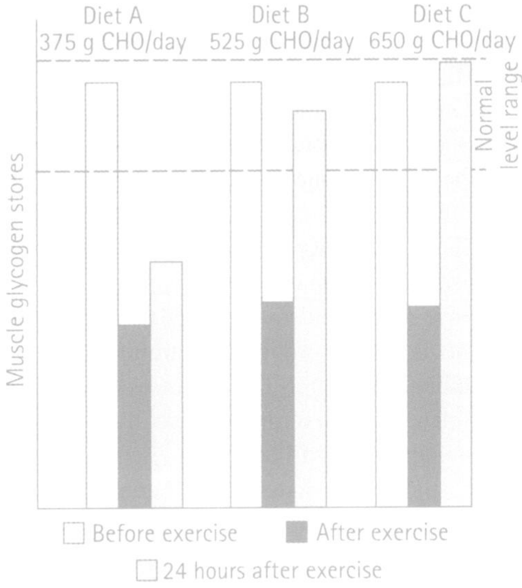

Figure 16.6 Effects of different amounts of carbohydrate in the diet on the refuelling of muscle glycogen in the 24–48 hours after exercise. (From Wootton, 1988. Reproduced with kind permission of Simon & Schuster, London.)

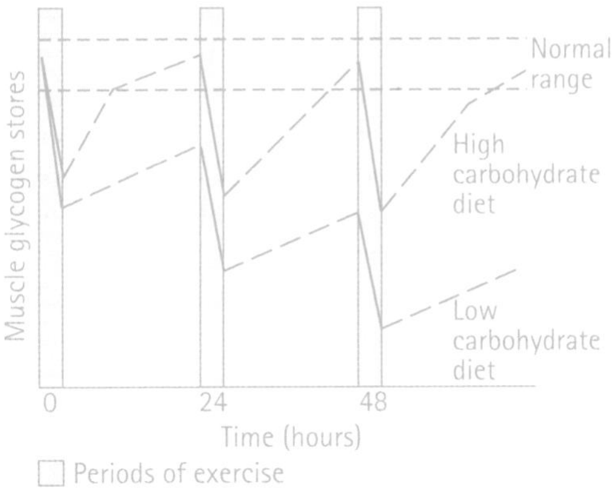

Figure 16.7 Effects of different amounts of carbohydrate in the diet on muscle glycogen levels during three consecutive periods of exercise over 72 hours. (From Wootton, 1988. Reproduced with kind permission of Simon & Schuster, London.)

diets, which in turn are greater than those in subjects fed a high fat/protein diet with low levels of carbohydrate. It has subsequently been shown that exercised muscle is capable of taking up carbohydrate in increased amounts in the first 1–2 hours after activity, which helps to replenish stores and permits exercise to be repeated on the following day (Figure 16.6). This increased capacity to store carbohydrate is believed to be at least partly the result of increased blood flow to muscles in the post-exercise period. Cell volume, influenced by osmotic changes is also a determinant of carbohydrate synthesis after exercise. These two findings highlight the importance of carbohydrate in the diet of the athlete.

During training

In practical terms, the diet during training should be based on carbohydrates, ideally supplying 55–60 per cent of the energy. This means that, if levels of protein are 10–15 per cent of energy, the amount of fat is 25–35 per cent. This is clearly very close to the general healthy eating guidelines. The carbohydrate should be a mixture of both simple and complex sources. In reality, an athlete who has very high energy needs would find it very difficult to consume the volume of complex carbohydrate this would represent. This would be exacerbated by the usual lack of time for eating, which is common among amateur athletes. Nevertheless, adequate intake of carbohydrate is essential if daily exercise is taken (Figure 16.7). A daily requirement of 8–10 g carbohydrate/kg body weight is recommended during periods of hard training. For training sessions that last for more than 60 minutes, it is also important to take carbohydrate at intervals starting after the first 30 minutes. This helps to maintain circulating blood glucose levels and prevents depletion of liver glycogen stores. Once these have been depleted, they cannot be replaced until exercise has stopped.

After exercise

When exercise stops, the muscles need to be refilled as quickly as possible with glycogen. The first priority after exercise is thus to consume some carbohydrate-containing food, which will be readily absorbed and deliver its glucose content to the muscles. The food chosen should have a high glycaemic index, which will cause a quick rise in blood sugar. During this time, it is recommended that at least 50–100 g carbohydrate is consumed (1–2 g/kg) within the first hour. (Foods grouped according to glycaemic index are given in Table 16.1.)

TABLE 16.1 Grouping of some commonly eaten foods according to glycaemic index

Foods with high glycaemic index (above 85)	Foods with moderate glycaemic index (60–85)	Foods with low glycaemic index (less than 60)
Bread (white or wholemeal)	Pasta and noodles	Apples, grapefruit, peaches, plums
Rice	Porridge	Beans
Breakfast cereals (e.g. cornflakes, muesli, Weetabix)	Grapes, oranges	Milk, yogurt and ice cream
Raisins, bananas	Crisps	Fructose
Potato, sweetcorn	Biscuits	Tomato soup
Glucose, sucrose, honey		
Soft drinks		
Maltodextrin drink (20%)		

Adapted from Williams and Devlin, 1992. Reproduced with the kind permission of the publisher.

Many athletes find that they do not want to eat immediately after exercise; in this case, a carbohydrate-containing drink is useful. This helps to achieve the goal of replenishment of carbohydrate stores, as well as providing some rehydration. Small carbohydrate-containing snacks eaten at frequent intervals are also helpful. It should be remembered, however, that too many high-sugar foods may pose problems for dental hygiene and appropriate advice should also be given on this. Where possible, a meal or large snack high in carbohydrate should be consumed within 2 hours.

Later on, foods with a lower glycaemic index are acceptable, as they cause a slower but more sustained increase in blood glucose levels, which can enter the muscles over a longer period of time to maintain the refuelling process. Protein supply is also important at this time to ensure sufficient levels of amino acids in the circulation for tissue repair and protein synthesis. This does not need to come from special protein supplements, but can readily be supplied from normal foods, such as a sandwich with cheese, lean meat or fish, a baked potato with beans, or a pasta dish with a meat- or cheese-based sauce. All of these provide a combination of protein and carbohydrate.

Protein needs

Many athletes believe that, to make full use of their muscles in exercise, they require a high protein intake. This stems from the idea that muscles are used up in some way in exercise and, therefore, require extra protein to restore them.

Activity 16.1

An athlete requires a daily intake of approximately 21 MJ (5000 Calories). Calculate the amount of carbohydrate this would represent according to the above guidelines.

Devise a day's menu to supply this amount of carbohydrate:

- using predominantly sources of complex carbohydrate
- including some simple carbohydrate.

Repeat the calculation using a target energy intake of 10.5 MJ (2500 Calories).

Compare the practicalities of consuming the two diets.

Protein makes a very small contribution to energy supply in exercise and is hardly used up at all. However, an exercising muscle does increase in mass over a period of time, so that when a person first starts to take regular exercise, more protein will initially be retained by the body. However, when equilibrium is reached, the additional food consumed to meet the energy needs should provide more than enough protein to meet the needs of the muscles for repair. Recommended levels for protein intake are in the region of 1.5 (1.2–1.7) g protein/kg body weight. There is no advantage in exceeding more than

2 g/kg, and such a high level may compromise the carbohydrate intake. Consequently, there will be insufficient glycogen for the muscles to exercise in training and any potential benefit of the extra protein will be lost anyway. The protein should always be balanced by an adequate energy intake, equal to 170 kJ (40 Calories) per gram of protein. There are many successful vegetarian athletes whose protein intakes are derived only from plant foods, and also athletes whose protein intakes do not exceed 10 per cent of the energy intake. It is the training that increases muscle size, strength and exercise capacity, and not the increased protein intake. Many athletes from developing countries do not have access to such high levels of protein, yet compete effectively on the world stage.

Dietary supplements

Athletes use a wide range of supplements, and surveys from various countries indicate that over 90 per cent of athletes studied are currently using, or have used dietary supplements in the past. Usage varies with the particular sport, level of competition and gender of the athlete.

Very few of the supplements used by athletes have been scientifically evaluated for efficacy to enhance performance, although, if the diet is inadequate, there may be a valid case for using the supplement.

Vitamin and mineral supplements

There is little evidence that vitamin supplements are of any benefit in an adequately nourished athlete. Studies that have claimed to show an improvement often give no indication of the initial nutritional status of the athlete and, therefore, their findings prove little.

The following two points are, however, important:

- Athletes who consume very little food in an attempt to maintain a low body weight appropriate to their particular sport may not meet their nutritional requirements for all micronutrients. A supplement may be indicated in this case.
- Intense physical activity produces free radicals, which may represent a health risk to the individual, if insufficient levels of antioxidant nutrients are present. Attention should be paid particularly to vitamin E and C intakes to ensure adequate status. There is some evidence that immune status is poorer in athletes who undertake heavy training. This may be linked to low levels of certain micronutrients needed for the components of the immune response, although stress responses may also be an important factor.

Mineral status is of concern in terms of calcium and iron, especially in female athletes, who may consume diets deficient in both of these nutrients. Low calcium status in young women, together with a low body weight, which results in amenorrhoea (loss of menstrual periods), may compromise bone density and lead to fractures and early osteoporosis. This condition has been described as 'fit but fragile'. The drive to maintain a low body weight may be so intense that a type of anorexic behaviour is seen, with obsessive avoidance of food that might cause weight gain, compulsive exercise, and amenorrhoea with resulting low bone density that may lead to frequent fractures. This is sometimes described as the female athlete triad. When competitive sport participation stops, normal menstrual activity is likely to return but it is possible that bone density does not recover to that expected for age. Most at risk are young females in whom high levels of exercise delay menarche and disrupt the phase of most rapid bone mass accretion.

Iron needs are higher in women because of menstrual losses; low-weight female athletes may cease to menstruate and thereby conserve some iron. However, evidence exists of a higher turnover of iron in athletes, possibly owing to increased destruction of red blood cells. This may result in increased needs and, if these are not met, then stores will decline and anaemia can develop, which will affect performance.

Creatine

Creatine phosphate is an important energy source for muscles during intense exercise. However, the content in muscle is limited. Creatine is obtained from the diet, predominantly in meat and animal products, but is also synthesized in the body from amino acid precursors, such as glycine and arginine. Vegetarian athletes have to rely on endogenous synthesis, which can provide enough creatine. However, since the early 1990s, creatine supplements have been available, which have been shown to enhance the content in muscle by up to 50 per cent. The scientific evidence supports a positive effect of creatine supplementation in repeated short bursts of intense activity. It does not enhance duration of prolonged effort. Creatine supplementation can result in an initial gain in muscle bulk of 1–2 kg after a loading dose (4×5 g doses daily) for 4–5 days. This is propbably due to swelling of cells, which may be accompanied by increased protein synthesis. A maintenance dose of 1–2 g daily is recommended. Subjectively, heaviness of muscles may be a reported side-effect. No clinically significant negative effects have been reported to date.

There are many other dietary supplements which are used by athletes. Some of these are mentioned in Chapter 17.

Fluid

Fluid is also an important consideration for athletes. Sweating is essential to lose heat and maintain body temperature. The sweat contains electrolytes, most notably sodium, potassium and chloride ions, derived from the plasma. However, the concentration of electrolytes in the sweat is different from that in the plasma, with the result that the remaining plasma may actually have higher concentrations of some electrolytes at the end of the exercise. Consequently, the top priority for replacement after exercise is water, to restore normal concentrations in plasma.

The issue is complicated by the observation that the best way to increase water absorption from the gut is to include some electrolytes in solution. This enhances water uptake and speeds rehydration. Many rehydrating solutions are available; most of them contain electrolytes (at less than 2.6 g/dL), together with varying amounts of carbohydrate. The carbohydrate is present in amounts that may be:

- lower than concentrations in body fluids (hypotonic solutions);
- the same as body fluids (isotonic solutions); or
- greater than body fluids (hypertonic solutions).

Absorption of these is most rapid from the hypotonic solution and slowest from the hypertonic solution. Drinking a hypertonic solution will not provide rapid rehydration and may actually aggravate matters, as fluid from the body is drawn into the digestive tract. However, hypotonic and isotonic solutions are useful in providing quick rehydration. The added benefit of the carbohydrate content when taken at the end of exercise is its contribution to refuelling the glucose stores. These solutions are also useful during prolonged exercise, when they help to maintain blood glucose levels and prevent dehydration, thus enabling performance to continue at an optimal level. Solutions that contain glucose polymers are now available; this enables more glucose to be contained in the drink without compromising the tonicity and, therefore, provide more potential energy in the drink.

Overall, many athletes do not consume a diet that is appropriate to optimize their sporting performance. This may be due to a variety of factors, including a lack of practical knowledge and time as well as a reluctance to take advice. More education about diet and nutritional needs of both athletes and those who have responsibility for their training is needed.

ALCOHOL ABUSE

Moderate amounts of alcohol (e.g. taken within the UK recommended limits of 2–3 units or 3–4 units per day for women and men, respectively) are believed to be beneficial to cardiovascular health, as described in Chapter 14. One unit of alcohol, as defined in the UK contains 8 g of alcohol, and is usually interpreted as the amount of alcohol in one standard drink (a half pint of regular beer, one glass of wine or one measure of spirits). However, amounts in excess of this taken over a period of time are likely to result in harm and to compromise health. The exact level of intake that may cause harm is difficult to define, as it is variable between individuals and depends on genetic predisposition. However, chronic intake of over 55 units per week for men and

35 units per week for women is defined as 'unlikely not to cause harm'.

It is very difficult to obtain a true assessment of the number of people whose health is damaged by alcohol. In Britain, figures quoted suggest that there are 250 000 people dependent on alcohol and a further one million at risk of dependence. The diagnosis may be difficult because so many people with an alcohol problem conceal this from those around them, often continuing to work and maintaining an external appearance of normality. It is only through alcohol-related disease, such as liver disease or encephalopathy (brain disease), that alcoholism may be diagnosed. In addition, alcohol taken in excess contributes to other diseases, such as cardiovascular disease and hypertension, ulcers, cancer and mental illness, as well as accidents and violence.

The pattern of alcohol abuse has changed in the last decade in Britain, with a rapidly increasing incidence in women. This reflects both the increased economic independence of women as well as the increased access to alcoholic drinks. Drinking among women has possible implications for the health of the fetus, if it is continued throughout pregnancy. High levels of alcohol ingestion may result in 'fetal alcohol syndrome', characterized by developmental abnormalities of the face, brain, heart and kidneys.

Young people are also drinking more, particularly in a 'binge' drinking pattern, when large amounts of alcohol are consumed in a relatively short space of time. Such high intakes may accelerate the damage caused.

The elderly, especially if affected by loneliness, are also recognized as a group at increased risk of excessive drinking. This may go unnoticed by primary health care staff until there is a crisis, such as a fall.

Nutritional implications

Food intake

Food intake can be affected by alcohol consumption in various ways, including the following.

- There is likely to be a reduced appetite or an overall lack of interest in food as a result of a preoccupation with alcohol. Inflammation of the stomach lining (gastritis) may result in pain on eating or cause vomiting.
- Access to food may be difficult, especially if the alcoholic has left home. Cafe or takeaway food may form a large proportion of the diet; this may not be particularly healthy or nutrient rich.
- Money available to buy food may be scarce and be preferentially spent on drink.

Digestion and absorption

Alcohol is an irritant to living tissue, resulting in a permanent state of inflammation along the digestive tract, and leading to vomiting and diarrhoea. Gut contents tend to be moved along rapidly and enzyme production may be impaired. This is particularly the case for the enzymes produced in the wall of the small intestine, which complete carbohydrate and protein digestion. The villi may be flattened and absorptive areas reduced. There may be secondary intolerance to sugars, which remain undigested and ferment in the large intestine.

Metabolic changes

Liver damage is recognized as one of the main consequences of alcohol abuse. The liver is also the site of activation, storage and metabolism of many of the nutrients in the body. These will be adversely affected. Some nutrients are specifically needed to metabolize and detoxify the alcohol, and requirements for these will increase.

Alcohol is a diuretic agent, increasing urine production. This will cause the loss of more water-soluble nutrients from the body. The pancreas may be inflamed, resulting in pancreatitis. Although this predominantly affects the production of digestive enzymes, there may also be implications for insulin release and thereby control of blood sugar levels.

Energy balance

There is controversy about the utilization of the energy content of alcohol. The theoretical energy yield is 29 kJ (7 Calories) per gram of ethanol. However, individuals consuming large amounts of alcohol in addition to a moderate food intake do not exhibit the weight gain one might expect from the excessive energy intake. This has led to the proposal that some of the potential energy from alcohol is liberated as heat rather than being converted into usable ATP. Some alcohol is metabolized via the microsomal ethanol oxidizing system (MEOS), which becomes more active at higher levels of alcohol intake. It is possible that this oxidation does not yield usable ATP, and constitutes a 'drain' for the excess energy. Alcoholics may, in fact, be underweight or overweight, and which of these occurs appears to depend on the total intake of food, rather more than the amount of alcohol consumed.

Abnormal findings

Fat metabolism by the liver becomes abnormal. The production of NADPH by alcohol metabolism drives fat synthesis, with large amounts accumulating in the liver. Circulating lipid levels, especially the very low density lipoprotein (VLDL) fraction, are elevated, increasing the risk of heart disease.

Control of blood glucose levels becomes less precise. This is partly the result of a failing production of insulin in the pancreas, but also because of reduced gluconeogenesis by the liver. There may be periods of hypoglycaemia (low blood sugar), with feelings of dizziness and faintness, and possibly blackouts.

The liver is one of the main sites for protein synthesis and degradation. In the liver of an alcoholic, protein degradation may continue at a relatively normal rate, but protein synthesis and, therefore, tissue repair declines. Levels of essential proteins will gradually decline, for example, the plasma proteins in the blood or the proteins that function as digestive enzymes.

Among the water-soluble vitamins, it is the B complex that is most affected. Multiple deficiency states may exist, involving niacin, riboflavin and pyridoxine, and resulting in sore mouth, diarrhoea, dermatitis and psychological disturbances. Megaloblastic anaemia is likely as a result of folate malabsorption. Thiamin deficiency is likely, as it is required for the metabolism of alcohol, and may, in addition, be lost in vomiting and diarrhoea. This deficiency will result in neuropathy, affecting hands and feet, making walking difficult. In its severe form, psychological disturbances with loss of memory and psychosis (Korsakoff's syndrome) may develop. Poor vitamin C status owing to a poor diet is also possible.

Absorption of fat-soluble vitamins may also be affected, especially if the production of bile from the liver is reduced. Particularly at risk is vitamin K, as there are generally small stores of this vitamin. Low vitamin D status has also been reported; it is believed that the breakdown of active vitamin D is induced by the alcohol.

Among the minerals, zinc is important, as it forms an essential part of the alcohol dehydrogenase enzyme. Levels may become depleted, affecting alcohol metabolism, wound healing, sense of taste and immune function. Electrolyte imbalances may arise because of vomiting and diarrhoea, and can lead to changes in muscle function. Iron status may be either high or low, depending on the beverages drunk. Spirits provide no iron (or any other nutrients), but some wines and beers may contain iron. However, blood loss due to intestinal irritation may cause iron depletion, and the alcoholic may become deficient despite an apparently adequate intake (see Figure 16.8).

INFLUENCE OF DISABILITY ON NUTRITION

The term 'disability' is used to cover a very wide range of physical or mental conditions that may influence the ability of an individual to function in the able-bodied world. The disability may be present from birth, or may have affected the person as a result of an accident or disease (such as Parkinson's disease, multiple sclerosis or stroke). The degree of disablement will be reflected in the extent to which functions are compromised. The disability may be progressive and deteriorating, or there may be gradual improvement. The perception of change may influence the person's willingness to look after themselves, and take an interest in their health and possible rehabilitation.

Some disabilities will have very little impact on nutrition; others may have profound effects. Those having the greatest effects will be those

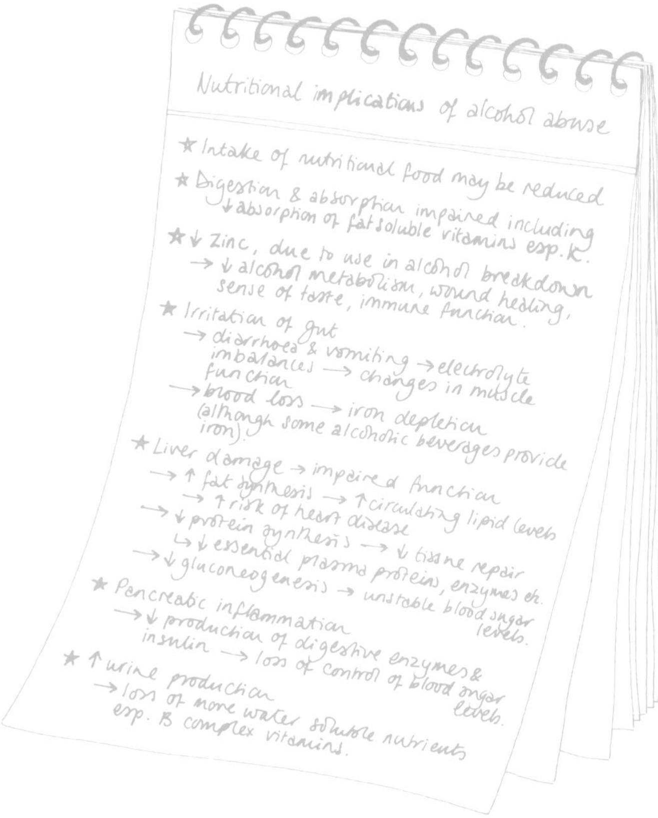

Figure 16.8 Nutritional implications of alcohol abuse.

that affect food intake, digestion and absorption, and metabolic needs.

Impact of disability on food intake

This is probably the largest area of potential difficulties. Food intake may be influenced by:

- factors affecting appetite;
- factors affecting the ability to obtain and prepare the food; or
- factors affecting the ability to ingest, chew and swallow the food.

Appetite

Appetite will be influenced by mental state, and thus can be affected by anxiety or depression. Physiological factors will also have an influence; for example, dulled sensation of taste, nausea, constipation or pain after eating will reduce appetite. A common side-effect of drug therapy is a dry mouth, which makes food ingestion difficult and unpleasant, and depresses the appetite for eating. Physical factors, such as lack of exercise and immobility, may also mean that the individual does not feel hungry.

Environmental factors, including monotonous menu presentation, especially if the diet has to be soft or puréed, and unpleasant surroundings may be off-putting. Eating snacks or sweets between meals may also be a major factor contributing to lack of appetite at mealtimes.

In a non-verbal individual affected by any of these factors, their unwillingness to eat and the carer's desire to provide food for eating may result in conflict and frustration.

Ability to obtain and prepare food

In the situation where the individual is responsible for his/her own food supply, both the mental and physical capabilities are important. Understanding what to buy to produce a meal is essential. The process of going out and buying the food may be compromised in many ways, including mobility, ability to communicate, to see/hear and to carry the food. All of these will determine the range of foods that are actually available to eat. Cooking skills and capabilities are also important.

Where a carer is responsible for all of these functions, the autonomy of the individual must be taken into account. The question of whether the food that is being prepared is actually what is desired needs to be addressed. Food is a very personal issue and another person's choice may not be our own.

Ability to ingest, chew and swallow food

Ingestion, biting, chewing and swallowing of food may be difficult in some disabilities. There may be tongue thrusting, spitting out, choking and dribbling. These may be linked, for example, to a lack of coordination, involuntary movements, lack of lip closure or cleft lip and palate. Careful techniques are required to provide useful nutrition. Appropriate modification of texture may be needed, with the use of thickeners to improve the appearance of meals and make them easier to eat. If the individual is responsible for his/her own feeding, hand to mouth coordination is needed.

Appropriate positioning is essential to facilitate swallowing and prevent regurgitation. Special feeding utensils are available to help the process; occupational therapists can help to develop skills required for feeding and advise on modified equipment. Becoming an independent feeder can lead to marked improvements in nutritional status.

Impact on digestion and absorption

Some individuals with disabilities may tend to regurgitate or ruminate food. Food that has been swallowed may later be brought back into the mouth and spat out. If this is continuous and severe, nutritional status will be threatened.

Drugs used to manage an underlying condition, such as tranquillizers, anticonvulsants, antibiotics, analgesics and antihypertensive drugs, may all affect the digestion and absorption of food from the gut. It is important that potential drug–nutrient interactions are anticipated and avoided by suitable timing of drugs and meals, wherever possible.

Laxatives may be used to treat constipation. A form of laxative that has no impact on nutrient absorption should be chosen and, if possible, dietary fibre and fluid intakes should be increased.

Impact on metabolism

Nutritional needs may be altered by increased or reduced energy expenditure, drug-induced alterations in metabolism and specific nutritional requirements related to the underlying condition. It is, therefore, important to monitor the nutrient needs of each individual. In children, growth should be monitored regularly, including height and weight; in adults, weight can be a useful indicator of adequate energy intake. However, other assessments of nutritional status may be required, particularly micronutrient status.

Nutritional consequences

If total food intake is small, there is a risk of malnutrition, resulting in poor physical and mental well-being, increased risk of infection and, in children, delayed growth. More often, however, sufficient food is eaten, but it may be low in nutrient density, perhaps because of the foods chosen or if it is diluted during purée production. Attention should also be paid to nutrient retention during preparation. Foods that are kept hot for periods of time lose vitamin content, and modification of texture may result in significant losses of water-soluble vitamins. If specific groups of food are omitted entirely, the individual may be left vulnerable to deficiencies; for example, if few fruit and vegetables are included, they may lack trace elements and folate. Constipation may be a problem if non-starch polysaccharide (NSP) intake is low. Laxative use, on the other hand, may deplete the body of fat-soluble vitamins.

Infection and the associated physiological stress will increase nutritional needs, especially for B vitamins and vitamin C, zinc and protein.

Involuntary muscle spasms may increase energy expenditure and result in weight loss, if this is not met. This is particularly common in children with athetoid cerebral palsy and autism, and with oral defects.

Specific drug–nutrient interactions should be anticipated by adjusting food intake. If appetite is very poor, a nutritional supplement may be needed to improve well-being to a point where adequate nutrition can be obtained through the diet.

In summary, there are many threats to the nutritional status of a person experiencing some disability. If these can be identified and anticipated, they should not result in nutritional deficiency. However, the most important criterion is to judge each case in the context of the specific circumstances.

SUMMARY

1. Several situations that provide an additional threat to nutritional status have been reviewed.
2. People suffering from food intolerance may need a modified diet. However, this should be devised with appropriate consultation with a dietitian, so that nutritional content is maintained.
3. In people with HIV infection or AIDS, nutrition can contribute to health, and every effort should be made to maintain nutritional status during periods of infection and debility.
4. Drugs that are used therapeutically can influence nutritional state. However, poor status with respect to nutrition in the patient may in its turn affect the metabolism of drugs and perhaps produce unexpected reactions.
5. Athletes have additional nutritional needs. These can be met from increases in food intake. A particular emphasis should be made on the carbohydrate content of the diet.
6. Disability may have short- or long-term implications for food intake. People affected by disability should have access to various aids and modifications that can improve their nutritional intake. Monitoring of health and weight is important.

STUDY QUESTIONS

1. a Think about the examples of challenges to nutritional status discussed in this chapter. Construct a table to identify which part of the food path (intake–processing–utilization) is actually affected in each of the cases.
   b Suggest other challenges to nutrition that could be analysed this way.
2. a What are the characteristic features of a food allergy?
   b Why is allergy to peanuts currently of concern?
3. Identify the main focus of nutritional advice to be given to HIV-positive subjects.
4. a In what ways does nutritional status affect drug utilization?
   b What are the possible implications of this in people who are ill and are receiving drug treatments?
5. a What do you consider to be the main difficulties encountered by an athlete that might prevent the consumption of an adequate diet?
   b How can some of these difficulties be tackled and overcome?
6. Prepare an article to appear in a newsletter for parents of children with disability, giving practical help about diet.

REFERENCES AND FURTHER READING

British Nutrition Foundation 2001: *Nutrition and sport*. Briefing Paper. London: British Nutrition Foundation.

Buttriss, J. (ed.) 2002: *Adverse reactions to food. The report of a British Nutrition Foundation Task Force*. Oxford: Blackwell Science.

DoH (UK Department of Health) 1995: *Sensible drinking. The Report of an Interdepartmental Working Group*. Wetherby: Department of Health.

DoH (UK Department of Health) 1997: *Peanut allergy*. Committee on Toxicity of Chemicals, Consumer Products and the Environment. London: Department of Health.

Gowland, M.H. 2002: Food allergen avoidance: risk assessment for life. *Proceedings of the Nutrition Society* 61, 39–43.

Grimble, R.F. 2001: Nutritional modulation of immune function. *Proceedings of the Nutrition Society* 60, 389–97.

Hughes, D.A. 2000: Dietary antioxidants and human immune function. *British Nutrition Foundation Nutrition Bulletin* 25, 35–41.

Maughan, R. 2002: The athlete's diet: nutritional goals and dietary strategies. *Proceedings of the Nutrition Society* 61, 87–96.

Prentice, A.M., Stock, M.J. 1996: Do calories from alcohol contribute to obesity? *British Nutrition Foundation Nutrition Bulletin* 21, 45–53.

Saarinen, U.M., Kajosaari, M. 1995: Breast feeding as prophylaxis against atopic disease: prospective follow-up study until 17 years old. *Lancet* 356, 1065–9.

Salomon, J., De Truchis, P., Melchior, J.-C. 2001: Nutrition and HIV infection. *British Journal of Nutrition* 87(Suppl. 1), S111–19.

Semba, R.D., Tang, A.M. 1999: Micronutrients and the pathogenesis of human immunodeficiency virus infection. *British Journal of Nutrition* 81, 181–9.

Terho, E.O., Savolainen, J. 1996: Review: diagnosis of food hypersensitivity. *European Journal of Clinical Nutrition* 50, 1–5.

Thomas, J.A. 1995: Drug–nutrient interactions. *Nutrition Reviews* 53(10), 271–82.

Ware, L.J., Wootton, S.A., Morlese, J.M. et al. 2002: The paradox of improved antiretroviral therapy in HIV: potential for nutritional modulation? *Proceedings of the Nutrition Society* 61, 131–6.

Williams, C., Devlin, J.T. (eds) 1992: *Foods, nutrition and sports performance*. London: E & F Spon.

Wootton, S. 1988: *Nutrition in sport*. London: Simon & Schuster.

Young, E., Stoneham, M.D., Petruckevitch, A. et al. 1994: A population study of food intolerance. *Lancet* 343, 1127–30.

17 OPTIMIZING NUTRITION

The aims of this chapter are to:

- discuss the concept of optimal nutrition;
- describe some of the foods that are available to the consumer that may be used to optimize health;
- describe the evidence to support the use of these foods.

On completing the study of this chapter you should be able to:

- explain what is meant by functional foods;
- evaluate the evidence for the role of non-nutritional factors in human health;
- debate the advantages and disadvantages of using designed food products to optimize health.

In the last few decades, the developed world has witnessed a shift in perception about the possible roles of food and nutrition. The fundamental role of food is to supply the basic nutrients for the maintenance of physiological function (and growth) in the body and fulfilment of social activity, while at the same time satisfying sensory needs. From this understanding come concepts, such as nutritional requirement and dietary reference values, which are discussed in Chapter 2. As our knowledge of the role of nutrients in the body and possible interactions with the prevention or development of diseases has developed, a further role for food has become apparent. This is the recognition that components of food, which may or may not have specific nutritional roles, may be beneficial to health. Thus, there has been a shift from discussing 'adequate' nutrition to considering 'optimal' nutrition.

This presents a challenge to nutritional scientists to decide, where relevant:

- how much is enough (to minimize deficiency);
- how much is best (to meet biochemical, physiological and other functions for normal health);
- how much can provide other benefits in non-nutritional ways;
- how much is too much and causes harmful effects.

Suitable indices are required in order to be able to define these limits, and this brings considerable methodological, practical and ethical challenges.

Traditional approaches have included balance studies, tissue saturation studies, measurement of body stores and functional studies. Many of these methods have been used to determine minimal requirements for nutrients.

The function of a nutrient within a specific target tissue or pathway can be used to determine its level of activity, and to explore the effects on this of changes in intake or blood level of the nutrient. Generally, it would be expected that increases in intake, or blood levels, up to a certain level would cause a dose–response change in activity of the measured function. At the point where activity ceases to increase, it can be assumed that maximal physiological (or optimal) function has been achieved.

With the current state of knowledge, the role of a nutrient is likely to be assessed in a rather general way, for example, in terms of its effect on antioxidant status, muscle strength or blood clotting. This is because, in most cases, the exact first biochemical point at which a particular nutrient is involved and at which it becomes limiting in deficiency may not be known. However, with developments in molecular biology, it may be possible in the future to explore the effects of nutrients on gene expression and determine their role precisely. A general function is also likely to be used to assess possible health benefits of a nutrient, perhaps in amounts greater than meet the functional needs.

There are many difficulties, however, in translating results obtained at the laboratory level into guidelines or targets for the intake of a particular nutrient. These can include:

- interactions between nutrients and other chemical components in food;
- uncertainties about the bioavailability of nutrients at the gut level;
- efficiency of transport to the target site;
- inter-individual variation;
- potential interaction between nutrients at different stages in the life cycle.

For all of the above reasons, research on optimal levels for the majority of nutrients is still at an early stage. The Food Standards Agency in the UK has an Optimal Nutritional Status Research programme, which has a number of objectives.

The first objective is the need to understand the links between optimal nutrition status and the maintenance of good health. This will explore the potential interactions between micronutrients at different life stages in the reduction of specific disease.

The second objective is to develop accurate measures of bioavailability of nutrients from foods. This will explore the processing of nutrients at the gut level and their transport to cellular sites. There are a number of subissues within this objective that have been identified:

- to measure the fraction of an ingested nutrient that meets functional demand at the target tissues;
- to develop functional markers of status for each micronutrient or group of micronutrients;
- to use human intervention studies to determine dose–response relationships of tissue function;
- to understand the extent of inter-individual variation in order to identify optimal nutritional intakes for the whole population and, therefore, provide advice that could reduce morbidity and mortality from chronic disease.

FOODS, FOOD COMPONENTS AND HEALTH CLAIMS

The growth of interest in the use of food to promote a state of health and well-being, and reduce the risk of disease has led to the rapid development of an industry that produces foods that claim to possess these characteristics. A health claim describes a positive relationship between a food substance in the diet and a disease or other health-related condition. This may include a lessening of the condition or a reduction in the risk of that condition.

Early research on these foods started in Japan in the 1980s, with the purpose of developing foods for specific health use (FOSHU). These were defined as 'processed foods containing ingredients that aid specific bodily functions in addition to nutrition'. Legislation allowed claims to be made about specific health effects of foods in certain categories. In the USA, the Nutrition Labelling and Education Act, enforced in 1994, allowed health claims to be made for ingredients for which there was recognized evidence of a correlation between intake and cure or prevention of certain diseases, although this does not necessarily mean that the evidence can be applied to the food itself.

The promotion of foods with health claims is much more restricted in the UK, where the law separates foods and medicines so that foods cannot be described as providing a medical health benefit. Therefore, foods cannot be labelled as 'preventing' or 'curing' a specific disease. As a result of growing concern about the unregulated market in the UK, the Food Advisory Committee produced a set of guidelines. These have been developed into a Code of Practice by the Joint Health Claims Initiative (JHCI), a panel of representatives from consumer, food industry and enforcement groups. This aims to help the food industry to make health claims that are within current legislative constraints. An expert committee is to review all claims to ensure that they are supported by scientific evidence, with the aim of producing a list of approved generic health claims for use by food manufacturers whose products meet the criteria. New submissions for products will also be considered. It is anticipated that this will allow consumers to receive information about health benefits without infringing current UK legislation.

There is a relatively high degree of public suspicion of processed foods in the UK, related to a number of food-related health scares in recent years. A meeting with consumers by the Foresight Task Force, set up by the Government in the UK in 2001, indicated that there is cynicism among consumers about the need for new products developed by the food industry, and the reasons for their development. It is evident, therefore, that products that might be valuable to optimize nutrition need to be clear in their presentation to the consumer.

This puts the onus on the food industry to follow the principles of scientific research and on regulatory authorities to ensure that systems are in place to protect the consumer.

The following points summarize stages in the process of developing such products or food components.

- Fundamental research techniques can identify possible interactions between a food component and a function relevant to health, thus generating hypotheses for study. Appropriate markers of this function need to be developed for the assessment. This is a problematic area, as few such markers exist.
- The hypothetical effect needs to be tested in appropriate models, including human studies, and safety assessments carried out. Trials should be carried out in a manner similar to drug testing, with the potential to demonstrate a dose–response relationship, and any potential risk be evaluated. The cost–benefit of the use of the food component should be analysed.
- The food component being studied should be able to be included in a variety of normal diets, in amounts sufficient to produce the desired effects, that is, they should remain 'foods'.
- Possible adverse effect of an excess intake of the component must also be examined (e.g. if the same component is included in a number of products, will this still be safe?).
- The differential effects of the component in people of different ages and states of health should be considered.
- The evidence relating to the product must be evaluated by an independent authority, which is empowered to approve the use of the product, and which can determine the nature and content of the health claim being made. This is a fundamental part of any food safety and labelling regulations that exist in a country.
- The information to the consumer about the product must be both clear and informative. It should include information about the target group or condition (if this is specific), the benefit claimed and the amount to be consumed.

Terminology

There is a confusing range of terms given to foods that have been specifically developed by the food industry to meet the demand for healthier foods.

SMART FOODS

This is a term that is being used in schools in the UK as part of the Design and Technology curriculum. The food industry uses the term 'modern' or 'novel' food materials. These are foods that have been developed through new or improved processes, generally by human intervention and, therefore, not through naturally occurring changes. This classification includes:

- foods with novel molecular structures, including fat substitutes and sweeteners;
- meat analogues, including novel proteins;
- foods produced by biotechnology;
- functional foods (also known as pharmafoods or nutraceuticals).

Foods with novel molecular structures

In relation to healthy eating initiatives, the most important components in this group are fat replacers and sweeteners. Both are useful in reducing the energy content of the diet. Fat replacers can be derived from carbohydrate or protein, or be lipid-based. In the case of carbohydrate- or protein-derived products, these can be used to substitute fat in the production of low-fat meals, and additionally act as stabilizers to prevent separation of ingredients. Lipid-based fat replacers are fatty acid esters with sugars, which are not absorbed from the digestive tract. These have the advantage of being stable at high temperatures and can, therefore, be used in fried or baked products, such as crisps and biscuits. An example of this group is Olestra, licensed for use in the USA.

Sweeteners are a well-established item in the diet of people wishing to reduce their energy intake. The main products used in the UK are saccharin, aspartame, acesulfame and cyclamate. All the intense sweeteners provide the sensation of sweetness in very small amounts because of their molecular structure and can, therefore, mimic the effect of sucrose, without supplying the associated energy. Aspartame is composed of phenylalanine and aspartic acid and, therefore, yields these amino acids when digested. However, the quantity consumed produces a negligible amount of energy. Because it contains phenylalanine, aspartame should not be used by people with phenylketonuria (PKU) who cannot metabolize it. Over 2000 products available in Europe contain aspartame.

This group of smart foods also contains modified starches, which are used in many food products that need to be stabilized or thickened, and has extended the range of 'instant' and 'ready to eat' products on the market.

Activity 17.1

1 Look in the supermarket for examples of 'instant' and 'ready to eat' products. Identify which of these contain modified starch that is acting as a stabilizer or thickening agent.

2 Prepare a number of drinks (e.g. cups of tea) with different sweetening agents – try to use examples of each chemical type, as well as sugar. Test these on several volunteers to study any perceived differences in taste and sweetness detected.

Meat analogues

This group of smart foods includes products made from soya protein (textured vegetable protein, tofu) or fungal proteins (Quorn) that have been extruded, spun, coagulated and moulded into products that resemble meat in texture. Flavours and additional nutrients may be added as part of the processing. These products are included in the diet of people who prefer not to eat meat, but may also be considered by some to be a healthier alternative to meat. This may not necessarily be the case, as levels of fat may be comparable to those in similar meat dishes and micronutrient levels may be lower.

Foods produced by biotechnology

Plant and animal breeders have for centuries tried to breed in the best characteristics of the species, and breed out the least advantageous ones. Biotechnology is the use of biological processes to make useful products. The use of yeast to make bread and beer, and microorganisms to make yogurt and vinegar are all traditional examples. In recent years, developments in molecular biology and genetics have made it possible to manipulate the genes of plants and animals to an extent that specific characteristics have been transferable. This has made it possible to produce new varieties of certain plants having desirable characteristics. Disease resistance can be enhanced by genetic modification so that insect or virus borne diseases no longer destroy the crop. This has been achieved for a substantial proportion of maize grown in the USA. Work is under way to increase disease resistance in the sweet potato, which could enhance yields three-fold.

One of the most successful 'genetically modified' (GM) plants has been the soya bean, which carries resistance to particular herbicides, thus allowing more effective treatment of the cultivated land with less herbicide and hence more efficient crop growth and less environmental damage. Varieties of maize and rice have also been developed, which have advantages in terms of nutrient composition or yield over the more traditional varieties. For example, the protein and vitamin A content of rice has been enhanced to improve dietary balance. It is anticipated that, in the future, more beneficial amino-acid profiles or higher meat yields can be engineered into animals. Higher levels of antioxidants are being bred into tomatoes. The removal of potential allergens from foods, such as wheat, is another exciting area of research, which would help individuals who are unable to consume gluten. Similarly, research on allergens in peanuts may yield a non-allergenic product. Slower ripening allows crops to be preserved better with fewer losses.

There is concern that introducing alien genes into plants may have adverse consequences for the humans who consume these, and a considerable amount of resistance to the introduction of foods containing GM components. Careful testing for safety and long-term trials are necessary to ensure that these products are safe. Clear labelling of products that contain GM ingredients is also called for by consumers, and European legislation has been reviewed in the light of concerns and will be monitored in the future.

Functional foods

This is the largest category of smart foods and also the most diverse. The functional food market in Europe was estimated to be worth $55 billion in 2000, and is rapidly expanding. A functional food may be defined as one having health-promoting benefits, and/or disease preventing properties over and above the usual nutritional value. This definition can cause difficulties in that some common foods could be considered to be covered by this definition. For example, many vegetables provide non-nutritive phytochemicals, which are believed to have health-promoting benefits but do not contribute to the accepted nutritional value of the vegetable. It has been suggested that functional foods might be better viewed as a concept that can help to optimize nutrition rather than a means to categorize them.

Nevertheless, it is useful to consider the different types of products that could come into this group.

- foods containing added (fortified) or reduced levels of nutrients – these may be nutrients that would normally be found in the product or ones that are not typical of the food;
- foods containing phytochemicals, that is, components with no known nutritional role that are promoted as such in the diet, or have added levels of some phytochemicals;
- foods containing added components that do not occur generally in the typical diet, with the specific aim of producing a functional effect;
- foods containing bacteria that are used to promote gastrointestinal tract function.

The following sections will consider examples of foods/food components in each of these categories and some of the evidence for their use as functional foods.

Fortified foods

This group includes foods that have been fortified with macronutrients or micronutrients. On a global basis, food fortification is an important strategy for combating specific nutrient deficiency that may be prevalent in a community. Notable examples of this include fortification of salt with iodine or the use of various vehicles as a medium for increasing iron intakes. In such national schemes, it is important to choose both an appropriate food for fortification, which represents a regular item in the diet, as well as the best form of the mineral or vitamin to maintain the stability of the food product, and maximize bioavailability of the nutrient.

There is no widespread single nutrient deficiency in the UK, yet there are a great number of fortified foods available aimed at promoting health rather than preventing deficiency. These include white bread and flour, which are required legally to have thiamin, iron and calcium added to restore the content to that found in wholemeal flour. This was introduced to protect the health of the population following World War II, but has been maintained ever since, although the nutritional need for this is arguable. In the USA, folate is added to flour; but this is not the

Figure 17.1 Examples of fortified foods.

case in the UK, following a decision taken by the Food Standards Agency in 2002, after a wide-ranging consultation. Margarine is required by law to be fortified with vitamins A and D, to provide levels of these vitamins that are comparable to those in butter. Many of the other spreading fats are also fortified with these vitamins. Breakfast cereals are voluntarily fortified with a wide range of nutrients; however, this is not a legal requirement. The range of nutrients added, and the level of fortification varies between products and from time to time in the same product (see Figure 17.1).

Infant milks and foods contain various added nutrients to enhance their nutritional value. There are guidelines on the levels of nutrients that should be provided in foods for infants. Other products that are fortified include instant mashed potato, bedtime drinks, yogurts, soft drinks, condensed milk and dried milk powder. The range of fortified foods available is not constant and it is interesting to note the information on food labels to keep up to date with products. Most of the examples mentioned above contain added nutrients that would be found in a more 'natural' form of the food. However, there are now exceptions to this, with nutrients being added that would not be found associated with the product. An example of this is the addition of calcium to orange juice. Currently, it is difficult to add some nutrients to foods because of the technological difficulties of dispersal, taint and stability of the products. However, micro-encapsulation of nutrients may expand this field further in the future. One group of nutrients being considered in this context is the n-3 fatty acids, which could be added to some foods in the future in this way. Similarly, calcium can be added to soya milk in an encapsulated form that avoids precipitation of the soya protein.

Activity 17.2

1 Look at some of the foods mentioned in this section in a grocery store or supermarket.
For each of the foods:
- **a** Note the added nutrients, how much is added and how this relates to the reference nutrient intake (RNI).
- **b** What fraction of the RNI does the food provide?
- **c** How much of the food would need to be eaten each day to meet the RNI – is this realistic and feasible?
- **d** Is there any indication on the label of the target consumer group for the product?

2 Try to find some examples of foods with added nutrients that would not normally be found in the food (as in the case of orange juice mentioned above). Why do you think these foods have been chosen for fortification with these particular nutrients?

3 List the advantages and disadvantages of fortifying foods with nutrients. If possible, think about the different situation in industrialized and developing countries. Discuss your findings with other members of your group.

Reduced content of nutrients

This group contains foods mostly for the weight-reduction market, with a wide range of products that are 'low calorie' and, therefore, to be used 'as part of a calorie-controlled diet'. These include individual products, such as drinks, biscuits, yogurts and whole meals, available as 'ready meals' that have been 'calorie counted'. A further range of foods are 'low-fat' products, which represent a separate area of the market. These are not necessarily lower in energy content than a corresponding regular product, as they may contain other energy-containing constituents within the formulation, but do meet regulations of having lower percentage fat than the regular product.

Specific alterations to other constituents may include reduced sugar or salt content. A number of specific dietary products are marketed to meet the demand for foods that are free from a specific component, such as gluten-free products for people with coeliac disease. Other examples may include products that are free from lactose, sucrose, milk or egg.

Foods containing phytochemicals

Vegetables and fruit have been promoted as part of a healthy diet for many years and, since the 1990s, there has been specific advice to include five portions, or 400 g, of these in the daily diet. Both fruit and vegetables contain a number of valuable nutrients but, in addition, it has been recognized that they are rich in non-nutritive substances, known as phytochemicals. These occur in plants and products made from plants at varying concentrations. Amounts are relatively low in the storage parts of plants, higher in the fruiting parts, and highest in the seeds and parts that are dried and concentrated for use as herbs and spices. The latter, however, are generally used in small amounts and, therefore, may not represent an important dietary source. In general, the phytochemicals are produced by the plant as a defence against predators, and are bitter, acrid or astringent in an attempt to make the plant unpalatable or toxic. As a result, humans too may find these substances unpleasant, and this may be a strong disincentive to consume foods that could be good for our health but may not agree with our palate. A challenge to the food industry, both in the past and future has been to breed varieties of plants in which the bitter taste is reduced, while at the same time attempting to ensure that the beneficial effects of the phytochemicals are preserved or enhanced by selective breeding. Extracting the active agent and adding it to other products is a possible developmental step. This has already happened with the use of isoflavones from soya in some types of bread.

The interest in phytochemicals stems from the strong link between diets rich in plant foods and lower rates of cancer and coronary heart disease. The diversity of these compounds creates an enormous task to study the roles of individual phytochemicals in disease prevention or risk reduction and, at present, the evidence often relates to groups of related compounds. Several different mechanisms of action have been identified, usually by *in vitro* study. These are briefly reviewed in the following sections.

Phenolic compounds, including flavonoids

Higher concentrations of phenolic compounds are generally found in young sprouting plants or seedlings than in the mature plant, in line with their role as protection against predators. Immature fruit, such as apple or grapefruit, are very bitter because of the presence of these compounds.

There are over 5000 different flavonoids; many are responsible for the colour of flowers, leaves and fruit. They are generally bitter or astringent. The various flavonoids differ according to their molecular structure and occur in different sources. Flavones, include rutin and quercetin, and are found in apple skins, broccoli, grapes, olives, onions and parsley. Quercetin is the most important contributor to the estimated intake of flavonoids, mainly from the consumption of apples and onions. Flavanones, including hesperetin, are predominantly found in citrus fruit and their peel, and contribute to the bitterness of these fruit. The catechins occur in green and black tea, and red wine (from both the seeds and skins of grapes). They contribute substantially to the bitterness of Japanese green tea. Catechins are also thought to be responsible for the bitter taste of chocolate. Finally in this group are anthocyanins, which are darkly coloured and occur in richly coloured fruit such as berries, cherries, grapes, wine and tea.

In addition, there are high-molecular-weight polyphenols, also known as tannins, which are found in sorghum, millet, barley, peas, dry beans and legumes, fruit, tea and wine. Tannins form insoluble complexes with proteins and starches, and reduce the nutritional value of foods.

The most researched property of all of the flavonoids and phenolic compounds is their antioxidant activity. This may include limiting the production of reactive oxygen species, stabilizing white blood cells and scavenging free radicals. All of these result in less low-density lipoprotein (LDL) oxidation and potential for endothelial damage. In addition, flavonoids have been proposed as having other roles including anti-inflammatory, antitumour, antithrombogenic, and antiviral roles. However, much of the supporting evidence is based on small studies or *in vitro* research, and conclusions cannot be drawn. More research on phenolic compounds and flavonoids is required, together with more information about the bioavailability of the compounds, and more analytical techniques for measurement of intake and excretion levels.

In the meantime, it is important that the known dietary sources of these compounds are encouraged in the diet, to maximize the diversity of intake and benefit from them.

Dietary phyto-oestrogens

Phyto-oestrogens are present in plant foods; the two major subclasses are isoflavones and lignans. The majority of interest has been focused on the isoflavones, of which the major examples are genistein and daidzein, which are found in soya beans and products derived from them including textured vegetable protein, tofu and soya milk. The richest source of lignans is flaxseed (linseed); however, many fibre-rich foods contain small amounts, including lentils, sweet potato and oat bran. More accurate analytical data are needed. A more potent phyto-oestrogen has recently been discovered in hops, and more sources may yet be discovered.

Phyto-oestrogens have been shown to exert a wide range of hormonal and non-hormonal effects in animal and *in vitro* studies. In addition, epidemiological evidence indicates that, in Asian countries, where the habitual daily intake of isoflavones is between 20 and 50 mg/day, there is a lower incidence in women of many hormone-dependent diseases, such as coronary heart disease, menopausal symptoms, osteoporosis and breast cancer. Women in communities where soya beans are eaten tend to have longer menstrual cycles, by 1–2 days. This can relate to 2 fewer years of menstruating life, less ovarian activity and possibly reduced breast cancer risk. In Japanese men, the incidence of clinical prostate cancer is significantly lower than in American men and prostatic tumours develop more slowly. Benefits in terms of coronary heart disease and osteoporosis also apply in men.

Interest in the phyto-oestrogens arose because of their structural similarity to mammalian oestrogen. The compounds were shown to act both as oestrogen agonists (mimicking the effects of the hormone), as well as antagonists (blocking the action of the hormone). The varying effects are attributable to the existence of two different oestrogen receptors in specific tissues, which result in varied responses. Target tissues include breast, ovaries and uterus, brain, bone, lungs, blood vessels, kidneys, adrenals, testes and prostate. In addition to oestrogen related responses, phyto-oestrogens have also been shown to alter steroid metabolism, increase sex-hormone binding in the blood, act as anti-oxidants and reduce thrombogenesis. At present, these effects have not been fully tested in clinical studies, although small short-term studies have reported benefits in menopausal symptoms and bone loss. There is much to discover about the bioavailability of the phyto-oestrogens from dietary sources, the levels achieved in the blood and at active sites, and the amounts required to produce a clinical effect. Studies also indicate that there is considerable individual variation in the metabolic fate of the compounds and this may make recommendations about dosage very difficult to predict. These compounds represent a challenge to the functional food market, in trying to balance a beneficial health effect with acceptability and safety. One of the problems with soya products is their bitterness; the food industry makes attempts to reduce this, but may at the same time remove the beneficial isoflavones.

Glucosinolates

These compounds occur mostly in the cruciferous vegetables (cabbage family), including broccoli, cauliflower, turnips, Brussels sprouts, cabbage and kale. *In vitro* studies suggest that glucosinolate compounds, such as sinigrin and progoitrin, induce enzymes that inactivate carcinogens by neutralizing their toxic properties and speeding their elimination from the body. In addition, products derived from glucosinolates during digestion, including isothiocyanates, are also reported to block the effects of carcinogens. Clinical studies have so far not been able to support these findings. However, diets high in cruciferous (and other) vegetables are linked in epidemiological studies with lower cancer rates, including lung and alimentary tract. One of the major practical problems for food scientists is the bitter taste of many of the vegetables in this family. Selective breeding, genetic modification and alteration of growing conditions are all being used to decrease bitterness and increase consumer acceptability, while protecting the content of active agents.

Carotenoids

Carotenoids are fat-soluble pigments found in many fresh fruit and vegetables. Initially, they were of nutritional interest because of the role of beta-carotene as a major precursor of vitamin A in the body; other carotenoids have lower levels of provitamin A activity. The total amount of carotenoids taken up from the diet is relatively small and a regular intake appears to optimize absorption. It is now known that some 600 carotenoids exist and at least 40 have been isolated in foods. The association between plasma levels of beta-carotene and cardiovascular disease has been reported in a number of epidemiological studies. However, supplementation trials using beta-carotene have not replicated the beneficial results. For example, a study in smokers resulted unexpectedly in a higher incidence of lung cancer and heart disease (Omenn et al., 1996).

Although a specific physiological role for carotenoids has not been clearly defined, they have been shown to possess antioxidant activity and, as such, are of interest in reduction of disease risk. It should be remembered that antioxidants donate an electron to stabilize a free radical. In so doing the antioxidant itself becomes unstable, with the potential to become a free radical and propagate a chain reaction. It is essential, therefore, that there are other antioxidants to repair and maintain the system. One such agent is believed to be vitamin C. This illustrates the importance of having adequate and comparable levels of various antioxidants in the body and may explain why large amounts of one of these may be more harmful than protective (see Chapter 14 for more on antioxidants). Thus, any supplement that provides additional carotenoids should also contain adequate vitamin C.

Lycopene, an acyclic form of beta-carotene, has been found to be a more potent antioxidant than beta-carotene itself. *In vitro* studies suggest that it protects LDL against oxidation. Lycopene is one of the major carotenoids in the Western diet, being found in tomato and tomato products. Intake levels are lower in developing countries. Other sources include pink grapefruit, watermelon, guava and apricot. An epidemiological association has been reported between low plasma levels of lycopene and prostate cancer in the USA. A study in Finland recently reported an excess incidence of acute coronary events and stroke in association with low levels of lycopene.

Lutein is a major pigment in chloroplasts and, as such, is one of the five most common carotenoids in the diet. Together with zeaxanthin (which is similar in structure), it is found in the macular region of the eye, which is the region of the highest visual discrimination, but also the most light-sensitive area. This area is, therefore, very vulnerable to damage by free radicals produced by light interacting with oxygen in the blood. Over time, this can result in macular generation (age-related macular degeneration; AMD) and blindness. This is the commonest cause of blindness in Western society. It is particularly common in smokers, in whom levels of lutein have been shown to be lower than the population average. Lutein absorbs blue light and, as an antioxidant, quenches free radicals. Lutein cannot be synthesized in the body and, therefore, a dietary intake is needed to maintain serum levels; active transport mechanisms concentrate lutein in the macula. There are high levels of lutein in breast milk. In addition, lutein is found in green leafy vegetables and in orange/yellow fruit and vegetables.

All of the phytochemicals discussed above have potential roles in risk reduction and health promotion. The evidence for most of them is, at present, based largely on *in vitro* or animal studies, with only a few clinical studies. However, epidemiological data support the link between intakes of fruit and vegetables in the prevention of a number of diseases. Food scientists can develop varieties in which the active agents are enhanced but, in the mean time, five servings a day of fruit and vegetables remains sound nutritional advice.

Foods with added components

Designing foods with a specific health purpose may involve adding an ingredient that is not usually present in foods, or present in only small amounts in the food.

Phytosterols are compounds that are structurally similar to cholesterol and are currently being used in a range of products as cholesterol-lowering agents. Phytosterols are thought to have been present in the diet of our ancestors in much greater amounts than occurs currently. Intakes of naturally occurring plant sterols are higher in vegetarians than in omnivores. The plant sterols currently used are extracted from soya bean oil or pine tree oil and are esterified to increase solubility. The most common are sitosterol, campesterol and stigmasterol. Products may contain plant sterol (unsaturated) or plant stanol (saturated) esters, and evidence shows that both have a similar capacity to lower circulating total and LDL cholesterol levels. The phytosterols reduce the absorption of cholesterol from the small intestine by forming insoluble particles with cholesterol, and by competing with cholesterol for bile that would facilitate absorption. Thus, a greater proportion of dietary cholesterol is excreted, although some of the phytosterol is absorbed. Absorption is estimated as no more than 5 per cent of the phytosterol. The liver does compensate for reduced cholesterol absorption by increasing synthesis of endogenous cholesterol, but the net effect is a reduction of total cholesterol in the body.

These effects are achieved with relatively small doses of the phytosterols. As little as 1 g/day may have an effective lipid-lowering effect, although a dose of 1.6 g/day of plant sterol is recommended. There appears to be a plateau effect with no further reduction of cholesterol seen at intakes above 3 g/day. The average reduction in cholesterol levels is in the region of 5–8 per cent from spread alone and, when combined with other lipid-lowering measures in the diet, or drug treatments, levels of cholesterol may be reduced by 10–15 per cent. The dispersal of the phytosterol within the food product appears to be the key determinant of its effectiveness.

There has been some concern expressed about the potential for reduced absorption of fat-soluble vitamins, as a consequence of phytosterol ingestion. Lower plasma levels of vitamin E and carotenoids have been reported, but these effects are considered to be marginal.

Although developed as an aid to the management of blood lipids levels in cardiovascular disease reduction, new evidence suggests that the plant sterols may also have a role in inhibition of tumour growth.

Plant sterols and stanols are currently marketed as a range of spreads, dairy goods, such as yogurt and cream cheese, and salad dressing.

Omega-enriched eggs

A range of eggs is on sale in the UK from chickens that have been fed on a vegetarian seed-rich diet containing n-3 fatty acids. This results in eggs enriched with these fatty acids. This illustrates how manipulation of the nutritional content of a product can be achieved. The eggs form a small part of the total egg sales in the UK, but can provide up to 70 per cent of the currently recommended level of n-3 fatty acids in one egg.

Clinical usage

In clinical nutrition, feeds are being produced that contain 'functional' components for which there is believed to be an additional need in particular circumstances. Glutamine is an important fuel source for rapidly dividing cells, for example, those lining the gastrointestinal tract and blood cells. Severely ill patients may be at risk of receiving insufficient glutamine to meet their increased demands. Supplemental glutamine may improve gut mucosal and immune functions, and reduce episodes of clinical sepsis. Trials have shown reduced mortality, lower infection rates and shorter hospital stay.

Arginine is also a conditionally essential amino acid in states of trauma and sepsis, and arginine-containing formulas may reduce complications in surgical patients.

Sports products

The sports nutrition market contains a wide range of functional foods for athletes that are promoted as supplying specific benefits over and above basic nutrition.

The development of sports drinks containing glucose polymers allowed more carbohydrate to be consumed, without undesirable effects in terms of sweetness and palatability as well as excessive osmotic effects. Products, such as high-energy bars, also provide a large amount of energy in a very small volume of food, allowing energy needs to be met. Glycerol is now included in some sports drinks as research has suggested that this can promote hyperhydration, although the evidence is equivocal.

A huge range of products that have potential use as ergogenic aids is marketed and can be considered as functional foods. Some of these are summarized in Table 17.1.

Although there is a theoretical potential for a metabolic effect for some of the functional products available for athletes, the actual ability of the substances to reach the target site and be incorporated into the cellular or subcellular metabolic machinery is usually not proven. Much more research is needed to examine possible beneficial effects of putative ergogenic agents, as well as their safety.

Foods containing bacteria

The contribution to human health of bacteria resident in the gut is increasingly recognized. More than 500 different bacterial species inhabit the human gut, amounting to about 1 kg in weight. Some of these are considered to be beneficial and health promoting, some benign and some harmful or pathogenic. The balance of these bacteria is important and a predominance of one group over another can alter the risk or progression of disease, and the health and function of the colon. Longevity had been noticed among groups of the world population who consumed fermented dairy products that were believed to reduce levels of toxin-producing bacteria, thus suggesting that the dietary intake may have an influence on the health of the bowel and the organism.

Far from being a passive excretory route, the bowel is now understood to be a metabolically active organ that provides a protective barrier for the host through effects on the immune

TABLE 17.1 Functional foods in sports nutrition

Dietary constituent	Suggested role	Strength of evidence
Amino acids		
Arginine, lysine, ornithine	Promote growth hormone secretion and aid muscle development	Weak
Glutamine	Prevents immunodepression, reduces infections	Some experimental evidence
Caffeine	Promotes fatty acid release, sparing glycogen stores	Can be beneficial, within legal limits
Carnitine	Central role in energy production, could enhance aerobic performance	Weak
Coenzyme Q_{10}	Needed for generation of ATP	Weak
Creatine	Increases capacity for repeated bouts of high-intensity exercise	Good
Ginseng	Increase mental energy and stamina	Weak
Sodium bicarbonate	Increased alkaline reserve to buffer lactic acid produced in anaerobic exercise	May be effective in specific circumstances. Gastrointestinal effects unpleasant

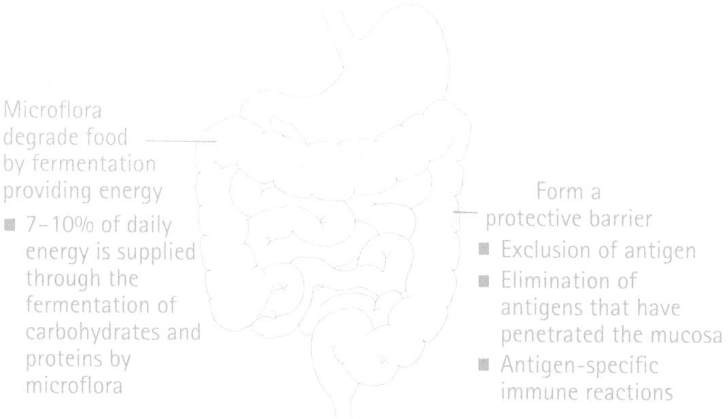

Figure 17.2 How microflora are used in the bowel.

system. The protection exists at various levels, in terms of physical exclusion of the antigen, elimination of antigens that have penetrated the mucosa and finally control of any antigen-specific immune reactions. In order to be able to perform these functions, the gut depends on both appropriate nutrients as well as a beneficial microbial balance.

In addition, metabolism in the bowel may provide between 7 and 10 per cent of the daily energy supply through the fermentation of carbohydrates and proteins (to a lesser extent). Some 60–80 g of the food ingested each day reaches the colon; the microflora degrade this by fermentation to lactic acid and short-chain fatty acids, as well as carbon dioxide, hydrogen, methane, phenolic compounds, amines and ammonia (see Figure 17.2).

In the past, there was a frequent challenge to the gastrointestinal tract by microorganisms present in the environment and in food, and this primed the immune system to function normally. Our increasingly clean and processed environment, with foods containing artificial sweeteners, preservatives and even antibiotic residues reduces the microbial challenge and results in an underperformance of the immune system. Modern lifestyle, with poor eating habits, stress and use of antibiotics can all contribute to alterations in the microflora. It is believed that this may be one of the mechanisms whereby there has been an increase in chronic inflammatory diseases, including eczema, asthma, allergies, Crohn's disease, inflammatory bowel disease and ulcerative colitis.

The gut of the newborn infant is sterile but becomes colonized soon after birth. The method of feeding determines the bacterial flora, with lactobacilli and coliform bacteria and bifidobacteria prevailing in the breastfed infant. Formula feeding induces a wider microflora, which additionally includes *Bacteroides*, clostridia and streptococci. After weaning the microflora becomes similar to that of the adult, with a predominance of anaerobic bacteria, which die in the presence of oxygen. Among these, the bifidobacteria and lactobacilli are considered to be beneficial to health, and some, such as certain *Eubacterium* spp., are benign but suppress the growth of harmful bacteria. Examples of the latter include proteolytic *Bacteroides* spp., many *Clostridium* spp. and pathogenic species of Enterobacteriaceae. Many other microorganisms are present in the bowel, some of which have not yet been characterized, and there is more research required.

Probiotics have been developed, therefore, as an aid to restore the immune function of the gut and to reduce the incidence or symptoms of associated clinical conditions. Thus, probiotics can be described as products that contain live microorganisms in fermented foods, which could promote good health by establishing an improved balance in intestinal microflora. The main organisms currently used are various species of lactobacilli and bifidobacteria, together with a non-pathogenic yeast, *Saccharomyces boulardii*.

A probiotic product must fulfil several criteria including safety, ease and reproducibility of production, and stability during storage.

Furthermore, the organisms should be able to survive in the digestive tract and colonize the bowel in adequate amounts to be able to provide benefit to the host. Although there is evidence from *in vitro* and animal experiments of beneficial effects of probiotics, clinical studies in humans are still at a relatively early stage. Most evidence exists for the reduction of diarrhoea and prevention of gastroenteritis, especially in infants and young children. In adults, antibiotic-induced and hospital-acquired diarrhoea has been shown to be better controlled with the use of probiotics as part of the treatment. Probiotics containing lactobacilli have also been used successfully in cases of lactose malabsorption. A study in older adults showed an improvement in several aspects of cellular immunity after 3 weeks of probiotic use, especially in those with low immune status at baseline. Some evidence of an immune system stabilizing effect has also been found in inflammatory bowel conditions and atopic eczema. There is still a lack of good evidence, however, that probiotics can prevent cancer, reduce plasma cholesterol levels or reduce levels of *Helicobacter pylori* infection in the stomach. Major advances in studying the mechanisms of action of probiotics, and gut structure and function *in vivo* are needed to further clarify the potential benefits and better target specific organisms for particular health needs.

Microorganisms require a substrate on which to grow and multiply. If this is not provided in the diet, the microflora can be compromised. This is the basis of the use of prebiotics, which are non-digestible food components that reach the colon where they can selectively stimulate the growth of beneficial microorganisms. In many ways, this definition is similar to that for components of dietary fibre, although these do not support the growth of one type of microorganism alone. Candidates for prebiotics are the oligosaccharides containing fructose (fructans). A naturally occurring example of this group is inulin, although other fructans are found in wheat, onions, bananas and chicory. Oligosaccharides containing xylose, galactose and mixtures of these sugars have also been studied. The most promising results have been obtained with fructo-oligosaccharides (FOS), which were shown to stimulate growth of bifidobacteria in the colon and change the balance of microflora. Lactulose (containing galactose and fructose) has also been used in a number of clinical trials and found to promote growth of lactobacilli. Prebiotics may be useful in the management of constipation, owing to the osmotic effect associated with increased bacterial fermentation. Increased acidity in the bowel has been suggested to be beneficial in the absorption of a number of minerals, most notably calcium.

As with all of the other functional foods, however, more randomized controlled trials are needed to confirm this effect and any associated health benefits.

Prebiotics are found in a range of foods in Europe, including dairy products, infant formula and bakery products (see Figure 17.3).

ORGANIC FOOD

The concept of organic food is in many ways the opposite end of the spectrum from the functional foods discussed above. Organic foods represent more traditional food production methods, without the use of man-made chemical agents to potentiate the yield or reduce pest damage. Organic farming systems rely on traditional concepts of crop rotation, the use of animal and plant manures, and biological methods of pest control. The market in organic foods has increased rapidly in the last 5–10 years, as consumers have become concerned about the perceived safety of mass or intensively produced foods. Such concerns include the presence of pesticide, growth promoter and antibiotic residues. In addition, there may be concerns about the presence of known (such as bovine spongiform encephalopathy; BSE), or unknown disease causing factors in the foods.

Although the primary concern may be one of food safety, organic food is also perceived as having superior sensory attributes and being 'healthier'. This is taken to mean that food produced organically has a higher nutrient content. Williams (2002), in reviewing the evidence on nutritional quality of organic food, notes that there is no evidence in the scientific literature to support these claims. There are methodological shortcomings in most of the publications that

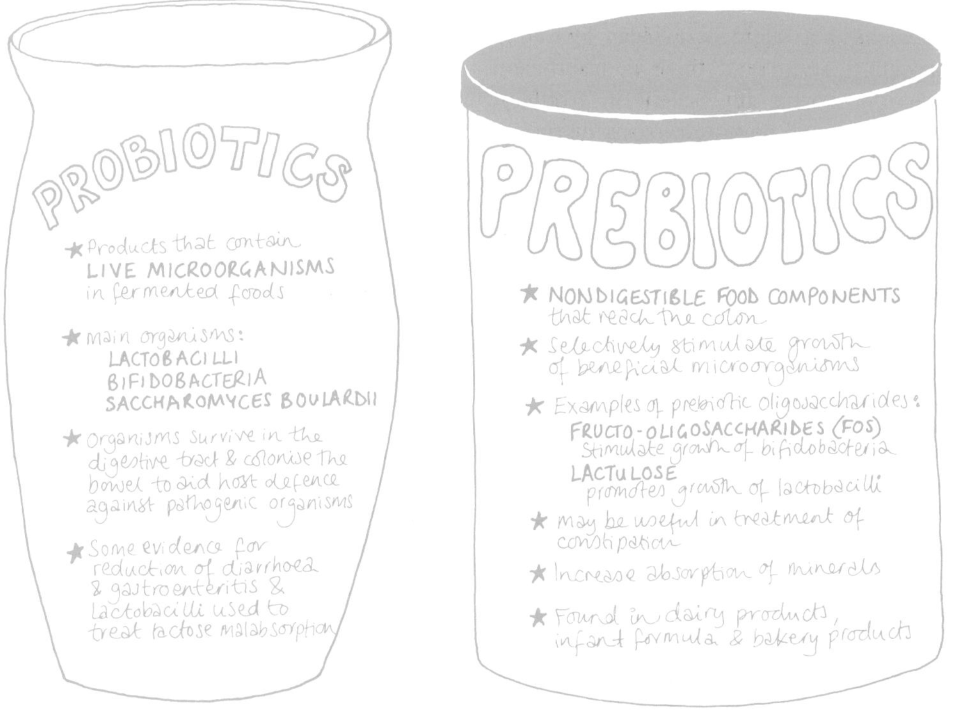

Figure 17.3 Probiotics and prebiotics.

report on nutritional quality of organic versus conventionally produced foods. Many cover a long time period, during which there have been many changes in the production methods. Comparisons of effects of feeding experiments in animals produce inconsistent and conflicting results. No studies of effects on human health have been performed. Some data show that conventionally produced vegetables, especially green leafy vegetables may have a lower vitamin C content. This is associated with a higher water content producing a dilution effect. Conventionally grown plants grow more quickly and are harvested sooner than those grown organically, resulting in a higher water content. Nitrate levels were also higher in the conventionally grown leafy vegetables, probably associated with fertilizer use. There is no evidence of a negative impact on health from these differences. An area of potential interest that has not been studied is the level of various phytochemicals contained in plants. These are produced by plants as a protection against adverse conditions or to combat attack by potentially damaging pests or diseases. It is possible that levels may be higher in organically grown products that are less protected by sprays. However, there has been no study of this area.

It should also be remembered that organic food may carry a higher level of microbial contamination, through the application of manure or the unchecked growth of fungi or bacterial contaminants.

Much of the organic food available for sale in the UK is imported. This has possible implications for its freshness and associated nutritional content. It is also more expensive than conventional produce. As a result, a substantial proportion of the population are unable to afford organic foods. If they choose to buy organic produce, this may be at the expense of other items in the diet that could have contributed more to a healthy balance. Where money is not an issue, individuals can buy organic produce without fear of compromising the balance of the rest of their diet.

In summary, it is more important to concentrate on consuming a diet in line with healthy eating guidelines, as there is much more good scientific evidence to support this than to worry about any risk to health of conventionally produced foods that might be avoided by eating 'organically'. At present, there is insufficient evidence to support any benefit to health of 'organic' food, and more research is needed to clarify these issues.

CONCLUSIONS

The concept of optimal nutrition opens a new era in the science of nutrition. Advances in knowledge about molecular biology and the characterization of the human genome will make it possible at some point in the future to study genetic polymorphisms that are associated with particular diseases. It is likely that these will also characterize individual responses to particular dietary components. We will also have a clearer view of the molecular mechanisms of nutrient action. An understanding of how genetic polymorphisms affect nutrient metabolism may make it possible to design specific dietary regimes to tackle nutritional problems, or disease risk. It is likely to become the responsibility of the food industry to develop products that help to fulfil these goals.

Nevertheless, although progress in recent years has been rapid, the preceding sections have indicated how little is known in some cases about mechanisms at cellular and tissue level. This is hindered by a lack of biomarkers and specific tools for identification of processes, for example, within the gut mucosa. Properly controlled large-scale clinical trials need to be performed to evaluate the potential benefits of products, and caution needs to be exercised when claims are made that have not been properly evaluated and cause confusion among consumers. Safety aspects must also be addressed, if new products are developed.

In the mean time, consuming a balanced diet following healthy eating guidelines is our best guarantee of optimizing nutrition from food. This, after all, is what has sustained the human race over thousands of years, and should not be forgotten in the rush for new designer foods that offer promises of better health and disease reduction.

SUMMARY

1. Optimal nutrition is a concept that encompasses positive benefits of food in the promotion of health.
2. Foods with altered nutritional contents have been produced to address some issues of 'healthy eating'.
3. Some of the more researched food components have been introduced into foods to produce potentially health-promoting products.
4. There are many other components of food that have no known nutritional role but may modify the risk of disease.
5. The use of bacteria to promote gut health is a novel approach to optimizing nutritional state.

STUDY QUESTIONS

1. Debate with a partner what are the arguments for and against more development of smart foods. You could consider:
   a. are they useful for all people?
   b. should they be targeted at specific groups? – if so, give examples
   c. which foods should be promoted and which allowed to disappear?
   d. are there other smart foods that you think might be useful?
2. You could imagine that you are an Expert Committee and have to decide on permission for the development of some new products. What would you need to know?
3. Survey a number of people in your community to discover how many buy organic foods.
   a. Which foods are commonly bought, and what are the perceived benefits of choosing these?
   b. What foods are they replacing in the diet, and does this lead to better or poorer balance of healthy items?

REFERENCES AND FURTHER READING

Buttriss, J., Hughes, J., 2000: A review of the MAFF optimal nutrition programme: aims and objectives. *British Nutrition Foundation Nutrition Bulletin* 25, 79–80.

Cassidy, A., Faughnan, M. 2000: Phyto-oestrogens through the life cycle. *Proceedings of the Nutrition Society* 59, 489–96.

Johnson, I.T. 2001: New food components and gastrointestinal health. *Proceedings of the Nutrition Society* 60, 481–8.

Kolida, S., Tuohy, K., Gibson, G.R. 2000: The human gut flora in nutrition and approaches for its dietary modification. *British Nutrition Foundation Nutrition Bulletin* 25, 219–22.

Marteau, P., Boutron-Ruault, M.C. 2002: Nutritional advantages of probiotics and prebiotics. *British Journal of Nutrition* 87(Suppl. 2), S153–7.

McConnon, A., Cade, J., Pearman, A. 2002: Stakeholder interactions and the development of functional foods. *Public Health Nutrition* 5(3), 469–77.

Omenn, G.S., Goodman, G.E., Thornquist, M.D. et al. 1996: Effects of a combination of beta carotene and vitamin A on lung cancer and cardiovascular disease. *New England Journal of Medicine* 334, 1150–5.

Rowland, I.R. 2002: Genetically modified foods, science, consumers and the media. *Proceedings of the Nutrition Society* 61, 25–9.

Schrooyen, P.M.M., van der Meer, R., De Kruif, C.G. 2001: Microencapsulation: its application in nutrition. *Proceedings of the Nutrition Society* 60, 475–9.

Various authors 1999: Symposium on optimal nutrition. *Proceedings of the Nutrition Society* 58, 395–512.

Williams, C.M. 2002: Nutritional quality of organic food: shades of grey or shades of green? *Proceedings of the Nutrition Society* 61, 19–24.

18 PUBLIC HEALTH NUTRITION AND HEALTH PROMOTION

The aims of this chapter are to:

- review and link some of the issues discussed in earlier parts of the book in relation to increasing health through improved nutrition;
- consider some of the obstacles to improving nutrition that may exist;
- describe strategies for health promotion and nutrition education that have been developed in recent years;
- consider future directions.

On completing the study of this chapter, you should be able to:

- discuss the importance of nutrition in prevention of chronic disease;
- recognize the stages involved in undergoing change and the barriers that may exist;
- describe and evaluate some of the strategies that exist to promote better nutrition.

To develop and implement policies for the prevention of a disease, it is important at the outset to make a realistic assessment of its prevalence and the extent to which it impacts on morbidity and mortality statistics in the population. Further, if these policies are to relate to dietary intake and nutritional goals, it is also important to make an assessment of the role of the diet in the aetiology of these diseases and how much gain can be expected from changes in the diet.

These are areas of controversy, generating quite polarized opinions. At one extreme, it is suggested that, because we cannot be certain that diet plays a role in a particular disease, we should do nothing, with the implication that to change could do more harm than good. On the other hand, others suggest changes based on very weak evidence, coming from a small database. However, between these extremes there is a broad consensus on desirable dietary change, based on evidence from large numbers of studies. Many of these have been re-evaluated using the technique of 'meta-analysis', which allows a number of studies with similar research criteria to be combined to increase the statistical power of the results.

The World Health Organisation (WHO), since its formation in 1948, has been working to improve the health of all the peoples of the world. In the last two decades, it has become clear that there have been changes in patterns of morbidity and mortality in many countries. These have arisen from:

- reductions in maternal and infant mortality;
- better control of infectious diseases through immunization and environmental improvements, although the spread of HIV infection has run counter to this trend;
- increased population life expectancies owing to advances in medical technology and lifestyle changes;
- improvements in diets in some areas.

However, in parallel with these, there has been a persistent rise in chronic non-communicable diseases, such as cardiovascular disease, cancers, diabetes, chronic respiratory diseases and osteoporosis. In the Western industrialized countries, these diseases have been well established for over

40 years and, in many of these countries, there have been decreases, especially in coronary heart disease incidence. However, there has been an upward trend in the countries of Eastern Europe and, most notably, in the developing countries.

Many countries whose traditional diet and lifestyle had been associated with a low incidence of non-communicable disease have been experiencing a period of food transition. This is typified by an increased consumption of animal protein and reduction in vegetable protein sources, generally associated with a higher fat intake. In addition, the intake of carbohydrate from the starchy staple, and minerals and vitamins from vegetables may begin to decrease. This has been noted in Japan, where the prevalence of obesity and coronary heart disease, both previously relatively rare conditions, has begun to increase. Countries such as China and those in South America are also experiencing this trend. In some of the poorer countries in the world, the gradual transition to a more Western diet, accompanied by rapid increasing urbanization and lower levels of physical activity (as well as smoking), is causing a rapid rise in chronic diseases. Because of the greater numbers of people in these countries than in the developed countries, mortality from chronic diseases has now outstripped on a numerical basis that in the developed world. There is also concern about the spread of overweight and obesity in these countries, and the potential for associated health problems, as has already happened in the industrialized world. These trends have been monitored by the INTERHEALTH programme of WHO, which studies the risk of the major non-communicable diseases in a number of populations around the world, as well as trends in diet and nutrition, and aims to promote and monitor community-based strategies for intervention.

In Europe, the WHO has been working to develop a Food and Nutrition Policy by 2005. This aims to increase awareness of the links between food growing, buying and eating, and the effects on health and environmental sustainability. This reflects a new approach inherent in many nutrition policies that incorporates concepts of social justice and the importance of fair access to food for all.

The European Community has also enshrined human health protection as a part of all its policies. This has led to the formulation of a public health framework, including an action programme, public health policies and legislation. The EURODIET project has been one aspect of this and aims to contribute towards a coordinated European Union (EU) and member-state health promotion programme on nutrition, diet and healthy lifestyles. Progress has been made on European dietary guidelines. Other objectives of this project include:

- translating these into food-based dietary guidelines within member states;
- promoting these to the population;
- identifying and overcoming barriers;
- a European Food Safety Authority to oversee the food supply from its production to consumption.

Despite some improvements in the incidence of coronary heart disease, it is estimated that, across Europe, the demand for treatment related to chronic diseases will continue to increase, because of the increases in the elderly population. It is, therefore, essential that changes in lifestyle and diet are introduced to reduce the incidence of these diseases, as clearly health services will not be able to cope with such huge increases in demand. There is, therefore, an economic benefit to be gained as well as the social gain for individuals.

Measures to prevent chronic diseases are needed and these are the goals of many strategies around the world. It is recognized that such strategies must take into account all aspects of the food chain:

- production policies;
- social policies determining access to the foods;
- education policies to increase awareness;
- dietary guidelines to inform choice.

They must, therefore, involve the governments as well as all those concerned with food. Policy makers also need to examine health impact effectiveness and cost effectiveness in their decision-making. In addition, there needs to be a commitment to the strategy, which is translated into action. Much has been learned in the last decade about public health approaches that are likely to result in changes in attitudes, behaviour, risk factors, morbidity and mortality. Attention is needed to public health nutrition, which is the promotion of good health though nutrition and physical activity, and the primary prevention of related illness in the population.

WHAT IS THE BASIS OF HEALTH-PROMOTING POLICIES AND WHAT IS PROPOSED?

There exists public concern in Europe about potential hazards associated with recent developments in a complex food chain. This concern focuses on new infections, such as bovine spongiform encephalopathy (BSE), *E. coli* 0157, novel viruses, and perceived environmental hazards from the use of genetically modified plants and food. Yet this concern is out of proportion to the effects on health from these sources, compared to the impact of dietary imbalances, which account for at least 100-fold more premature deaths and considerably more ill health. About one-third of all premature deaths in Europe are diet related and many are preventable. The cost of this burden of ill health is in excess of that caused by tobacco use. Despite this, the budget in most European countries for health promotion is on average, less than 1 per cent of the total health budget.

Dietary links

Over 100 expert reports, produced throughout the world over the previous 20 years, have been in broad agreement about both the major chronic diseases threatening health and the dietary changes that are needed to reduce their incidence. The change in disease incidence over the last 40 years has made it increasingly clear that changing environmental factors, including diet, are involved in their aetiology. Although we are now discovering more about the role of genes in the susceptibility to disease, these are rarely the sole factor in its development and, at present, are believed to play a much less important role than other environmental factors, such as activity and diet. It is also unlikely that genetic changes or mutations would have produced such major changes in a relatively short time span. The dietary trends seen around the world point to alterations in the balance of nutrients in the diet, which parallel, in most countries, the changes in disease incidence. Inevitably, there are exceptions that need explanation. In some cases, a satisfactory explanation can be proposed; in others it awaits further research. Additional dietary concerns are also emerging, as our understanding of disease increases. Table 18.1 shows some of the proposed linkages between chronic disease and dietary factors.

Specific nutritional problems are also important. Anaemia is increasingly recognized as a problem among the female population, affecting adolescent girls in particular. Consumption of foods with low bioavailability of iron contributes to this problem, and can result in reduced physical performance and lowered cognitive function. In addition, where it exists in pregnant women, poor iron transfer to the fetus will impact on its early development.

The increasing number of older adults results in a higher prevalence of low vitamin D status. This appears to be associated with low sunshine exposure, even in Southern European countries. Bone pain, difficulty in walking and accelerated bone demineralization may all occur.

In Europe, there is still a problem with iodine deficiency, affecting populations in the central parts of the landmass and in mountainous regions. The use of iodized salt is an important public health measure but education about its need is required. The consequences for maternal health and, in particular, the normal development of the fetus are profound, if deficiency exists.

Lifestyle and social factors

In addition, other aspects of lifestyle are important. There is convincing evidence that physical activity is an essential component of health and interacts with dietary aspects in a number of ways including:

- activity increases energy expenditure and is, therefore, crucial for the maintenance of energy balance and normal weight;
- activity increases physical fitness and the sense of well-being, and may be important

TABLE 18.1 Summary of chronic diseases and other health problems with possible dietary links

Disease	Dietary excess	Dietary lack
Heart disease	Saturated fats Total fats *Trans* fatty acids	Antioxidant nutrients *n*-3 fatty acids Dietary fibre Folate
Hypertension	Salt ?Total fat Alcohol	Calcium Potassium
Diabetes (Type 2)	Energy intake (via obesity)	
Cancers	Total fat/energy ?Meat ? Salt	Antioxidant nutrients Fruit and vegetables Dietary fibre ?Dairy products
Gallstones	Energy intake (link via obesity)	Dietary fibre
Osteoporosis	? Salt ?Animal protein	Calcium ?Vitamin D Fruit and vegetables
Dental disease	Sugar	Fluoride Dietary fibre
Arthritis	Total energy (linked to obesity)	
Liver cirrhosis	Alcohol	?General dietary deficiency
Dementia		?Folate ?Vitamin C

in the control of blood pressure, prevention of colon cancer, regulation of blood glucose levels and lowering of blood lipid level;

- weight-bearing activity maintains bone health and limits demineralization of bone in later life;
- activity helps to maintain muscle mass and sense of balance, which is important with increasing age to preserve independence and prevent falls.

The most prevailing social factor that impacts on diet and health is that of poverty. This has increased substantially throughout Europe in the last two decades, as a result of rising unemployment, more insecure and low-paid work, and pressures experienced by governments in providing social security. All the evidence shows that the health experience of these groups is worse than in the better off, with an average of 5 years lower life expectancy. This is attributable to many factors, including dietary choices, lack of physical activity, access to shops and leisure facilities, stressful life experiences and an increased burden of illness. Many dietary goals have now recognized the need to address such social inequalities.

On the basis of existing evidence, the EURODIET team has put forward population goals for nutrients, some foods and lifestyle features, consistent with the prevention of major public health problems. These are based on a review of the scientific literature and represent the consensus view. These population goals are intended to form the basis for food-based dietary guidelines to be developed, or that have already been developed within individual countries, which reflect the national diet. The population goals for Europe are shown in Table 18.2.

There has been debate about who should be the target population for dietary goals. Those

TABLE 18.2 Population goals for nutrients, foods and lifestyle factors, consistent with the prevention of major public health problems in Europe (Eurodiet Core Report, 2001)

Component	Population goal	Background information
Physical activity level (PAL)	PAL >1.75	Maintenance of energy balance and cardiovascular health
Adult body weight	Body mass index (BMI) 21–22	An optimal individual BMI may be 20, and Asians may be susceptible to weight-related diseases above BMI 23–24
Dietary fat (% energy)	<30%	The goal is for the prevention of overweight. Higher fat intakes up to 35% may be consumed with high levels of physical activity
Fatty acids (% energy)		These intakes are recommended in relation to blood lipid levels. Stearic acid has little effect on these. A lower ratio of *n*-6:*n*-3 acids than at present is recommended
Saturated	<10%	
Trans	<2%	
MUFAs	10–15%	
n-6 PUFAs	4–8%	
n-3 PUFAs	2 g linoleic 200 mg very long chain	
Alcohol (where consumed) g/day	24–36 (men) 12–24 (women)	The lower values are optimum
Carbohydrates (% energy)	>55%	Rich in non-starch polysaccharides and of low glycaemic index
Dietary fibre (g/day)	>25 (or 3 g/MJ)	Based on Southgate method of analysis
Sugary foods (occasions/day)	<4	To reduce the risk of dental decay; frequency of consumption is a major factor. Important for lifelong oral health
Fruit and vegetables (g/day)	>400	These have many health-promoting properties, including non-nutritional components
Folate from food (μg/day)	>400	Bioavailability from food is only 50% of that of folic acid; needed for pregnancy and for normal homocysteine levels
Sodium (as sodium chloride; g/day)	<6	Population benefits are greater than those obtained if only hypertensive subjects adopt the guideline
Iodine (μg/day)	150	Essential for normal development
Exclusive breastfeeding	About 6 months	Promotes immunological responses, lower risk of infection and atopic disease, reduced risk of breast cancer in mother

MUFAs, monounsaturated fatty acids; PUFA, polyunsaturated fatty acids.

individuals with most risk factors and the most severe risk factors will be in greatest need of intervention. However, they represent only a small proportion of the total population and, therefore, reducing their risk will make little impact on overall population morbidity and mortality. On the other hand, the majority of the population will have moderate levels of risk. Improvement in these risk factors will have less success on an individual basis (because the

Activity 18.1

What common themes are apparent in Table 18.1 that could form the basis for coordinated dietary advice?

If you were presented with this group of suggested links between diet and disease, what specific dietary changes might you recommend?

Check these with the targets suggested in Table 18.2.

original risk is less) but, taken for the population as a whole, will amount to a greater reduction in the population's risk of morbidity and mortality.

Hence, many strategies, such as the European goals shown here, are now targeted at the whole population, because this will bring the greatest reduction in risk. It also provides more social support for changes in dietary patterns. This does not, however, exclude an additional policy directed at those most at risk, with more intensive and specific targeting at this group. Of course, before this can happen, the problem of identifying those with greatest risk must be overcome!

From goals to guidelines

In order to achieve the population goals, practical advice must be developed. It is recognized that across Europe there are different dietary patterns, so national guidelines must take into account the existing culturally determined diet. Of course, there are many differences between intakes of individuals within any one country and these can provide an opportunity to study which existing dietary pattern comes closer to the desirable goals. In recent years, dietary guidelines have moved from being nutrient based to being food based (see Chapter 3). In other words, instead of recommending that consumers 'eat more fibre' and 'eat less fat', foods that contain these nutrients are used in the recommendations. Clearly, this is easier for the consumer to understand, as it coincides with how we buy and select our daily food.

Many countries are now publishing food-based guidelines, with the emphasis on foods and the numbers of servings to be eaten; these can also be used to develop advice for populations at higher risk, such as those produced by the American Heart Association in 2000. These recommend the inclusion of fruits and vegetables, whole grains, low-fat dairy products, legumes, fish and low-fat meats. Achieving and maintaining a healthy body weight through physical activity is included as a guideline.

Several stages have been identified in compiling food-based dietary guidelines. These include identification of:

- the major food sources of the nutrients recommended (e.g. from tables of food composition);
- the foods contributing substantially to the intake of the population (e.g. from national food surveys);
- existing food patterns that show differing levels of intake of key nutrients (e.g. from individual dietary intakes studies);
- key foods that explain the major variation in intakes of specific nutrients in the diets of high and low consumers.

With this information, it should be possible to identify the most important foods or eating patterns that could be targeted for change in order to move all dietary intakes towards achievement of a dietary goal. If this can be done for several key nutrients or foods, then many goals can be achieved. Guidelines can be formulated to include choice of products, menu planning, portions and frequencies of eating that have a sound basis within the target population. A further strategy may be to change the supply of food, by modifications to existing products (e.g. lowering the fat content, fortifying with a nutrient) or introducing new products.

Consideration of the population goals suggests some common themes. Reduction of fat intake and attention to the balance of fats with a reduction of saturated fat, and attention to polyunsaturated fats, especially those of the n-3 family addresses a number of health issues. The reduction in energy intake that will ensue may be beneficial for weight loss but, in many people, it will have to be counterbalanced by an increase in other energy sources. Most appropriate is an increase in complex carbohydrates from cereals, grains, pulses, roots, vegetables and fruits. These will provide not only starch, but also intrinsic sugars, dietary fibre and a wide range of micronutrients. Among these will be folate, the antioxidant nutrients and other non-nutritional factors, such as the phytonutrients, which are considered to be important as protective factors (see Chapter 17). A shift in the diet to fewer, or at least lower-fat animal products may also occur as fat intakes are reduced.

Thus, a series of nutrient goals may be achieved by the same changes in the diet. In theory, this should make the giving of dietary advice more straightforward, as the basis of a 'healthy diet' will apply whatever the client's needs. Clearly, there will be differences in emphasis, for example, if weight needs to be lost, or if the appetite is small, as in older sedentary people or in young children.

In Britain, the Nutrition Task Force devised the National Food Guide (the Balance of Good Health), which has been adopted throughout many areas of nutrition education as the basic framework for achieving the nutrient goals (see Chapter 3).

The role of the Nutrition Task Force cannot, however, be viewed in isolation. It was part of an overall strategy, emanating from the 'Health of the nation' paper, which has involved many in the move towards actually 'adding years to life' and 'life to years'. Since its publication, public health initiatives related to nutrition have remained on the political agenda. The Department of Health has recognized the importance of nutrition in a series of National Service Framework documents, published since 2000. These indicate the standards of service and care in relation to coronary heart disease, mental health, older people and diabetes, and, in each case, include a role for nutrition. Most recently, the Food Standards Agency (FSA), created in 2000, has become responsible for the public's health and consumer interests in relation to food. One of the key aims is to secure long-term improvements in the health of the population by working to reduce diet-related ill health, within the UK Strategic Framework for Nutrition. The main elements of this are:

- securing a sound evidence base for action to promote a healthy diet;
- developing appropriate means of informing the general population;
- identifying and addressing barriers to changing dietary behaviour;
- evaluating and monitoring the effectiveness of action taken.

This framework is intended to form the basis for developing realistic and effective programmes for the future.

It is possible to illustrate how this might work by considering the Nutrition Strategy developed by the Food Standards Agency Wales. The strategy aims to improve the diet of all the people in Wales, but certain groups have been prioritised, owing to their poor diet and health, and, therefore, have the greatest potential gain from improved nutrition.

The top priority groups were identified as infants, children and young people, and socially disadvantaged and vulnerable groups. The second priority groups were women of child-bearing age, especially pregnant women, and men, especially middle aged men.

The main recommendations include:

- increase the uptake of a healthy balanced diet to meet recommended levels for nutrients and micronutrients;
- increase fruit and vegetable intake;
- develop and manage initiatives to prevent and manage obesity and overweight;
- ensure that schemes and policies are in place to assist improvement in healthy eating;
- provide information and training to key players;
- ensure that the public is well informed about the need for dietary improvement;
- ensure that local initiatives are in place to tackle the main barriers to improving nutrition;
- develop and promote initiatives with the food industry to improve healthy eating, especially relating to access to specific foods;
- evaluate the impact of activities resulting from the strategy.

Key players in delivering the strategy will include policy and decision-makers, health, nutrition and catering professionals, practitioners and educators at national and local levels, and the food production and the retail industry.

Recruiting and training volunteers to become involved with local projects is important. The approach is, therefore, multi-dimensional and flexible, and able to focus on specific targets and develop local initiatives suited to the needs of particular communities. Settings for the interventions can be very diverse. They may include schools, workplaces, health care locations, the commercial sector (e.g. supermarkets), local clubs or day centres, or even street markets.

A systematic review of interventions to promote healthy eating in the general population has shown that the most effective appear to:

- adopt an integrated, multidisciplinary comprehensive approach;
- involve a complementary range of actions;
- work at individual, community, environmental and policy levels.

Information provided by itself is insufficient to produce change. Thus, any attempt to implement food-based dietary guidelines needs to learn from previous work and adopt the lessons from other interventions. In so doing the difficult challenge of changing diets to improve health will make progress.

WHAT IS HEALTH PROMOTION?

The above discussion illustrates some of the principles of health promotion, these will now be considered in their own right.

The Ottawa Charter for health promotion, developed by the WHO (1986) outlines an approach to health promotion that includes:

- building healthy public policies;
- creating supportive environments;
- developing the personal skills of the public and practitioners;
- re-orienting health services;
- strengthening community action.

It, therefore, demonstrates that health promotion involves more than just providing people with knowledge about the functions of the body and ways of preventing illness, and thus helps them to maintain well-being. This part of the process can be better described as health education, or if it is carried out in the nutritional context, then it is nutrition education.

Nutrition education, in turn, has been described as the process that assists the public in applying knowledge from nutrition science, and the relationship between diet and health to their food practices. Having the knowledge, however, is insufficient in itself to effect change. This can be witnessed all around us most vividly in the context of smoking. Almost everyone knows that smoking is injurious to health, yet a substantial proportion of the population continues to smoke. For knowledge to be translated into action, the environment must be supportive of the change and thereby enable it to happen. This includes the political context, the social environment and the individual's personal environment. In addition, the person making the change must have the desire and the belief that this is achievable, by the means available to them.

Thus, health promotion must be seen in a wide context. It includes:

- having in existence the political and community structures that can make health-promoting changes possible;
- providing the information about health-promoting measures to all interested and involved parties;
- developing in the individual the desire to want to change towards a healthier set of practices;
- showing the individual that they have the ability to do this.

Briefly, health promotion has been described as 'making healthier choices the easier choices'.

In the context of nutritional improvements, the introduction of nutritional goals is accepted as the responsibility of governments in most countries of the world. This was not always so. The first advice formulated about reducing fat intakes for the prevention of coronary heart disease was developed by the American Heart Association. This government-led approach had been perceived by some as unwarranted interference by the State in food intake, which is a purely personal matter. Nevertheless, without appropriate support from the government in establishing food production policies and legislation, for example, for clear nutritional labelling, the consumer is left without adequate information to make a choice.

Activity 18.2

Applying this in the nutrition context, the nutritionist or dietitian wants people to adopt healthier eating practices. Ways must be found to make these 'the easier choices'.

- Who will need to be involved? Think of all the parties concerned in the food production chain.
- What does the consumer need to know about the healthier choice?
- How will the consumer be convinced to try this out?
- What might the obstacles be and how can they be tackled?

In working through this activity, you should find yourself referring back to the key points made above about health promotion.

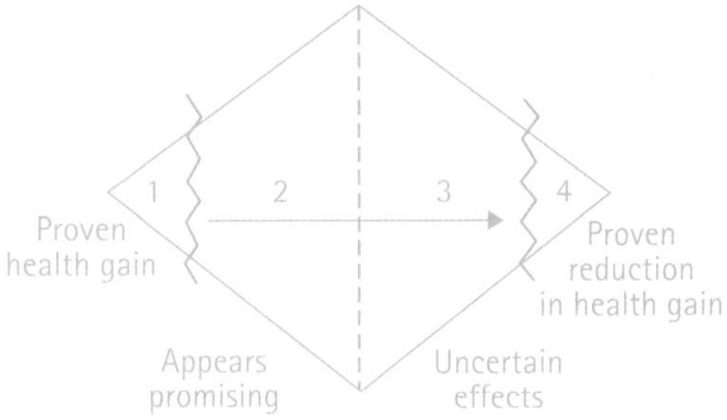

Figure 18.1 The health gain rhomboid.

Health promotion incorporates a number of related phases:

- planning;
- intervention;
- evaluation.

Planning

This is arguably the most important stage and can determine the success or failure of the programme. Most importantly, the issue that is to be addressed must be identified. In coming to this decision, the planners balance the perceived needs with the possible benefits. This may be illustrated in the form of the 'health gain rhomboid' (shown in Figure 18.1). At the two extremes, there are very few interventions that have been assessed and shown definitely to provide health gain, or to diminish it (i.e. at 1 or 4, respectively). Interventions classified as 2 would generally be considered worthwhile, but there may be an equal number at 3 that have not been fully evaluated and whose benefits to health promotion are uncertain. Where decisions have to be taken about the use of a finite amount of resources, most planners will chose interventions in the area 2, rather than 3.

A further element of the planning process is to identify the target group, since particular interventions may be more appropriate and relevant to certain groups. This type of planning and consultation was undertaken in the preparation of the 'Health of the nation' paper. During this period, a very large number of possible goals and targets were discussed, with supporters of each putting forward strong arguments. Eventually, only a small number of goals were identified, although these were chosen because they were believed to be the most appropriate to achieve the maximum health gain. This has also been described in the case of the Food Standards Agency Wales Nutrition Strategy.

A further aspect of planning includes taking account of the nature of the problem, for example, by collecting data about morbidity and mortality statistics. Perhaps also at this stage it is important to consider the lifestyle aspects of the target community. When this is being done at national level, the variation among communities within the country makes this more difficult.

Finally, general aims and specific objectives are formulated, taking into account the nature of the existing problem and the potential change expected. This, in turn, depends on existing knowledge, attitudes and behaviours of the target group. A very important consideration is the readiness to change on the part of the target. This has been studied extensively and a model developed that shows change as a process comprising several stages (Table 18.3). It will be necessary to consider what aspects of the programme will facilitate people moving from one stage to the next in the change process.

In the UK, the information about food intakes is available from National Food Survey data and from National Dietary and Nutrition Survey data.

TABLE 18.3 Model for stages of change

Stage of change	Associated behaviour
Pre-contemplation	Not considering any change or need for change
Contemplation	Thinking about changing, but not yet prepared to start the process
Preparation	When the change seems possible and benefits are perceived, ready to change
Action	Actually doing things differently. May need much support and reassurance; may slip back to earlier stages
Maintenance	New behaviour becomes part of the healthier lifestyle

Adapted from Prochaska et al., 1992.

Intervention

An obvious but important element of this stage of the process is the decision on the methodology to be used. This should take into account information about previous uses of this methodology and their level of success. Constraints that might exist must be taken into account. For example, if the promotional material is presented in a written form, this necessitates that the target group can, and wants to, read. Computer-based images may be more appealing to young people than the written word. Thus, the methodology must be flexible and adaptable to meet the objectives with all of the targets.

The FSA Wales is employing a variety of interventions. Breakfast clubs have been set up in some schools, which can provide a healthy start to the day and encourage children to interact. Nutrition and health education activities in the workplace are increasing awareness of the links between diet and cancer in middle-aged men. Midwives working with vulnerable groups are teaching about meal planning and budgeting to reduce the numbers of low birthweight babies. Local grocers are involved in delivering fruit to schools as part of a school tuck shop scheme. Fitness training in a local club for young people is being linked with some nutrition education as well as smoking, drugs and alcohol education.

Evaluation

The process of health promotion may be seen as cyclic. The evaluation of one programme may generate questions and proposals for an improved programme, which can start with another planning stage. No programme can be brought to a conclusion without evaluating what it has achieved. In the case of health promotion, changes in some of the measures that were used at the planning stages may be indicative of success. These may include morbidity data, measures of quality of life or, in the case of nutrition programmes, changes in patterns of food purchasing. On the other hand, outcomes may be programmes and policies that need to be taken up in subsequent interventions. In its 'Eat well II' report, the Department of Health (1996) published an evaluation of the first 2 years of operation of the Nutrition Task Force initiatives. Follow-on initiatives have since been introduced, so the original outcomes have been superseded by new interventions.

The FSA Wales Nutrition Strategy is aiming for some quantitative outcomes, for example, in terms of knowledge about portions and increased consumption of fruit and vegetables in priority groups, as well as a balance of the diet closer to recommendations by 2010.

The national progress towards a healthier diet in the UK is more difficult to follow. However, there are indications that intakes of fat are falling, although rates of obesity are increasing. Intake of fruit has increased, although vegetable intakes are static. There is increased knowledge about recommendations to increase fruit and vegetable intake and reduce intakes of fat. Yet, generally food intake patterns remain resistant to change. Many studies demonstrate that people are not making changes for a number of reasons. These include:

- confusion over the message (e.g. what is a portion);
- perception that the messages are frequently changing and the professionals cannot agree;

- belief that the subject's diet is already healthy, so the messages do not apply to them;
- inadequate/incorrect knowledge about which foods contain particular nutrients;
- concern that healthy food is unappealing;
- perceptions about the cost of healthy food;
- beliefs about the availability of healthy foods, both in local shops and in catering venues;
- lack of interest.

For all of these reasons, progress is inevitably slower than nutritionists and other health professionals would like it to be. However, if goals are made specific, measurable, achievable and realistic, then after a set time some progress is generally found to have occurred. It is important to recognize that such small steps will eventually add up to more substantial change. Trends in the incidence of chronic disease will take longer to become apparent. Evaluation is, therefore, essential to ensure that all changes are recorded and lessons learned from them.

HEALTH-PROMOTION INITIATIVES AND THE INDIVIDUAL

Most individual consumers may know little about national initiatives and are dependent on changes in their own immediate environment to provide them with opportunities to improve their nutrition. This section will consider what difference health-promotion initiatives might make to the individual.

Information and education

The National Food Guide continues to be published as *The balance of good health* (FSA, 2001). It is an example of food-based dietary guidelines and, as such, should be readily understood by consumers. It is used widely by retailers and health professionals, and has been adapted for use with groups, such as ethnic minority groups and diabetics.

Past advice had tended to focus on single nutrients. Thus, consumers heard the message that they should 'eat more fibre', for example. They follow this advice by buying wholemeal bread and eating a wholegrain breakfast cereal, but continue as before with their previous diet. This may still be high in fat, low in fruit and vegetables, high in salt, or even all of these, but the consumer may believe that he/she is now eating 'a healthy diet'.

This focus on single nutrients has also led to an enormous increase in consumption of supplements, with up to 30 per cent of some groups in the population taking supplements regularly. This again reflects the message about 'antioxidant nutrients', which are being consumed in tablet form rather than by amending the diet. It is possible that it is the chemical substances found alongside these antioxidants that may actually be the biologically important agents.

The balance of good health moves away from this approach and provides a whole diet picture. It can be used in many ways, both as an educational tool in settings ranging from schools to antenatal clinics, a meal-planning guide or even a shopping list; and provides a non-verbal illustration of the balanced diet, which can be very useful in allowing each person to understand the guide in their own way.

Although we are exposed to many messages about nutrition and health throughout the week, some are more likely to persuade us than others. The effectiveness of a message is determined by the wording. Messages need to be:

- reasonable (we should understand the message, and the reason for it);
- practical (we should find the change possible); and
- compelling (we should want to do it).

We are more likely to be influenced by messages that fit in with existing belief systems, rather than those which seem alien to us. In devising messages, the health promoter must be sure that he or she understands the belief systems of the target group, so the messages will be understood and acted on. A common failing is that health promoters make assumptions about their target group's level of understanding; this can lead to misunderstanding of the message.

Schools

A network of 'School Nutrition Action Groups' has been set up as school-based healthy alliances between schoolchildren, staff and caterers, together with a community dietitian. These groups aim to develop a health-promoting environment in the school, establishing, monitoring and evaluating a consistent food policy with health as the main objective, and providing healthy options on the school menu, at lunchtime and for snacks. It allows pupils, caterers and teachers to have involvement and ownership of school meals provision. The existence of good examples of healthy food aims to serve as an educational model. There is now more teaching of food and nutrition in schools, and computer-based packages to facilitate this have been produced by the British Nutrition Foundation. The introduction of new guidelines on school meals in 2001 should help to integrate the educational and food-based messages.

The NHS and health professionals

It is recognized that the majority of people will turn to members of the primary health care team if they want specific nutritional advice. However, many studies have indicated that doctors may be uncertain about nutritional advice and, although they appreciate that it is important, often have not included nutrition in a consultation. This may be influenced by a number of factors, including lack of time, inadequate teaching materials, low confidence and patient non-compliance. The practice nurse in the primary health care setting is more likely to provide nutritional advice and may have more time to do so. The importance of training in nutrition for many groups of health professionals is now widely recognized and included in the curriculum. A recent report by the Royal College of Physicians (2002) confirmed that nutrition of patients was a doctor's responsibility and should be supported by appropriate training in nutrition. A study of nutrition intervention in primary care (Moore and Adamson, 2002) found that there were good levels of nutritional knowledge among members of the primary care team. Diet was discussed with a proportion of patients, although practical aspects of food were not well covered. There is thus evidence of progress in widening the availability of nutritional information to patients. Multi-disciplinary nutrition teams have been established in many hospitals to ensure adequate feeding of at-risk patients in this setting.

Media/advertising

A major source of information for the lay person is the media and advertising. Because the most eye-catching news items are the ones that aim to surprise or shock, it is the sensational aspects of nutrition that tend to reach prominence in the media. An expert opinion, which apparently disagrees with the accepted viewpoint, becomes newsworthy and is published in the press. Where a number of experts have agreed, however, this is often not considered important and so receives no publicity. Thus, the overall impression given is that 'experts' always contradict one another, and there is no point in following any advice, as it is inevitably contradicted within the next few months. Regrettably, this is believed by many and frequently cited as the reason for not following any dietary advice. Information from professionally accredited nutritionists and state registered dietitians is sound and based on scientific evidence. Unfortunately, a proportion of the information provided by the media is not.

The food chain

The food industry is in a very powerful position to determine the nutritional quality of the diet consumed. It is, therefore, essential that health promoters work with the industry. The potential for the development of modified products or new products with a healthier nutritional profile is there, and whether they appear on the supermarket shelves depends on the manufacturers.

In the UK in recent years, there has been a huge growth in the consumption of ready-made and convenience food products, and, therefore, a great responsibility rests with the food industry with respect to these. The provision of comprehensive nutritional labelling can help the consumer decide whether products are healthy or not. Eating a diet containing many pre-prepared meals makes it difficult to achieve the holistic view of the diet, as many complete dishes span various segments of the Balance of Good Health, and make it impossible to gauge exactly how much of each component has been eaten. It is probably easier to achieve the balanced diet using more basic foods than predominantly composite dishes. Unfortunately, many people have little time and/or perhaps ability to do this, and may resort to eating a largely pre-prepared diet. There is evidence that cooking skills are gradually declining in parallel with the more hectic lifestyle and the use of ready meals. This highlights the importance of the food industry in making sure that this type of diet is balanced and healthy. A further challenge for the food industry is to respond to the drive for an increase in fruit and vegetable intake. Traditionally, there has been very little profit margin for the sale of fruit and vegetables, as minimal processing is required. However, if public health is to be improved and the food industry is to be involved, new and more creative ways of promoting plant-based foods will need to be developed.

Catering outlets also have a great responsibility, as over one-third of the meals now consumed in the UK are eaten away from home. Guidelines on healthy catering practice for hospitals, restaurants, fast-food outlets and in the workplace are available, with awards for good practice. Recommendations for the training of caterers have been drawn up. These initiatives should make it easier for consumers to be able to choose healthy eating in all outside venues, although, in practice, this is not always the case.

Constraints

Change is difficult for most people. Even if the health promotion is well designed and appropriately targeted, there may be some for whom it is not appropriate or for whom it is not possible to change. Some groups that are more difficult to reach by health-promotion programmes are:

- those on a low income;
- the elderly;
- people in minority ethnic groups;
- single men;
- children – who need specifically focused programmes.

A targeted policy

It is useful to consider a more targeted policy as an illustration of how the process described above can be applied within a more specific health promotion context. The Folic Acid Campaign in the UK, initially commissioned by the Department of Health in 1995, is an example of a policy that was specifically targeted (see Figure 18.2).

The planning stage reviewed the evidence in the literature that the estimated risk of neural tube defects (NTDs) was progressively reduced with an increasing dose of folic acid intake, and that supplementation with folic acid would significantly impact on the risk of NTD in the population. A daily dose of 400 μg folic acid was indicated as appropriate to achieve a reduction in NTD incidence of at least 50 per cent. The primary target group for the campaign were women intending to become pregnant and the aim was to reduce the incidence of NTDs, such as spina bifida, in their offspring. However, since almost half of the conceptions in the UK are reported to be unplanned, the target audience was initially expanded to all women of child-bearing age, and later to young people, as future parents. It was thus intended that, as an outcome, all women would gain an awareness of the importance of folic acid supplementation.

The intervention stage of the campaign was designed to increase the baseline intake of folate from foods, as well as promote the use of folic acid supplements at the appropriate time before conception and during early pregnancy. This entailed developing cooperative partnerships with food producers and the commercial sector to increase the availability of fortified products, as well as an increased range of appropriate supplements in order to increase access to the vitamin in shops. The increased demand was to come as a result of dissemination of the message about the importance of folate, by health professionals, teachers and journalists. Manufacturers of pregnancy testing kits were also involved at this stage. Many diverse strategies were used to disseminate the message about folate. These included leaflets and posters, a new labelling symbol for foods fortified with folic acid, promotion of fortified products by advertising, and development of teaching packs for use in schools.

The campaign finished in 1998, although many elements of the promotion of folic acid remain in place as part of health promotion. Initial evaluation results indicated an increase in

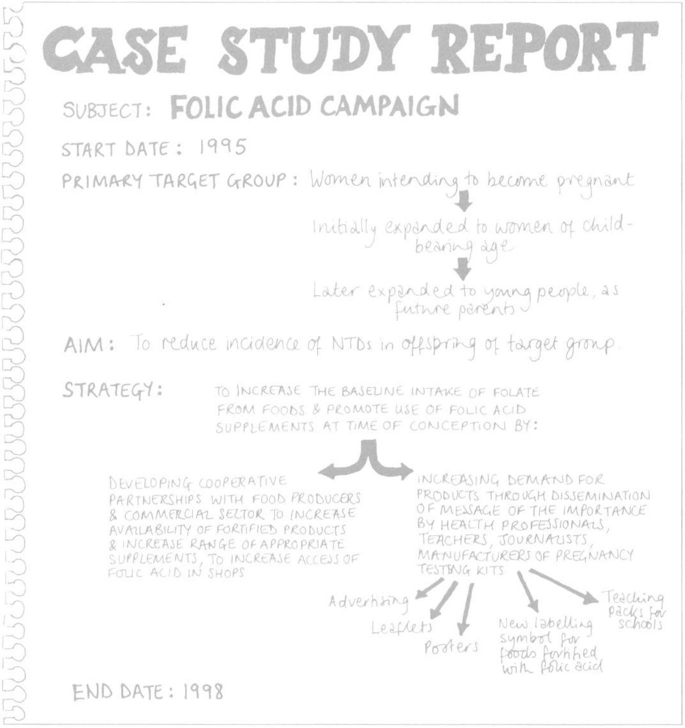

Figure 18.2 The folic acid campaign. NTDs, neural tube defects.

awareness about the issue among women, wider availability of folic acid supplements and fortified products, and an increased usage of folic acid supplements. However, women whose pregnancies are unplanned remain at risk as a result of low uptake of folic acid at the critical time around conception. The campaign can thus be viewed as only partly successful and demonstrates that the challenge of achieving change, with a simple supplement and at a highly vulnerable time of life, is enormous.

ECONOMICS OF HEALTH PROMOTION

It is generally assumed that health promotion is inexpensive and will reduce health care costs. Thus, many see health promotion as a way of saving money. However, although it is possible that money may be saved through health promotion, this cannot be the primary objective. Health promotion involves various cost inputs, most obviously in the form of resources, such as health professionals, their time and materials. There generally needs to be an input in the form of government action whether through legislation or financial 'pump priming'. In addition, better health is also achieved by efforts on the part of individuals, which are more difficult to evaluate economically.

To evaluate the cost–benefit of health promotion, it is necessary to identify what is gained as a result of the programme and what has been forgone by diverting these resources from elsewhere (see Figure 18.3).

Because the outcomes of nutritional health promotion are often difficult to measure, decisions of this nature are rarely straightforward. Various measures of health gain may need to be used that show incremental advantages, rather than simply the ultimate goal of reducing chronic disease incidence. Balanced against this are the costs of treating these diseases and the loss of earnings that chronic disease can cause. Each case may need to be evaluated separately and on its merits. However, the more information is provided about nutrition and health and the more that people can be empowered to make their own choices in an informed way, the greater will be the potential benefit for health.

A health economist might wish to compare the costs (C) of a programme to reduce obesity, against the potential saving in the treatment of diabetes (D) associated with obesity. If C is greater than D, then clearly the programme would appear not to be cost effective as it stands. However, if one also could show that reducing obesity would cause a potential saving in treatment for arthritis and hypertension (A + H), it is now possible that the combined savings (D + A + H) could be greater than the cost C. In this way, a multiple benefit can make the programme cost effective.

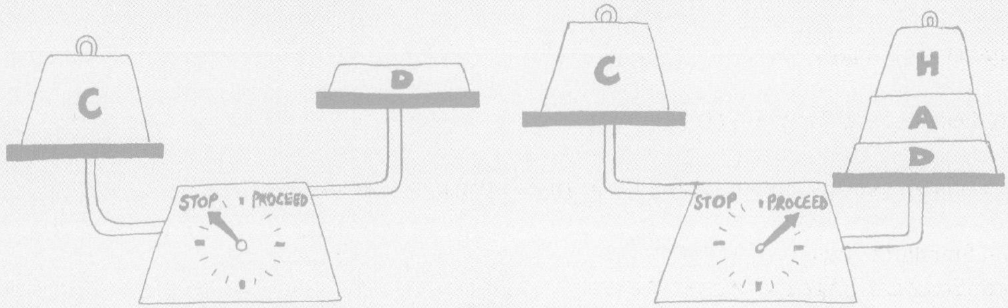

Figure 18.3 Economics of health promotion.

SUMMARY

1. Nutrition plays an important part in the causation of chronic disease. It is, therefore, essential that dietary change is introduced to reverse the high prevalence of some diseases.
2. Guidelines have been established by various national and international bodies that propose change.
3. The consensus on change recommends reductions in fat, increases in starchy carbohydrates, fruits and vegetables.
4. Health promotion can facilitate change.
5. Health promotion involves partnerships between the various players in the food system and the citizen, in a process of education and empowerment.

STUDY QUESTIONS

1. Improving health involves more than just an awareness of dietary guidelines. What other aspects of life must be considered and changed to make dietary improvements possible?
2. List the major participants in the food chain and indicate how you think each could be involved in promoting healthier eating.
3. Discuss with colleagues:
   a. Where they have obtained information about healthy eating (if at all)?
   b. Have they understood the information?
   c. Have they acted on the information? If not, why?
4. Do you believe that nutrition information available generally to the public is adequate and/or an appropriate way of producing changes in the diet?
5. Survey newspaper articles describing nutritional issues over a period of 3–4 weeks. Try to look at a 'popular' newspaper and one which is considered to be of higher 'quality'.
   a. Are issues handled differently and, if so, in what way?
   b. Do you find either of the article types more credible?
   c. As a result of reading the articles are you encouraged to change your diet?
   d. What can you conclude from this investigation?

REFERENCES AND FURTHER READING

DoH (UK Department of Health) 1994: *Eat well!* An action plan from the Nutrition Task Force to achieve the Health of the Nation targets on diet and nutrition. Wetherby: Department of Health.

DoH (Department of Health) 1996: *Eat well II.* A progress report from the Nutrition Task Force on the action plan to achieve the Health of the Nation targets on diet and nutrition. Wetherby: Department of Health.

DoH (Department of Health) 2000: *Folic acid and the prevention of disease.* Report on Health and Social Subjects 50. London: The Stationery Office.

Eurodiet core report 2001: Nutrition and diet for healthy lifestyles in Europe: science and policy implications. *Public Health Nutrition* 4(2A), 265–73.

Eurodiet Working Party 2. 2001: A framework for food-based dietary guidelines in the European Union. *Public Health Nutrition* 4(2A), 293–305.

Food and Agriculture Organisation/World Health Organisation (FAO/WHO) 1998: *Preparation and use of food-based dietary guidelines.* Geneva: WHO.

Food Standards Agency 2001: *The balance of good health.* London: FSA.

Food Standards Agency Wales 2002: *Nutrition Strategy for Wales,* Consultation Document. London: FSA.

Gillespie, A.H., Shafer, L. 1990: American Dietetic Association position paper on nutrition education for the public. *Journal of the American Dietetic Association* 90, 107–10.

Gregory, J., Foster, K., Tyler, H., Wiseman, M. 1990: *The dietary and nutritional survey of British adults.* London: HMSO.

HEA (Health Education Authortiy) 1994: *Introducing the National Food Guide: The balance of good health.* Information for educators and communicators. London: HEA.

Jackson, A.A. 2001: Human nutrition in medical practice: the training of doctors. *Proceedings of the Nutrition Society* 60(2), 257–63.

James, W.P.T. 1988: *Healthy nutrition: preventing nutrition-related diseases in Europe.* WHO Regional Publications, European Series, No. 24. Copenhagen: WHO Regional Office for Europe.

Margetts, B.M., Thompson, R.L., Speller, V. et al. 1998: Factors which influence 'healthy' eating patterns: results from the 1993 HEA health and lifestyle survey in England. *Public Health Nutrition* 1(3), 193–8.

Moore, H., Adamson, A.J. 2002: Nutrition interventions by primary care staff: a survey of involvement, knowledge and attitude. *Public Health Nutrition* 5(4), 531–6.

Posner, B.M., Franz, M., Quatromoni, P. and the INTERHEALTH Steering Committee 1994: Nutrition and the global risk for chronic diseases: the INTERHEALTH Nutrition Initiative. *Nutrition Reviews* 52(6), 201–7.

Prochaska, J.O., DiClemente, C.C., Norcross, J.C. 1992: In search of how people change. *American Psychologist* 47, 1102–14.

Roe, L., Hunt, P., Bradshaw, H. et al. 1997: *Health promotion interventions to promote healthy eating in the general population – a review.* London: Health Education Authority.

Royal College of Physicians 2002: *Nutrition and patients: a doctor's responsibility.* London: Royal College of Physicians.

World Health Organization 1986: *The Ottawa Charter: principles for health promotion.* Copenhagen: WHO Regional Office for Europe.

World Health Organization 1990: *Diet nutrition and the prevention of chronic diseases.* WHO Technical Report No. 797. Geneva: WHO.

INDEX

TABLE 4.5 Dietary reference values for protein for adults

Gender/age	Estimated average requirement (g/day)	Reference nutrient intake (g/day)
Males		
19–50 years	44.4	55.5
50+ years	42.6	53.3
Females		
19–50 years	36.0	45.0
50+ years	37.2	46.5

From DoH, 1991. Crown copyright is reproduced with the permission of Her Majesty's Stationery Office.

TABLE 7.6 EAR for energy for adults in megajoules per day (Calories/day)

Age (years)	Males	Females
19–50	10.60 (2550)	8.1 (1940)
51–59	10.60 (2550)	8.0 (1900)
60–64	9.93 (2380)	7.99 (1900)
65–74	9.71 (2330)	7.96 (1900)
75+	8.77 (2100)	7.61 (1810)

From DoH, 1991. Crown copyright is reproduced with the permission of Her Majesty's Stationery Office.